Introductory
SOIL MECHANICS
and FOUNDATIONS

Introductory
SOIL MECHANICS
and FOUNDATIONS

Second Edition

GEORGE B. SOWERS

Consulting Engineer, Lt. Colonel, Corps of Engineers, AUS (Res)

GEORGE F. SOWERS

Professor of Civil Engineering, Georgia Institute of Technology
Consulting Engineer, Law Engineering Testing Company

THE MACMILLAN COMPANY : NEW YORK

Seventh Printing, 1968

Previous edition copyright 1951 by
The Macmillan Company

Library of Congress catalog card number: 61–5509

The Macmillan Company, New York
Collier-Macmillan Canada, Ltd., Toronto, Ontario

Printed in the United States of America

PREFACE to
the SECOND EDITION

The ten-year period since the first edition was prepared has witnessed the rapid development of soils engineering. New methods for analysis and design have appeared and old ones have been changed. As a result, it has been necessary to revise completely the original text.

The original plan of a concise introduction to soil mechanics and foundations has been retained, and even greater emphasis has been given to the basic principles that govern soil behavior, rather than to step-by-step rules for design.

Over two-thirds of the text has been entirely rewritten. The importance of mineralogy, physicochemical forces and structure, and their relation to shear strength, consolidation, compaction, and soil stabilization are stressed throughout the revision. The newer concepts of bearing capacity of shallow foundations and of piles are treated, and more space is given to the rational application of the basic principles to foundation analysis and design. Material has been added on drainage, classification, soil expansion, anchored bulkheads, stability, and earth dam design, to give a more balanced coverage of these topics.

The authors are indebted to the many users of the text in both the academic and design professions who have offered helpful criticisms and suggestions for the revision. Finally, Professor Sowers wishes to express his thanks to the Georgia Institute of Technology, and to Dean Paul Weber, Dean Jesse Mason, and Professor R. E. Stiemke, Director of the School of Civil Engineering, for the sabbatical leave that made this revision possible.

PREFACE to
the FIRST EDITION

The rapid development of the field of soil mechanics or soil engineering has been accompanied by a demand for engineers who understand its principles and who appreciate the advantages of utilizing soil mechanics in the solution of problems of design and construction. Of course specialists, with detailed knowledge of theory and practice, are necessary on many jobs. More important, however, are civil and architectural engineers who have sufficient knowledge of soil mechanics to apply its principles to their routine problems and to make intelligent appraisals of recommendations made by specialists.

This book was written for undergraduate civil and architectural engineering students who are not soils specialists and also for practicing engineers who encounter soil problems in their everyday work. It stresses the rational, scientific approach to soil and foundation problems and explains how the theories are applicable in situations that engineers are likely to encounter in practice.

Prerequisites for a study of this text are: first, an introduction to geology; second, a thorough knowledge of applied mechanics; third, some understanding of structural design; fourth, an appreciation of construction procedures; and last, an inquisitive and open mind. Soil mechanics is not a difficult subject, but it does involve some new and different concepts that sometimes seem to contradict what students have already learned.

The material presented in this text is not original with the authors. Modern soil mechanics is the result of the efforts of engineers from every part of the world. We have made extensive use of the works of Dr. Karl

Terzaghi, Dr. Arthur Casagrande, Mr. R. D. Chellis, and many others who have played a part in the development of this field of engineering. We have attempted to acknowledge all sources of material presented in the text; if any references have been omitted or if we have failed to give proper credit, it has been done unintentionally.

We are indebted to Mr. Norman F. Williams of Southern Services, Inc. for his suggestions and criticisms and to Mr. George H. Nelson and others of the staff of the Law-Barrow-Agee Laboratories, Inc. for their suggestions and encouragement. Our thanks are due Mr. A. E. Cummings of the Raymond Concrete Pile Co., Mr. F. L. Jenkins of the Western Foundation Corporation, and Mr. George Flay of the Drilled-in-Caisson Corporation for their review of portions of the chapter on deep foundations.

We are grateful to the Independent Pneumatic Tool Company, the Wm. Bros Boiler and Manufacturing Company, the Barco Corporation, R. G. LeTourneau, Inc., the Raymond Concrete Pile Company, Mr. R. D. Chellis, and the Law-Barrow-Agee Laboratories, Inc. for furnishing some of the photographs used in the text.

Mr. Zenon Chen and Dr. K. C. Ho contributed valuable assistance in reviewing problems and preparing many of the drawings and Mrs. Frances L. Sowers in editing the text and preparing the map of frost penetration.

CONTENTS

NOMENCLATURE
and SYMBOLS

The following symbols are used throughout this text. They conform in general to *ASCE Manual of Engineering Practice No. 22*, "Soil Mechanics Nomenclature," published in 1941 and the "Glossary of Terms and Definitions in Soil Mechanics," *Proceedings ASCE*, Vol. 84, SM 4, Oct. 1958.

A area (sq ft or sq cm)

a_v coefficient of compressibility (sq ft per lb or sq cm per kg)

b width (ft or cm)

C_c compression index (dimensionless)

C_u uniformity coefficient (dimensionless)

c shear strength of saturated clays in quick shear or apparent cohesion (lb per sq ft or kg per sq cm)

c_v coefficient of consolidation (sq cm per sec, sq ft per min, sq ft per day)

d diameter of capillary tube (ft or cm)

D diameter of soil particle (mm)

D_D relative density

D_{10} diameter of 10 per cent size (mm)

E modulus of elasticity (lb per sq ft or kg per sq cm)

e void ratio (dimensionless)

e_0 void ratio at time compression or shear begins

F force (lb, kips, or kg)

G_s specific gravity of solids (dimensionless)

H height of retaining wall, thickness of soil stratum (ft or cm)

h head (ft or cm)

i hydraulic gradient (dimensionless)

K_0 coefficient of earth pressure at rest (dimensionless)

K_A coefficient of active earth pressure (dimensionless)

K_P coefficient of passive earth pressure (dimensionless)

k coefficient of permeability (ft per min or cm per sec)

L length or distance (ft or cm)

LL liquid limit (dimensionless)

m stability number (dimensionless)

n porosity (dimensionless)

P resultant of earth pressure over an area (lb, kips, or kg)

P_A resultant of active earth pressure (lb, kips, or kg)

P_P resultant of passive earth pressure (lb, kips, or kg)

PL plastic limit (dimensionless)

PI plasticity index (dimensionless)

p pressure (lb per sq ft, kips per sq ft, or kg per sq cm), also normal stress on failure plane

$\bar{p}$ effective stress at failure, effective pressure (lb per sq ft or kg per sq cm)

Q discharge (cu ft per sec or cu cm per sec); total load (lb, kips, or kg)

q pressure on soil (lb per sq ft, kips per sq ft, or kg per sq cm)

q_a allowable soil pressure (lb per sq ft, kips per sq ft or kg per sq cm)

q_0 ultimate bearing capacity of soil (lb per sq ft or kg per sq cm)

q_r compressive strength from triaxial shear test (lb per sq ft or kg per sq cm)

q_s safe bearing capacity (lb per sq ft, kips per sq ft, or kg per sq cm)

q_u unconfined compressive strength (lb per sq ft or kg per sq cm)

r radius

S degree of saturation, shear force (lb)

SF safety factor

s shear strength (lb per sq ft or kg per sq cm)

T time factor

T_0 surface tension (lb per ft or gm per cm)

t time (sec, min, or days)

U per cent consolidation uplift force

u neutral stress (lb per sq ft or kg per sq cm)

V volume (cu ft or cu cm)

W weight (lb, gm, or kg)

w water content

z depth (ft or cm, measured positive downward)

α angle of plane with major principal plane, also angle of failure plane with major principal plane

β angle of face of earth dam, embankment or backfill behind a retaining wall with respect to a horizontal plane

γ unit weight (lb per cu ft or gm per cu cm)

γ_w unit weight of water (lb per cu ft or gm per cu cm)

γ' unit weight of soil submerged in water (lb per cu ft or gm per cu cm)

γ_d weight of soil solids in cubic foot of soil (lb per cu ft or gm per cu cm)

Δ change or increment (used as prefix)

δ angle of wall friction

ϵ strain (dimensionless)

ν Poisson's ratio

ρ contact settlement (ft or cm)

σ normal stress (lb per sq ft, kips per sq ft, or kg per sq cm)

$\bar{\sigma}$ effective normal stress

$\sigma_1, \sigma_2, \sigma_3$ principal stresses

σ_c preconsolidation load

σ_h horizontal stress

σ_0 initial stress

σ_v vertical stress

σ_α normal stress on plane making angle of α with major principal plane

τ shear stress

τ_α shear stress on plane making angle of α with major principal plane

ϕ angle of internal friction

1... The NATURE of SOILS

The site for a supermarket was strategically located at the intersection of two main streets, but most of the property was a hillside. In order to provide level space for the building and for the parking of automobiles, a wide cut was made at the toe of the slope. Of course this resulted in a steeper hillside, but since the soil appeared to be very stiff, the builder assumed that it would be safe. A few months later the owner of the property noticed that the rear corner of his new building, 20 ft from the toe of the cut, was rising. At the same time the driveway between the building and the hill was narrowing. The builder diagnosed the cause as sliding of the earth at the toe of the slope, and he erected a concrete retaining wall to restrain the movement. Instead of stopping the slide, the wall moved with the hill toward the building. Frantically the contractor drove steel sheet piling between the building and the hillside to support the concrete wall and the hill. The movement continued at the same rate. Finally, in desperation, he constructed a horizontal reinforced concrete beam against the sheet piling and supported the beam with steel H-piles driven at an angle and bearing on rock. The hillside, the wall, the sheeting, and the beam continued to advance on the building.

An investigation of soil conditions disclosed that the stiff clay in the hillside absorbed water and expanded when the weight on the soil was reduced by the cutting at the toe. The expansion took place slowly, and therefore the freshly excavated slope was stable. The expanded soil was much weaker than in its original state and was incapable of supporting itself on the new-cut slope. The retaining wall and the sheeting were designed on the basis of the ordinary formulas and were incapable of resisting the unsupported mass in motion on the hillside.

The project was not large and the cost of the excavation and the build-

1

ing was just over $100,000. The cost of the retaining wall, the sheet piling, and the concrete beam was $80,000, or nearly as much as the original project, but they were of no value in correcting the difficulty. As a result the entire project was a financial disaster because correction of the foundation fault would be more expensive than the value of the building.

Such failures are not uncommon and they illustrate the need for careful, scientific soils engineering on even small projects. While the soil conditions encountered in the preceding example were unusual, they could have been detected by an investigation costing less than $1,000, and a design for the hillside and the structure could have been prepared within the economic limits of the project.

Traditionally, soil problems have not received the attention they deserve from engineers and constructors. Too often designs have been based on handbooks written years ago, experiences with other sites that are not representative, or even on guesses about the soil properties. Only extremely generous safety factors (as high as 20 in some cases) have prevented serious failures. Too often construction operations involving soil have been based on blind trial and error, but costly failures and dead workmen are a high price to pay for experience.

1:1   Definition of Soil and Rock

The reason for the lack of a rational approach to problems of soil design and construction has been a lack of understanding of the complex nature and behavior of soils. Until the twentieth century engineers considered soil to be a sort of witch's brew—a mysterious mixture that was incapable of scientific study. Great advances in the techniques of studying soils have led to a better understanding of their nature and to rational methods in design and construction.

Definition of Soil   To a farmer, soil is the substance that supports plant life, whereas to the geologist it is an ambiguous term meaning the material that supports life plus the loose material or mantle from which it was derived. To the engineer the term *soil* has a broader meaning.

Earth, or *soil*, in the engineering sense is defined as *any unconsolidated material composed of discrete solid particles with gasses or liquids between.* The maximum particle size that qualifies as soil is not fixed but is defined by the function involved. For footing excavations and trenches where hand excavation is employed, and for the construction of fills in layers, the limiting size is 12-in. diameter (about 85 lb), the maximum size a man can lift. Where power shovels are used for excavation, the limit is sometimes given as ½ cu yd (about 1 ton).

Definition of Rock   Rock is defined by the engineer as any indurated material that requires drilling, wedging, blasting, or other methods of brute force for excavation. The minimum degree of induration that qualifies as rock has been defined by a compressive strength of 200 psi. In all cases the dividing line between soil and rock is not definite; there is a continuous series of materials from the loosest soil to the hardest rock, and any division into two categories must be arbitrary. In preparing engineering documents, such as specifications, the engineer must define the limit so that all who are affected will be in agreement.

Soils include a wide variety of materials such as the gravel, sand, and clay mixtures deposited by glaciers, the alluvial sands and silts and clays of the flood plains of rivers, the soft marine clays and beach sands of the coast, the badly weathered rocks of the tropics, and even the cinders, bed springs, tin cans, and ashes of a city dump. Soils can be well-defined mixtures of a few specific minerals or chaotic mixtures of almost anything. Problems in soil engineering, therefore, cannot be solved by simple data from some handbook but must be handled as unique situations requiring both scientific analysis and engineering judgment.

1:2   Development of Soil Engineering

Construction involving soil began before the dawn of history. Some of the first construction operations were the digging of holes to bury the dead or to dispose of excrement and the building of earth mounds for worship and burial. Earth, in the form of sun-dried brick or of mud daubed on interlaced sticks or reeds, was used in building houses.

The builders of the ancient civilizations, such as those of India and Babylon, have left numerous examples of their ability to handle soil problems. Some earth dams in India have been storing water for more than 2000 yr. The cities of Babylon were placed on fills to raise them above the flood plains, and the buildings were erected on stone mats that spread the loads to the weak soils below. These builders were skilled artisans who learned from their own bitter experiences or from the success and failures of others. During the Middle Ages craftsmen improved the art of construction involving soils, by the process of trial and error. They received little help from the early scientists, who felt that problems involving the soil were beneath the dignity of a gentleman.

Since the eighteenth century, however, the need for better structures led scientists and engineers to study soil problems and to try to analyze them like other problems in structural design. Such eminent investigators as Coulomb and Rankine, who are well known in the fields of physics and applied mechanics, turned their attention to the mechanics of soil masses. They started from mathematical expressions of soil strength or from crude experiments on piles of sand and from them developed expressions for earth pressure on walls and the bearing capacity of foundations. This procedure was logical and when applied to other problems in mechanics led to theories that are still in good repute. The theories they developed for soils, however, often proved to be dismal failures. Retaining walls failed, buildings settled, and excavations caved in when designed in accordance with theory.

The tremendous increase in the size of the structures in the early twentieth century and the need for greater economy in their construction forced many brilliant engineers to re-evaluate the work of the earlier investigators and to develop new and more realistic methods of analyzing soil masses. The work of Fellenius in Sweden, Kogler in Germany, Hogentogler in the United States, and above all the contributions of Karl Terzaghi in both Europe and the United States brought about the birth of a new phase of civil engineering—*soil mechanics*, and its application to practical problems, *soils engineering*. Since the middle 1930's soil mechanics has become an indispensible tool to the planner and designer and an aid to the builder who must work with the ground.

Types of Problems in Soils Engineering   Two distinct types of problems are involved in soils engineering. The first type deals with soils as they actually occur in nature. Buildings ordinarily are founded on undisturbed soils, excavations and highway cuts are made through natural soil deposits, and drainage networks are constructed to remove water from existing soil masses. The second type of problem involves soils as raw materials for construction. Fills for highways and railroads, earth dams and levees, and airport and highway subgrades use soils as construction materials. The soils are changed from their original characteristics into new materials in a way similar to that in which sand, cement, and stone are made into concrete.

In handling either type of problem, the engineer must keep one thought uppermost in his mind—he is dealing with highly complex materials and with variable ingredients that at times will appear to defy all laws of nature. With careful study based on scientific analysis and sound judgment, even the most difficult problems can be analyzed. The numerical results often are not accurate in more than one or two significant figures, but in most cases the accuracy is as good as that obtained in calculating the stresses in a structure caused by assumed live loads.

1:3 Phases of Soil Composition

Three-Phase Composition Since soils by definition include all un-consolidated materials, we may expect them to be composed of many different ingredients in all three states or phases of matter—solid, liquid, and gaseous. The interrelations of the weights and volumes of the differ-ent phases are important because they help define the condition or the physical makeup of a soil. The definitions and terms attached to these relations must be clearly understood before the engineer can gain an understanding of the properties of soils.[1:1]

The volumes and weights of the different phases of matter in a soil can be represented by a block diagram or graph such as Fig. 1:1.[1:2] The

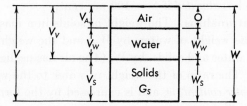

Fig. 1:1 Block diagram showing relationship of weights and volumes of solids, air, and water in a mass of soil.

total volume or weight is denoted by the entire block; the solids, by the lower section; the liquids, by the middle section; and the gases, by the upper section. For all practical purposes the gases may be considered to be air (although methane is occasionally found in some soils containing decaying organic matter), and the liquids are ordinarily water (although in some instances the water may contain small quantities of dissolved salts). The composition of the solids, however, varies considerably and will be discussed in detail in Art. 1:4.

Volume Relationships The volume of the solids in a mass of soil is denoted as V_s, the volume of the water V_w, and the volume of the air V_a. The volume of the mass of soil, including air, water, and solids is V. The space between the solid particles that is occupied by air and water is called the *voids* and its volume is denoted V_v. The ratio of the volume of voids to the volume of solids is expressed by the *void ratio, e,* as

$$e = \frac{V_v}{V_s}. \tag{1:1}$$

The void ratio is always expressed as a decimal. A second way of expressing the relation between voids and solids is the *porosity, n,* which is
defined by

$$n = \frac{V_v}{V} \times 100 \text{ per cent} \tag{1:2}$$

and is always expressed as a percentage.

The *degree of saturation, S,* expresses the relative volume of water in the
voids and is always expressed as a percentage,

$$S = \frac{V_w}{V_v} \times 100 \text{ per cent.} \tag{1:3}$$

A soil is said to be *saturated* if $S = 100$ per cent.

Weight Relationships   The weight of solids in a mass of soil is denoted by W_s; the weight of water, by W_w; and the weight of the entire
mass, including water and solids, by W. (The air has negligible weight, so
it is neglected.) The ratio of the weight of water to the weight of solids
is termed the *water content, w,* and is expressed by the formula

$$w = \frac{W_w}{W_s} \times 100 \text{ per cent.} \tag{1:4}$$

The *unit weight* of the soil mass is the ratio of the weight of the mass
to the volume of the mass. It is denoted by the Greek letter γ (gamma)
and is expressed in pounds per cubic foot or in grams per cubic centimeter:

$$\gamma = \frac{W}{V}. \tag{1:5}$$

The *unit weight of water,* γ_w, is 62.4 lb per cu ft or 1 gm per cc.

The *specific gravity* of a substance is the ratio of its weight to the weight
of an equal volume of water. The specific gravity of a mass of soil (including air, water, and solids) is termed *mass specific gravity.* It is denoted by
G_m and may be expressed by the formula

$$G_m = \frac{\gamma}{\gamma_w} = \frac{W}{V\gamma_w}. \tag{1:6}$$

The *specific gravity of the solids, G_s,* (excluding air and water) is expressed by

$$G_s = \frac{W_s}{V_s \gamma_w}. \qquad (1:7)$$

Specific gravity is a dimensionless ratio and therefore has no units. It is the same in both the metric and English systems of measurement. Numerically the specific gravity and unit weight are equal in the metric system but not in the English system.

Computations Involving Relationships The relations between volumes and masses are very important in many types of soil calculations such as those to determine the stability of a soil mass, to estimate building settlements, or to specify the amount of compaction necessary to construct an earth fill. These calculations are the arithmetic of soil mechanics and must be mastered before proceeding further. In making each calculation, a block diagram showing the relation of the different phases should be drawn and the different data entered on it as shown in the following examples.

Example 1:1 Calculate the unit weight, void ratio, water content, porosity, and degree of saturation of a chunk of moist soil weighing 45 lb and having a volume of 0.43 cu ft (Fig. 1:2). When dried out in an oven, the soil weighed 40 lb. The specific gravity of the solids was found to be 2.67.

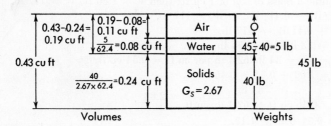

Fig. 1:2 Block diagram showing computations for weights and volumes in Example 1:1.

(1) $V = 0.43$ cu ft, $W = 45$ lb, $G_s = 2.67$, $W_s = 40$ lb.

(2) $W_w = 45 - 40 = 5$ lb.

(3) $\gamma = 45$ lb/0.43 cu ft $= 105$ lb per cu ft.

(4) $G_m = 105/62.4 = 1.68$.

(5) $V_w = \dfrac{5 \text{ lb}}{62.4 \text{ lb/cu ft}} = 0.08$ cu ft. $\quad V_w = \dfrac{W_w}{\gamma_w}$

(6) $V_s = \dfrac{40 \text{ lb}}{62.4 \text{ lb/cu ft} \times 2.67} = 0.24$ cu ft.

(7) $V_v = 0.43 - 0.24 = 0.19$ cu ft.

(8) $V_a = 0.19 - 0.08 = 0.11$ cu ft.

(9) $e = 0.19/0.24 = 0.79$.

(10) $n = (0.19/0.43) \times 100\% = 44\%$.

(11) $S = (0.08/0.19) \times 100\% = 42\%$.

(12) $w = (5/40) \times 100\% = 12\%$.

Example 1:2 Calculate the void ratio and specific gravity of solids of a saturated soil whose unit weight is 117 lb per cu ft and whose water content is 41 per cent (Fig. 1:3).

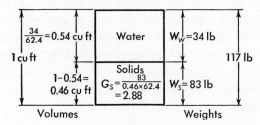

Volumes   Weights

Fig. 1:3 Block diagram showing computations for weights and volumes in
Example 1:2.

(1) $\gamma = 117$ lb/cu ft, $w = 41\%$, $S = 100\%$.

(2) Assume a mass of soil of 1 cu ft; then $V = 1$ cu ft, $W = 117$ lb.

(3) $W_w/W_s = 0.41$; $W_w + W_s = 117$ lb,
  $W_s + 0.41\,W_s = 117$ lb,
  $W_s = 83$ lb; $W_w = 34$ lb.

(4) $V_v = V_w = 34$ lb$/62.4$ lb per cu ft $= 0.54$ cu ft.

(5) $V_s = 1.00 - 0.54 = 0.46$ cu ft.

(6) $G_s = \dfrac{83 \text{ lb}}{0.46 \text{ cu ft} \times 62.4 \text{ lb/cu ft}} = 2.88$

(7) $e = 0.54/0.46 = 1.17$.

1:4 Composition of Soil Solids

The solids, or the soil grains as they are often called, play a major part in determining the properties of a soil. According to the engineering definition of soil, almost anything can become a soil solid. The most important materials, however, fall into three groups: the products of rock weathering, the products of organic decay, and man-made materials.

Rock Weathering Rock weathering is the breakdown of intact masses of rock into smaller pieces by mechanical, chemical, or solution processes. *Mechanical weathering*, or *disintegration*, is a combination of grinding, shattering, and breaking that reduces the rock to smaller and smaller fragments that have the same mineral composition as the original rock. It is caused by the freezing of water in cracks and pores, the impact of water, the abrasion of gravel and boulders carried by mountain streams and rivers, the pounding of water waves on beaches or cliffs, the sand blast of sand-laden desert winds, the expansion and contraction of rock by violent temperature changes, and by the plowing action of glaciers. *Chemical weathering*, or *decomposition*, is a chemical alteration of the rock minerals to form new minerals that usually have chemical and physical properties completely different from their parent materials. It is caused by the reaction of the minerals with water, dissolved carbon dioxide and oxygen from the air, organic acids from plant decay, and dissolved salts present in the water. *Solution* is the dissolving of soluble minerals from the rock, leaving the insoluble minerals behind as a residue. All three processes occur simultaneously but at different rates, depending on the climate, topography, and the composition of the original rock. In general, decomposition predominates in warm, humid regions and in areas with flat topography, and disintegration predominates in dry regions and areas with rugged topography. Solution obviously is predominant in humid regions underlain by soluble rocks.

One of the most important rock minerals is *silica*, silicon dioxide, usually present in the crystalline form of quartz. It is not subject to chemical weathering and is practically insoluble (it may dissolve at an extremely slow rate in water containing bases), but it will break down mechanically. However, in its crystalline form it is hard and tough with no planes of weakness; and so it breaks into irregular, angular fragments that require considerable abrasion to reduce them to finer and finer particles.

Feldspars constitute a second important group of rock-forming minerals that consist of potassium, sodium, calcium, or similar aluminum silicates. They are brittle, with pronounced planes of cleavage, and they break easily to form small prismlike particles. The feldspars are very susceptible to chemical breakdown, and the mechanical disintegration accelerates the chemical processes to such an extent that feldspar fragments are rarely found in soils in humid regions. The decomposition products of the feldspars are exceedingly variable, depending on the type of feldspar and on the weathering conditions, but they can be described in three groups; complex hydrous aluminum silicates, soluble or semi-soluble carbonates of sodium and similar metals, and silica (usually in a colloidal suspension). The hydrous aluminum silicates comprise a family called the *clay minerals*, that are physically very different from the feldspars from which they came.

Micas comprise a second family of silicate minerals that often contain iron and magnesium in addition to their potassium. The mica flakes are soft and resilient, with a pronounced cleavage. They split easily and break to form still smaller, thinner flakes. Their chemical breakdown is similar to that of the feldspars, producing the clay minerals, carbonates, and silica, but in addition various oxides of iron are formed from those containing iron. The chemical weathering of the micas is not so rapid as that of feldspar; and so mica is often present in soils in humid regions.

The *ferro-magnesian* family of minerals (including hornblende, olivine, pyroxene) are complex aluminum silicates that contain both iron and magnesium. They are moderately hard and tough, with no pronounced cleavage, and break mechanically into irregular dark-colored fragments. They alter chemically to form iron oxides, clay minerals, and the other products of silicate decomposition.

The *carbonate* minerals (calcite and dolomite) break down mechanically into both irregular and prismlike fragments. These are rather rare, however, because the minerals are so easily dissolved. The carbonates are carried away by percolating water, leaving behind any insoluble impurities such as silica, clay minerals, or iron oxide that were present in the original rock. Soils that are produced by rock weathering, therefore, are predominately quartz and clay minerals, with varying amounts of mica, iron oxide, and ferro-magnesian minerals. In very dry regions fragments of feldspar and the carbonate minerals may be present, while the amounts of clay minerals are small.

Clay Minerals[1:3]   The clay minerals are a highly complex family of hydrous aluminum silicates, having physical and chemical properties greatly different from each other, yet all with the same general composition. With a few exceptions they are extremely fine-grained crystals that resemble mica flakes in their appearance, as shown in Fig. 1:4. Structurally they are made up of repeating groups of atoms, linked together with chemical valence bonds to form sheets. One form consists of repeating groups of silicon atoms surrounded by oxygen atoms to make a *silica sheet*. A second form, the *alumina sheet*, consists of groups of aluminum atoms surrounded by oxygen atoms or hydroxyl (oxygen–hydrogen) atoms. The sheets are extremely thin, only about 5 to 10 angstrom units (0.000 000 5 to 0.000 001 mm), but are of indefinite extent in their length and width. The clay minerals consist of stacks or books of such sheets, with the character of the clay determined by the composition of the individual sheets and on their order of stacking.

To the soil engineer, three families of the clay minerals have proved to be most important: the *kaolinites*, the *montmorillonites*, and the *illites*.

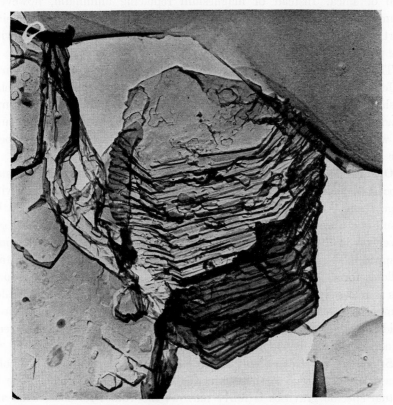

Fig. 1:4   Electron photomicrograph of kaolinite, showing individual plates overlapping to form a stack; magnified 7400 diam. (Courtesy of Electron Microscopy Laboratory, Engineering Experiment Station, Georgia Institute of Technology.)

The kaolinites consist of alternating silica and alumina sheets in a repeating sequence to form a stack of indefinite thickness. Sometimes these stacks are so thick they can be seen with an optical microscope, but usually they are submicroscopic. *Halloysite*, a peculiar member of the kaolinite family, develops curved sheets which form elongated tubes rather than stacks. The montmorillonites consist of an alumina sheet sandwiched between two silica sheets. The alumina sheet has been altered by the substitution of magnesium atoms for some of the aluminums, leaving an unbalanced electrical charge. The sandwiches, or units, stack together loosely, with water between, but separate easily. The illites are similar to the montmorillonites, with one alumina sheet between two of silica. Instead of magnesium replacing aluminum, however, aluminum replaces silicon, with the deficiency in electrical charge being partially made up by potassium ions. The illite units stack together with the potassium ions between them.

The identification of the clay minerals is extremely difficult. Three different procedures are employed: the electron microscope, which yields a shadow of the particle; x-ray diffraction, which indicates the atomic spacing; and differential thermal analysis, which measures the amount of water released from the mineral at different temperatures. At best the analysis is semiquantitative and is frequently inconclusive.

Organic Decomposition   Organic materials are a part of many surface soils and of soils deposited in swampy areas that are filled with vegetation. When the vegetable matter is only partially decomposed, the result is a fibrous material that is largely cellulose. Hydrogen sulfide gas given off in the process may partially dissolve in the water or become trapped in the soil voids. If the decomposition continues, various organic colloids form, imparting a greenish or black color to the soil. Methane gas is released which also can be trapped in the soil voids. Organic decomposition results in an acid-reducing environment which converts iron oxides to the ferrous state and which promotes the weathering of rock minerals and the development of kaolin-type clays.

Specific Gravities of Soil Solids   The specific gravity of a soil solid phase is the average of those minerals that are included. The range in actual specific gravities is fairly narrow; the values for most soils are between 2.65 and 2.75. Table 1:1 lists the specific gravities of common soil minerals.

1:5   Grain Size

The range in the sizes of soil particles or grains is almost limitless; the largest grains are by definition those that can be moved by hand, while the finest grains are so small they cannot be identified by an ordinary microscope. The particles produced by mechanical weathering are rarely smaller than 0.001 mm in diameter and are usually much larger, for nature's grinding processes are not very efficient and the small grains often escape further punishment by slipping through the voids between the larger grains. The products of chemical weathering, including iron oxides and the clay minerals, are tiny crystals which occasionally are larger than 0.005 mm in diameter but which are usually very much finer.

Table 1:1 SPECIFIC GRAVITY OF MINERALS

Mineral	Specific Gravity, G_s,
Quartz	2.66
Micas	2.8–3.2
Limonite (iron oxide)	3.6–4.0
Clay minerals	2.2–2.6
Cellulose (fibrous vegetable matter)	1.5

Grain Size Tests Two methods are commonly used to determine the grain sizes present in a soil. Calibrated sieves or screens having openings as large as 4 in. and as small as 0.074 mm (U.S. Standard No. 200) are used for separating the coarser grains. Sieves with smaller openings are available but are impractical for soil work. The portions finer than 0.1 mm can be measured by sedimentation. This is based on the principle that the smaller the size of a particle, the more slowly it settles through water. This method is unsatisfactory for grains smaller than 0.0005 mm because such particles are kept in suspension indefinitely through molecular agitation. For particles that have a near-spherical shape, both the sieve and the sedimentation tests give the same results in the size range in which they overlap. For flat particles, however, the sieve measures the intermediate dimension, or width, while the sedimentation indicates the

Table 1:2 STANDARD SIEVE SIZES

U.S. Standard		British Standard		Metric Standard	
No.	Diameter (mm)	No.	Diameter (mm)	No.	Diameter (mm)
4	4.76	5	3.36	5000	5.00
6	3.36	8	2.06	3000	3.00
10	2.00	12	1.41	2000	2.00
20	0.84	18	0.85	1500	1.50
40	0.42	25	0.60	1000	1.00
60	0.25	36	0.42	500	0.50
100	0.149	60	0.25	300	0.30
200	0.074	100	0.15	150	0.15
		200	0.076	75	0.075

diameter of a sphere that settles at the same rate through water as the soil particle. This equivalent diameter is approximately the grain thickness. Particles smaller than 0.0005 mm can be measured by an electron microscope, but the data are of little use in soil engineering. Particles larger than 4 in. are measured by calipers.

Grain Size Scales Because of the extreme range in grain sizes, scientists and engineers have attempted to break the entire scale into smaller divisions. Many methods have been proposed, but all are arbitrary and no one method is better than another. A convenient scale, adopted by the ASTM, is shown on Fig. 1:5. The coarsest division is

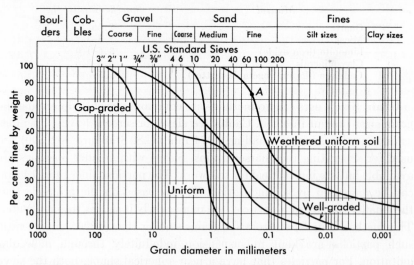

Fig. 1:5   Grain size chart and ASTM-ASCE grain size scale.[1:1]

gravel, which includes all soil grains larger than a No. 4 sieve. *Sand* includes all particles smaller than the No. 4 sieve and coarser than a No. 200. The grains smaller than the No. 200 sieve are the *fines*. This fraction is sometimes subdivided into *silt sizes*, the particles coarser than 0.002 mm, and *clay sizes*, the particles finer than 0.002 mm. Unfortunately any attempt to designate clay by particle size is misleading, for some soils finer than 0.002 mm contain no clay minerals and some clay mineral grains are larger than 0.002 mm.

Grain Size Chart   A better method of representing the different grain sizes in a soil is the logarithmic chart shown in Fig. 1:5. The entire range in grain sizes, plotted on a logarithmic scale, forms the horizontal divisions, while the percentages by weight of the soil grains that are finer than a given size form the vertical divisions. For example, point *A* on Fig. 1:5 means that 83 per cent by weight of that soil is finer than 0.2 mm. A curve drawn through all the points that represent a single soil is known as the *grain size curve* of that soil. The interrelation of the different grain sizes in a soil can be seen from the shape of grain size curve. A steep curve indicates that the grains are nearly the same size, and such a soil is termed *uniform*. A flat curve shows a wide range in grain sizes; such a soil is termed *well-graded*. Humps in the curve indicate that a soil is composed of a mixture of two or more uniform soils. Such a soil is *gap-graded*. A steep curve in the sand range that gradually becomes a long, flat curve in the fines range may indicate a soil that was formed by mechanical weathering and later altered by chemical weathering.

Effective Size and Uniformity   The *effective size* of the grains is defined as the size corresponding to 10 per cent on the grain size curve. It is given the symbol D_{10}. It has been found that the effective size is related to the ease with which water passes through the soil. A numerical measure of soil uniformity is the *uniformity coefficient*, C_u, proposed by Hazen. It is defined by the relation

$$C_u = \frac{D_{60}}{D_{10}}. \tag{1:8}$$

Soils with the value of C_u less than 4 or 5 are termed *uniform;* soils whose C_u is greater than 10 are termed *well-graded.*

1:6   Grain Shape

The shape of soil grains is fully as important as the size in determining the physical properties of the soil mass, but since shape is difficult to measure by an exact laboratory test, it is often neglected. Three classes of grain shapes have been defined: *bulky* grains, *scalelike* or *flakey* grains, and *needle-like* grains. Of these only the first two are important, for needle-like grains occur only rarely.

When the length, width, and height of the soil particle are about the same, as in particles of sand or gravel, the shape is termed *bulky*. Bulky grains are formed by the mechanical breakdown of rock. They are rarely less than 0.001 mm in diameter and can be examined readily with a good magnifying glass or with a microscope (Fig. 1:6).

When bulky grains are first formed by crushing or grinding of rock they are rough and sharp and are described as *angular*, as in Fig. 1:7a. After tumbling and wearing against one another for countless centuries, the sharp edges are worn down and the grains become more and more like small ball bearings and are termed *well-rounded*. Between these two extremes the soil grain may be successively *subangular*, *subrounded*, and *rounded*, as shown in Fig. 1:7. Small particles of river sand deposited close to their point of origin tend to be angular or subangular, while

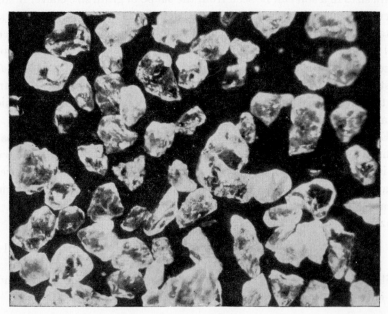

Fig. 1:6 Photomicrograph of a bulky-grained beach sand; magnified 54 diam. (Photo by G. B. Sowers.)

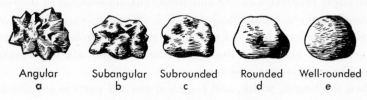

Angular   Subangular   Subrounded   Rounded   Well-rounded
a   b   c   d   e

Fig. 1:7 Shapes of bulky particles.

the larger particles deposited in the same way are often subrounded and rounded. Beach sands that have been tossed about by the waves are usually subangular to subrounded, while beach gravels are rounded to well rounded. Wind-blown sands tend to be well rounded, while very fine-grained, water-borne sands tend to remain angular. The microscopic examination of soils is a fascinating experience in which a common river sand is seen to be a mass of shining quartz fragments, and the dirty brown grains in a beach sand may be found to be tiny garnets.

Flakey or *scalelike* grains have the same shape as a sheet of paper or a flake of mica; they are extremely thin compared with their length and width. Some flakey grains larger than 0.001 mm are formed by the mechanical breakdown of mica, but most are the minute submicroscopic crystals of the clay minerals.

Effect of Grain Shape Soils composed of bulky grains behave like loose brick or broken stone. They are capable of supporting heavy, static loads with little deformation, especially if the grains are angular. Vibration and shock, however, cause them to be displaced easily. Soils composed of flakey grains tend to be compressible and deform easily under static loads, like dried leaves or loose paper in a basket. They are relatively stable when subjected to shock and vibration. The presence of only a small percentage of flakey particles is required to change the character of the soil and to produce the typical behavior of a flakey material.

1:7 Interreaction of Water and Soil Particles[1:4]

If equal volumes of dry sand and water are mixed together in a container, some of the water will fill the voids in the sand and the excess will merely rise above the sand surface. If more or less water is used, the effect on the sand will be the same (provided there is enough to fill the soil voids), and the only difference will be the amount of the excess water that covers the sand. The sand feels gritty, either dry or wet, and does not appear to be affected by the water. If equal volumes of dry montmorillonite clay (such as commercial bentonite) and water are mixed, the water will disappear and a sticky, greasy-feeling mass will be formed. If two volumes of water to one of montmorillonite are used, the result will be similar: The water will disappear and a sticky mass will be formed. The only difference is that the second mass will be somewhat softer than the first. In the case of the clay mineral, there is a reaction between the solid and the water, which results in a change in the characteristics of both. This phenomenon is termed *adsorption*, the binding of the water to the solid surface, and it has a profound effect on the physical properties of any soils containing minerals which exhibit it.

The exact causes for adsorption are not clearly understood, but they appear to be the result of electric charges in the particle surface. These arise from at least four sources: (1) the unsatisfied molecular bonds at the edges of the crystals and at broken edges of other particles; (2) the electrical unbalance caused by substitution of an atom of lower valence, such as magnesium (+2) for aluminum (+3), in the sheets of clay minerals such as montmorillonite; (3) the non-uniform distribution of electric charge within the particle surface; and (4) the disassociation of hydrogen ions from the particle surface in water. The intensity of the charge is greatest in the clay minerals but small in the soil fragments, where it is probably limited to the broken edges. The total electric charge per unit of soil volume depends on the surface area of the particles and the broken edges as well as the intensity of the charge. In the soil fragments with a small charge and a small surface area, compared with the volume, the total charge is negligible. In the clay minerals, which are flat and fine-

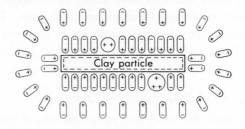

⊕ Cation   Tightly adsorbed water layer   Loosely adsorbed water layer

Fig. 1:8   Adsorbed water and cations surrounding a clay particle.

grained and which have relatively high intensities, the total charge is very high.

Molecules of water, an electrolyte, are polar, with one side positive and the other side negative, owing to the non-symmetrical orientation of the hydrogen and oxygen atoms. These polar molecules cling to the soil particles, as iron filings to a magnet, and create a layer of water around the particle in which the molecules are oriented in a definite direction, as shown in Fig. 1:8. In montmorillonite clays and some illites the water also enters between the layers in a stack, causing the stack to expand and the soil to swell. In the kaolinites the water is largely confined to the outer surfaces and the broken edges. Depending on the intensity of the electric charge that holds them and on the availability of water, these layers may be thin or very thick. The innermost layers are so tightly attached that they assume the physical properties of ice, whereas the outer layers are less securely bound. The thickness of the icelike layers may be as much as 10 angstrom units (or 0.000 001 mm), and the total water thickness may approach 400 angstrom units. (These values are of the same order of magnitude as the thickness of the crystal sheets in the clay mineral.)

Soils in which the adsorbed layer is thick in comparison with the grain thickness are greatly different from those with little or no adsorbed water. The most pronounced characteristic of the former is their ability to deform plastically without cracking when mixed with varying amounts of water. When little water is present in a soil containing clay minerals, the grains are extremely close together and are therefore strongly attracted to each other by the same force that acts between all bodies, depending on their mass and separation. This attraction holds the particles together, creating a relatively rigid mass. With increasing amounts of adsorbed water, the particles are forced to separate; the particle attraction becomes smaller and the mass is less rigid. With sufficiently large amounts of water the solid particles are separated far enough so that their mutual attraction is negligible and the soil becomes a fluid.

Effect of Ions In addition to water the soil particles attract any ions that may be present in solution. The predominately negative electric charges of most clay minerals attract positive ions or cations such as hydrogen, sodium, potassium, iron, and aluminum to the particle surface, although some negative ions may be attracted to local points of positive charge. The ions partially neutralize the attraction of the particle for water. Because of their bulk and their strong valence bonds, certain cations such as calcium have a greater ability to do this than others, such as sodium. By introducing a strong concentration of calcium ions into the soil by the addition of lime or calcium chloride, it is possible to force a soil to substitute calcium cations for others already present and adsorbed. This process is termed *base exchange* and it makes it possible to modify the water-adsorbing characteristics of a clay mineral and thereby the properties of the soil. Use is made of this principle in soil stabilization, to be discussed in Chapter 8.

Cohesive and Cohesionless Soils Soils in which the adsorbed water and particle attraction work together to produce a mass which holds together and deforms plastically at varying water contents are known as *cohesive soils* or *clays* (largely because this cohesive quality results from some proportion of clay minerals). Those soils that do not exhibit this cohesion are termed *cohesionless*. Soils composed of bulky grains are cohesionless regardless of the fineness of their particles. Many soils are mixtures of bulky grains and clay minerals and exhibit some degree of varying consistency with changes in moisture. These, too, are termed cohesive soils if the effect is significant. Obviously there is no sharp dividing line between cohesionless and cohesive, but it is often convenient to divide soils into these two groups for the purpose of study.

1:8 Atterberg Limits

The Swedish soil scientist Atterberg developed a method of describing quantitatively the effect of varying water content on the consistency of fine-grained soils. He established stages of soil consistency and defined definite but arbitrary limits for each.

Table 1:3 ATTERBERG LIMITS

Stage	Description	Boundary or Limit
Liquid	A slurry; pea soup to soft butter; a viscous liquid	
		Liquid limit (LL)
Plastic	Soft butter to stiff putty; deforms but will not crack	
		Plastic limit (PL)
Semisolid	Cheese; deforms permanently but cracks	
		Shrinkage limit (SL)
Solid	Hard candy; fails completely upon deformation	

Each boundary or limit is defined by the water content that produces a specified consistency; the difference between the limits represents the range in water content for which the soil is in a certain stage or state.

The *liquid limit* (LL) is defined as the water content at which a trapezoidal groove of specified shape, cut in moist soil held in a special cup, is closed after 25 taps on a hard rubber plate. The *plastic limit* (PL) is the water content at which the soil begins to break apart and crumble when rolled by hand into threads $\frac{1}{8}$ in. in diameter. The *shrinkage limit* (SL) is the water content at which the soil reaches its theoretical minimum volume as it dries out from a saturated condition. This is described in Art. 2:8.

In themselves the Atterberg limits mean little, but as indexes to the significant properties of a soil they are very useful. The liquid limit has been found to be directly proportional to the compressibility of a soil. The difference between the liquid and plastic limits, termed the *plasticity index* (PI), represents the range in water contents through which the soil is in the plastic state. It is inversely proportional to the ease with which water passes through the soil. The most important use of the Atterberg limits is in classifying fine-grained soils. Soils with thick adsorbed layers have high plasticity indexes; soils with thin adsorbed layers have low plasticity indexes. Soils with high liquid limits have high ratios of particle surface area to particle volume, whereas soils with low liquid limits have low ratios. The Atterberg limits are particularly useful in identifying and classifying cohesive soils, which will be discussed in Chapter 3.

1:9 Soil Structure

The mineral grains, water, and air are put together in many different ways to form the materials we identify as soils. Their arrangement is known as the *structure* of soil. A nearly limitless variety of structural arrangements is possible, depending on the character of the particles, the adsorbed water, and the manner in which the soil is formed. For the purpose of study, most of these can be placed in three groups: cohesionless, cohesive, and skeletal. However, some soils encountered have combination structures or arrangements that are completely different. Therefore the soils engineer must study each soil carefully and should not draw from any arbitrary grouping unwarranted conclusions regarding the soil behavior.

Cohesionless Structures The cohesionless soils are composed largely of bulky grains that can be represented by spheres or similar regular, equidimensional bodies. The simplest arrangement of such particles is similar to oranges stacked on a grocer's counter: Each grain is in contact with those surrounding it. Such a structure is termed *single grain* and is typical of sands and gravels.

Depending on the relative positions of the grains, it is possible to have a wide range in void ratios. If we pack uniform, rounded grains in a box, with each directly above the one below as shown in Fig. 1:9a, a structure with a void ratio of about 0.90 is formed. If we place them so that each succeeding layer falls into the depression between the spheres in the layer below, as in Fig. 1:9b, a structure with a void ratio of about 0.35 is formed. The arrangement corresponding to the higher void ratio is described as *loose*, and that corresponding to the lower is described as *dense*. Various arrangements of the same grains could be made to produce any void ratio between these two limits.

Similar variations in void ratio are possible in cohesionless soils having irregular grain shapes and mixed sizes. The highest void ratio possible for a given soil (and still have each particle touching its neighbors) is the *maximum void ratio*, e_{max}. The smallest void ratio is the *minimum void ratio*, e_{min}. The approximate minimum void ratio of a soil is determined by compacting it by combined tamping and vibration until no further densification is possible. The tamping must not be so vigorous that the soil grains are fractured, however. The approximate maximum void ratio is found by pouring the dry soil through a funnel into a graduated cylinder.

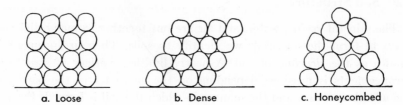

a. Loose   b. Dense   c. Honeycombed

Fig. 1:9   Cohesionless soil structures.

For uniform spheres, $e_{max} = 0.90$ and $e_{min} = 0.35$, and the range in e between the limits is 0.55. Soils with angular grains tend to have both higher maximum and minimum void ratios than spheres, but the range is usually somewhat smaller. Soils with mixed grain sizes, on the other hand, usually have lower values for e_{max} and e_{min}, and the range in e is also smaller than for uniform spheres. Soils with flakey particles often have much higher values for e_{max} and e_{min} because the flakes bridge over large voids.

Table 1:4   TYPICAL VOID RATIOS AND WEIGHTS OF SINGLE GRAINED STRUCTURES

Soil Description	Void Ratio		Unit Weight (lb/cu ft)	
	Maximum	*Minimum*	*Minimum*	*Maximum*
Uniform subangular sand	0.85	0.50	118 (sat)	131 (sat)
			89 (dry)	110 (dry)
Well-graded subangular sand	0.70	0.35	123 (sat)	139 (sat)
			97 (dry)	122 (dry)
Very well-graded silty sandy gravel	0.65	0.25	125 (sat)	145 (sat)
			100 (dry)	132 (dry)
Micaceous sand and silt	1.25	0.80	110 (sat)	122 (sat)
			75 (dry)	94 (dry)

The relation between the actual void ratio of a soil and its limiting values, e_{max} and e_{min}, is expressed by the *relative density* or relative void ratio D_d:

$$D_d = \frac{e_{max} - e}{e_{max} - e_{min}} \times 100 \text{ per cent.} \qquad (1:9)$$

A natural soil is said to be loose if its relative density is less than about 50 per cent; dense, if it is higher.

The properties of loose, single-grained structures are greatly different from those of dense soil. The loose soil, with its grains perched directly on top of one another, is inherently unstable. Shock and vibration cause the grains to move and shift into a more dense, stable arrangement. The rounded particles are particularly unstable when loose, but even angular grains exhibit instability if their void ratios are sufficiently high. Dense, single-grain structures are inherently stable and are only slightly affected by shock and vibration. Both loose and dense structures are capable of supporting static loads with little distortion.

Honeycombed Structure   Under some conditions it is possible to arrange cohesionless bulky grains in crude arches so that the void ratio exceeds the maximum for the single-grain arrangement. Such a structure has a negative relative density and is termed *honeycombed*, Fig. 1:9c. Honeycombed structures can develop when extremely fine sand or co-hesionless silt particles settle out of still water. Because of their small size they settle slowly and wedge between each other without rolling into more stable positions, as do the larger particles. The structure also may develop when damp, fine sand is dumped into a fill or a pile without densification, a condition often termed *bulked*.

The honeycombed structure is usually able to support static loads with little distortion, similar to the way in which a stone arch carries its load without deflection. Under vibration and shock, however, the struc-ture may collapse. In some cases this merely results in rapid settlement of the soil mass. In others the collapse sets off a chain reaction of soil failure that converts the entire mass momentarily into a heavy liquid capable of filling an excavation or swallowing a bulldozer. Fortunately such struc-tures are not common and usually occur in lenses and pockets of limited extent. Because of the hazards involved, however, the engineer should view all water-deposited silts and very fine sands with suspicion until void-ratio tests prove them to be stable.

Cohesive Structure—Dispersion and Floculation   In cohesive soils the structure is determined largely by the clay minerals and the forces acting between them. The clay particles in water are acted upon by a complex series of forces, some of which, including the universal attractive forces and mutual attraction to individual cations, tend to pull the particles together; others, such as the electric charge on each grain and the electric charges on the adsorbed cations, cause the particles to repel one another. The forces of both attraction and repulsion increase, but at different rates, as the distance between particles decreases. In a dilute suspension with wide particle spacings, the total repulsion usually exceeds the attraction. The particles remain apart and stay in suspension or settle very slowly while bounding about from the agitation of the water molecules, a motion termed *Brownian movement*. Such a system is termed *dispersed*. Dispersion can be increased by adding materials which increase the repulsion forces without increasing the attraction. Dispersing agents like sodium silicate and sodium tetraphosphate are used in the sedimentation test for soil grain size to ensure that the indi-

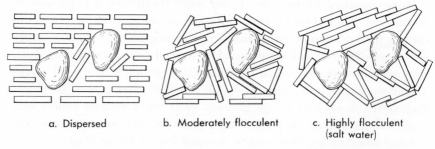

a. Dispersed   b. Moderately flocculent   c. Highly flocculent
                                               (salt water)

Fig. 1:10 Cohesive soil structures. (Adapted from T. W. Lambe.[1:5,1:6])

vidual particles do not stick together and give a false indication of their equivalent diameter.

When the particle spacing is extremely small, as in a soil of a low water content, the attraction exceeds the repulsion and the particles hang together in a cohesive solid or semisolid, separated by their adsorbed layers. This effect can also be produced in a dilute suspension by reducing the repulsive forces. The addition of an electrolyte supplies ions to the soil particles, which partially neutralize the particle charges and thereby reduce their repulsion. The particles then attract each other even though widely spaced, and they move together and stick in a heterogeneous loose arrangement termed a *floc*. Such flocs often contain hundreds of individual particles and are sometimes visible to the naked eye.

Dispersed Structures The structural arrangement formed from a dispersed soil is shown diagrammatically in Fig. 1:10a. The repulsion between the particles as they come close causes each one to position itself for the maximum grain-to-grain distance in a given volume soil. The resulting structure is very much like flat stones laid on top of one another to form a wall. The bulky grains are distributed throughout the mass and cause localized departures from the pattern. This arrangement is termed an *oriented*, or a *dispersed*, structure. It is typical of soils that are mixed or remolded, such as by glacial action (glacial till), or of soils compacted under wet conditions in a man-made fill, or developed by sedimentation in the presence of a dispersing agent. Soils having a dispersed structure are likely to be dense and watertight. Typical void ratios are often as low as 0.5 but can be as high as 1 or 2, depending on the type of clay and the water content.

Flocculent Structures The arrangement in a flocculent structure is shown in Fig. 1:10b and c. It forms from a soil-water suspension which initially is dispersed, such as the suspended solids carried by a river. A sudden introduction of an electrolyte like salt water brings about flocculation. The particles stick together in a haphazard way, with the edge of one particle touching the face of another and with bulky grains scattered throughout. Considerable free water is trapped in the large voids between the particles, in addition to the adsorbed water already immobilized by the clay. Flocculent structures are typical of water-deposited clays. The degree of flocculation depends on the type and concentration of clay particles and on the electrolyte. Deposits formed in the sea, which is a strong electrolyte, are frequently highly flocculent, with void ratios as large as 2 to 4. Fresh-water deposits, acted on by the weak electrolytes brought by rivers from different regions, are likely to be only partially flocculent or even dispersed. By way of contrast, organic acids from plant decay in shallow ponds and marshes may produce a high degree of flocculation.

Flocculent soils are light in weight and very compressible but are relatively strong and insensitive to vibration because the particles are tightly bound by their mutual attraction. A peculiar characteristic is their sensitivity to remolding. If the undisturbed soil is thoroughly mixed without the addition of water, it becomes soft and sticky as though water had been added to it. In fact water has been added, for the bond between the particles has been destroyed so that the free water trapped between them has been released to add to the adsorbed layers at the former points of contact. This softening upon remolding is termed *sensitivity* and will be discussed at more length in the next chapter. Construction operations in flocculent clays are difficult because the soils become softer as equipment works on top of them and may develop into a sea of mud even in dry weather.

Composite Structures   Composite structures (Fig. 1:11) consist of a framework of bulky grains arranged like the cohesionless bulky grain arrangements and held together by a binding agent. A wide variety of such structures can develop, depending on the relative amounts of the binder and the bulky grains, the type of binder, and the method of deposition.

A number of different types of binder are found. Clay that has been highly compressed or dried, so that it is stiff or hard, and calcium car-

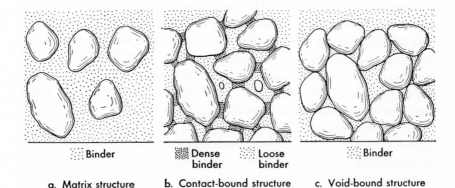

::: Binder   ▓ Dense   ::: Loose   ::: Binder
                      binder   binder

a. Matrix structure   b. Contact-bound structure   c. Void-bound structure

Fig. 1:11   Composite soil structures.

bonate are the most widespread. They are usually strong but may be weakened by water. Various iron oxides and colloidal silica from rock weathering also are encountered as binders and are relatively insensitive to softening by water.

In the *matrix* structure the volume of the bulky grains is less than about twice that of the binder so that the bulky grains float in a binder matrix, as shown in Fig. 1:11a. If the binder is clay, this is merely another form of a cohesive structure, and the physical properties are essentially those of a cohesive soil. With other binders the matrix structure is a form of rock whose physical properties depend on either the binder or the bulky grain, whichever is the weaker.

When the volume of the bulky grains is more than about twice that of the binder, skeletal structures develop. These take two forms: *contact bound* and *void bound*, depending on the position of the binder between the grains. In the contact-bound structure, the binder is concentrated between the points of contact of the bulky grains, holding them apart as stones are set in mortar. It can form in a number of ways. When bulky grains and clay settle simultaneously out of water, some of the clay is caught between the bulky grains and is compressed by the increasing weight of the sediment into a relatively rigid solid. A soft clay–water mixture occupies the voids between the grains but probably contributes little to the binding. The reweathering of a soil composed largely of quartz and with some feldspar, mica, or partially weathered clay can form a contact-bound structure in which the material in the voids is altered or leached away, leaving the material caught between the contact points of the grains largely unaltered. Contact-bound structures also form when large amounts of bulky grains and small amounts of clay are mixed and then consolidated or compacted. This occurs naturally by glacial action where the ice mass plows up and mixes the materials and the weight of the ice compacts the resulting *till* to a rocklike solid. It occurs artificially where clay–sand or clay–gravel mixtures are used in constructing highway or airfield subgrades.

Contact-bound structures are relatively rigid, incompressible, and resistant to shock and vibration as long as the binder remains strong. When the voids are large and open so that water can seep through them, the calcium carbonate and clay binders may soften. If the bulky framework is loose or honeycombed, the weakened soil will collapse like a loose cohesionless soil. If the bulky framework is dense, the softened binder will extrude into the voids, resulting in some settlement and weakening.

In the void-bound structure, the bulky grains touch each other and the binder occupies the voids between them. This structure develops when the bulky grains are deposited first and the binder subsequently is deposited between them. Water seeping through a bulky grained soil can precipitate calcium carbonate, iron oxides, or silica to form a cemented sand or gravel which is rigid, strong, and dense. This structure also forms by the weathering of a rock such as granite, which consists of a framework of interconnected quartz grains with feldspar and micas between. The decomposition of silicate minerals leaves a quartz framework supported by clay minerals. Clay and fine bulky grains washed into a coarse sand or gravel deposit also can act as binders but not to the same degree as the binders that are precipitated. The void ratio of void-bound skeletal structures may be as low as 0.2, but typical values are 0.3 to 0.5.

The soil is rigid and incompressible and not likely to be softened by water.

Macrostructures   The continuous structure of natural soils is often altered by local conditions to develop a *macrostructure* or secondary structure. The primary cause is reweathering, and it is most pronounced in the uppermost few feet near the ground surface. The most prominent feature is cracking, caused by shrinkage and plant roots that divide the soil into blocks or columns. A second form is aggregation, in which clumps of grains are developed by reflocculation from organic acids and colloids, giving the soil a crumbly texture. A third form is cracking from faulting or shear. Discontinuities from the introduction of alien materials into the cracks are another form. A soil with a pronounced macrostructure is often characterized by planes of weakness and patterns of color that mark former cracks.

REFERENCES

1:1   "Glossary of Terms and Definitions in Soil Mechanics," *Journal of the Soil Mechanics and Foundations Division, Proceedings, ASCE*, Vol. 84, SM4, October, 1958.

1:2   A. Casagrande, *Notes on Soil Mechanics, First Semester*. Harvard University, Cambridge, 1939.

1:3   R. E. Grimm, *Clay Minerology*, McGraw-Hill Book Co., Inc., New York, 1953.

1:4   "Physico-Chemical Properties of Soil, A Symposium," *Journal of the Soil Mechanics and Foundations Division, Proceedings, ASCE*, Vol. 85, SM2, April, 1959.

1:5   T. W. Lambe, "The Structure of Inorganic Soil," *Proceedings, ASCE*, Separate 315, Vol. 79, October, 1953.

1:6   T. W. Lambe, "The Structure of Compacted Clay," *Journal of the Soil Mechanics and Foundations Division, Proceedings, ASCE*, Vol. 84, SM2, May, 1958.

Suggestions for Further Study

1. J. Feld, "Early History and Bibliography of Soil Mechanics," *Proceedings, Second International Conference on Soil Mechanics and Foundation Engineering*, Vol. I, Rotterdam, 1949.

2. References 1:3 and 1:4.

3. T. W. Lambe, *Soil Testing for Engineers*, John Wiley & Sons, Inc., 1951.

4. *Procedures for Testing Soils*, American Society for Testing Materials, Philadelphia, 1958.

PROBLEMS

1:1 The total weight of a chunk of moist soil is 330 lb. Its volume is 3 cu ft. The water content was found to be 27 per cent and the specific gravity of solids to be 2.72. Find e, n, S, and the weight per cubic foot.

1:2 A 50-cc sample of moist soil weighs 95 gm. It is dried out and found to weigh 75 gm. The specific gravity of solids is 2.67. Find e, n, w, S, and the weight per cubic foot of moist soil.

1:3 A 558-cc volume of moist soil weighs 1010 gm. Its dry weight is 918 gm and its specific gravity of solids is 2.67. Find e, n, w, S, and the weight per cubic foot of moist soil.

1:4 A 75-cc sample of moist soil weighs 120 gm. It is dried out and found to weigh 73 gm. The sample is assumed to be saturated, since it occurred below the ground water table. Compute its unit weight, w, e, n, and G_s.

1:5 A 120-gm sample of soil is 50 per cent saturated. The specific gravity of solids is 2.71 and the water content is 18 per cent. Compute the unit weight, e, and n.

1:6 A saturated soil has a water content of 38 per cent and a specific gravity of solids of 2.73. Find e, n, and the weight per cubic foot.

1:7 A saturated soil has a water content of 40 per cent and a unit weight of 114 lb per cu ft. Find e, n, and G_s.

1:8 A saturated soil has a water content of 47 per cent and a void ratio of 1.31. Find the weight per cubic foot and G_s.

1:9 A sand has a porosity of 37 per cent and a specific gravity of solids of 2.66.
   a. Compute e.
   b. Compute unit weight of sand if dry.
   c. Compute unit weight if sand is 30 per cent saturated.
   d. Compute unit weight if sand is completely saturated.

1:10 A soil has a unit weight of 109 lb per cu ft and a water content of 6 per cent. How much water in gallons should be added to each cubic yard of soil to raise the water content to 13 per cent? Assume that the void ratio remains constant.

1:11 A soil has a unit weight of 128 lb per cu ft and a water content of 12 per cent. What will be the water content if the soil dries out to a unit weight of 123 lb per cu ft and the void ratio remains unchanged?

1:12 A highly organic soil (peat) weighs 70 lb per cu ft saturated. The specific gravity of the solids is 2.35.
   a. Find e.
   b. Find the unit weight if the soil dries out without a change in void ratio.
   c. What would happen if the dried soil were subjected to a rising water table that reaches the ground surface?

1:13 How much difference in the unit weights and specific gravities of solids is there between a soil composed of pure quartz and a soil composed of 70 per cent quartz, 20 per cent mica, and 10 per cent iron oxide? Assume both soils are saturated and have void ratios of 0.63.

1:14   Plot on five-cycle semilog paper the grain size distribution curves from the following data. Compute the effective sizes and the uniformity coefficients of each. Record the percentage of sand, silt, and clay sizes according to the ASTM grain size scale.

Per cent Finer by Weight

Sieve No.	Lagoon Clay, Beaufort, S.C.	Glacial Till, Columbus, O.	Beach Sand, Daytona Beach, Fla.	River Sand– Gravel, Columbus, Ga.	Weathered Sandstone, Jasper, Ala.
½ in.	. . .	94	. . .	98	
No. 4	. . .	68	. . .	86	100
10	. . .	50	. . .	60	82
20	. . .	35	100	39	76
40	. . .	22	98	26	70
60	100	18	90	4	60
100	95	15	10	. . .	43
200	80	11	2	. . .	27
0.045 mm*	61	10	. . .	. . .	23
0.010 mm*	42	7	. . .	. . .	13
0.005 mm*	37	5	. . .	. . .	8
0.001 mm*	27	2	. . .	. . .	3

* From sedimentation test.

1:15   A soil has a liquid limit of 56 and a plastic limit of 25. The water content of the soil as it is excavated for use in a fill is 31 per cent.

     a. Compute the *PI* of the soil.

     b. Is the soil likely to be stiff or soft when compacted at its existing moisture content in a fill?

     c. What would a light rain do to the consistency of this soil?

1:16   Compute the typical unit weight in pounds per cubic foot of:

     a. Dense, well-graded, subangular, dry sand.

     b. Dense, well-graded, subangular, saturated sand.

     c. Loose, uniform, rounded, dry sand.

     d. Loose, uniform, rounded, saturated sand.

     e. Honeycombed, saturated silt.

     (Assume typical values for e and G_s.)

2... The PHYSICAL
PROPERTIES of SOILS

The design of every engineering structure requires an understanding of the physical properties of the materials to be used. In a soil the most important physical properties are those related to the water in the soil and those related to the behavior of the soil under stress. Permeability is a measure of the ability of water to pass through the soil and is especially important in the design of earth dams and the construction of drainage systems. Compressibility and consolidation deal with the changes in volume of a soil under load as encountered in the settlement of structures. Shear strength is an expression of the ability of a soil to sustain stress without failure and is particularly important in determining the bearing capacity of soils beneath foundations and the safety of earth masses against movement. Elasticity, the relationship between stress and strain, is important in determining the pressure of soils on retaining walls.

2:1 Surface Tension

Moisture in soil can be present in two forms: the adsorbed films surrounding the grains, and free water occupying part of or all the voids between the grains. If the voids are completely filled with water, the soil is saturated and the moisture is said to be continuous; if the voids are only partly filled, the moisture is discontinuous forming wedges of water between adjacent grains and moisture films around them (Fig. 2:1). The boundary between air and water in the voids is particularly important. The unbalanced molecular attraction of the water at this boundary gives rise to *surface tension*, a force acting parallel to the surface of the water in all directions, similar to the tension in a tightly stretched rubber membrane.

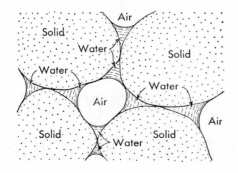

Fig. 2:1 Moisture wedges between soil grains.

Surface Tension Phenomena   Surface tension has many manifestations in soils. If a hole is dug in the ground, the soils encountered will be found to be saturated long before the ground water table (the level of water in a large pit or well) is reached. This results from capillary rise of water in the soil voids which form irregular tubes or pores. If a sample of a saturated clay is dried, it decreases in volume in the process. Surface tension acting in the soil voids acts to compress the soil structure and decrease the volume of the sample. A dried soil will absorb water rapidly and often will disintegrate in the process. The force of surface tension is partly responsible. Dry sand will run out between the fingers if one tries to mold it into a ball, but moist sand can be packed and formed easily. The tension in the moisture films between the grains is responsible for this moist strength. If the moist sand is immersed in water, the tiny moisture films will no longer exist, and the sand will again run between the fingers.

Capillary Tension   Surface tension is a force in the boundary between air and water acting parallel to the water surface. It has a magnitude of about

$$T_o = -0.005 \text{ lb/ft},$$
$$T_o = -0.075 \text{ gm/cm}$$

at 70 F. It decreases with increasing temperature and increases with decreasing temperature. (In soil mechanics *tension* is denoted by a negative sign.) The attraction of water for soil particles or clean glass is of the same or greater magnitude as surface tension, so there is a tendency for the boundary to extend itself along any such solid material. If the extension of the air–water boundary surface is prevented by some force such as gravity, the surface is stretched, forming a curved surface called a *meniscus* and developing a tensile stress in the water. This stress is known as *capillary tension*, and it may be computed for a cylindrical tube by considering the force developed by the stretched meniscus (Fig. 2:2). If α is the angle of contact between the meniscus and the solid

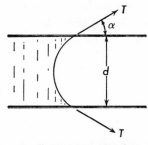

a. Capillary tension developed by meniscus

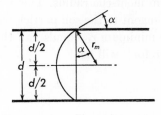

b. Meniscus radius

Fig. 2:2 Capillary tension and meniscus radius in uniform tube of diameter d.

material and d is the diameter of the tube, the total unbalanced force, F, developed along the perimeter of the meniscus is

$$F = \pi d T_o \cos \alpha. \tag{2:1a}$$

Since the area of the tube A is

$$A = \frac{\pi d^2}{4}, \tag{2:1b}$$

the capillary stress, u, is found to be

$$u = \frac{F}{A} = \frac{4 T_o \cos \alpha}{d}. \tag{2:2}$$

(Note that u has a negative sign when the value of T_o is substituted in the equation.)

   Meniscus Radius   The relation of capillary tension to the radius of the meniscus, r_m, can be found by considering the geometry of the meniscus (Fig. 2:2b):

$$\frac{d}{2} = r_m \cos \alpha. \tag{2:3}$$

If the expression for meniscus radius is substituted in the formula for capillary tension, then

$$u = \frac{2T_o}{r_m}.$$ (2:4)

It can be seen that for water in contact with air, the capillary tension is dependent only on the meniscus radius, and it varies inversely with it.

Maximum Tension   The maximum tension will occur with a minimum meniscus radius. This will occur when the surface of the meniscus is tangent to the soil particles and $\alpha = 0$. In a cylindrical tube, therefore, the minimum r_m equals half the tube diameter.   The maximum tension, therefore, will be

$$u_{max} = \frac{4T_o}{d}.$$ (2:5)

2:2   Capillary Tension in Soils

The interconnected pores or voids in the soil form irregular but definite capillary tubes. The maximum tension that can develop will vary from point to point, depending on the pore diameter and the degree of saturation. In a saturated pore in a cohesionless soil, experiments show that the effective pore diameter for capillary tension is approximately one-fifth D_{10}.

If a soil mass is completely saturated and inundated, the air–water boundaries disappear and capillary tension becomes zero. When a saturated soil is exposed to open air, capillary tension develops as soon as evaporation creates meniscuses at the surface. Since the soil moisture in a saturated soil is continuous, the water-tension stress developed at the air–water boundary is felt throughout the mass in a way similar to the way pressure applied at one point in a continuous body of fluid is transmitted throughout the body. The water, however, also obeys the law of hydrostatics:

$$\Delta u = \gamma_w \, \Delta z,$$ (2:6)

where z is measured positive downward. Therefore, below the elevation of the meniscus, the tension decreases; or, in other words, the pressure increases.

The capillary rise of water in a soil above the ground water table illustrates the combined effect of capillary tension and hydrostatic pressure. At the ground water elevation, a free surface, the water pressure u is zero. Below the water table the pressure increases in accordance with equation 2:6. Above the water table it decreases in the same way as shown in Fig. 2:3. The limiting negative stress in the water is the maximum capillary tension, $u_{\max}$. The height, h_c, to which the water can rise above the surface of zero pressure is found by equating the expression for hydrostatic pressure with that for maximum capillary tension:

$$h_c = \Delta z, \qquad \Delta u = u_{\max} = \frac{4T_o}{d},$$

$$h_c \gamma_w = \frac{4T_o}{d},$$

$$h_c = \frac{4T_o}{\gamma_w d}. \tag{2:7}$$

In a partially saturated soil the moisture may be either *continuous* or *discontinuous*, depending on whether the moisture wedges (Fig. 2:1) are

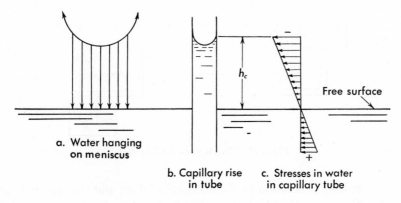

a. Water hanging on meniscus

b. Capillary rise in tube

c. Stresses in water in capillary tube

Free surface

Fig. 2:3 Capillary rise of water.

interconnected or discrete. If it is continuous, the variation of water stress with elevation follows equation 2:6, and the meniscus radius in each wedge adjusts itself to conform to the water stress. If the moisture is discontinuous, the stress in the water at any point is independent of the elevation and is determined only by the meniscus radius.

The height of capillary saturation in soils varies from a few inches in sands to over 100 ft in some clays, and a zone of partial saturation extends even higher, as will be discussed in Chapter 4. If the soil is homogeneous, the approximate height of rise can be computed from the effective grain size by using the relationship between pore diameter and grain size. The actual capillary rise and the maximum tension are seldom as great as the computations indicate, since in natural soils, cracks and seams are present which are so large that they rather than the soil pores control the capillary tension.

2:3 Permeability

The voids in a soil are not isolated cavities that hold water like storage reservoirs but are interconnected, small, irregular passageways through which water can flow in the same way as it flows through other conduits.

Laminar and Turbulent Flow   Two completely different types of flow can exist. *Turbulent flow* is characterized by chaotic, irregular movements of the fluid particles and by energy losses that are roughly proportional to the square of the velocity of flow. This type takes place at relatively high velocities in large diameter conduits such as in pipes carrying air or water. In *laminar flow* the water particles move in a

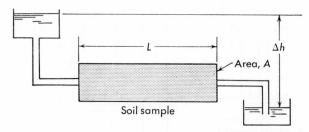

Fig. 2:4   Simple permeability test.

smooth, orderly procession in the direction of flow, and the energy losses are directly proportional to the velocity. Laminar flow takes place at low velocities in small conduits and is characteristic of all soils except the coarsest gravels.

Darcy's Law   A French physicist, Darcy, studied flow of water in soils by using apparatus similar to Fig. 2:4. He placed a sample of length L and cross-sectional area A in a tight-fitting tube with open ends. A reservoir of water was connected to each end of the tube. The level of the water in one reservoir was a distance of Δh above that in the other. (The term *head loss* is often applied to this difference in level, Δh.) He found by experiments that the flow of water, Q, in cubic centimeters per second was directly proportional to the area A and to the ratio $\Delta h/L$ (which is termed the *hydraulic gradient* and given the symbol i). This relation is expressed by

$$Q = kiA, \tag{2:8}$$

in which k is the constant of proportionality and is given the name *coefficient of permeability*, or simply *permeability*. This formula is true as long as laminar flow exists; it has been found to apply to all soils finer than coarse gravel, as long as the hydraulic gradient is less than 5.

Coefficient of Permeability The coefficient of permeability is a constant (having the dimensions of a velocity) that expresses the ease with which water passes through a soil. Ordinarily it is reported with the dimensions of centimeters per second or feet per minute but occasionally for very impervious soils, feet per day may be used.

The magnitude of the permeability coefficient depends on the viscosity of the water and on the size, shape, and area of the conduits through which the water flows. Viscosity is a function of the temperature: the higher the temperature, the lower the viscosity and the higher the permeability. Ordinarily the permeability is reported at 68 F (20 C). At 32 F (0 C) it is 56 per cent, and at 104 F (40 C) it is 150 per cent of the value at 68 F. The influence of the factors that determine the size and shape of the conduits is less specific and no valid mathematical expression for their effect has been derived. For clean cohesionless soils the permeability varies approximately as $(D_{10})^2$. Hazen's formula[2:1] for permeability of clean sands is

$$k = C(D_{10})^2, \qquad (2:9)$$

in which k is given in centimeters per second, D_{10} in millimeters, and C is a constant whose value ranges between 1 and 1.5. At the best, this formula gives only an indication of the order of magnitude of the permeability of clean sands. In soils having cohesion, the effect of grain size is even more pronounced, for part of the soil moisture around the fine clay particles is immobilized in the adsorbed layers. Void ratio is a factor in most soils, with the permeability approximately proportional to e^2. Grain shape and gradation are also important, particularly in the coarser soils, but it is difficult to express their effects quantitatively. The degree of saturation is a major factor because air in the voids reduces the cross-sectional area and may block some voids completely.

Permeability Tests Because of the numerous, complex factors that influence the permeability coefficient, only crude estimates of its magnitude can be made from a knowledge of the character of the soil. Therefore tests must be performed to obtain the coefficient with any certainty. The simplest test is the *constant head*, shown diagrammatically in Fig. 2:4. It is used primarily on sands and gravels. For fine sands and silts *the falling head* test is used. The upper reservoir of Fig. 2:4 is replaced with a vertical standpipe. During the test, the level of water in the standpipe falls, and the volume of water that flows is equal to the volume difference in the standpipe. Extreme care is essential in testing fine-grained cohesionless soils to avoid migration of the soil particles caused by excessive hydraulic gradients. For clay soils either the constant or falling head test is employed. The quantity of seepage is so small that great care is necessary to avoid leaks and evaporation which could be many times greater than the flow through the soil.

2:4 Permeability of Natural Soils

The range in permeability of natural soils is even greater than the range in grain size. The following table can be used as a standard for describing a soil's permeability and as a guide for rough estimates.

Table 2:1   RELATIVE VALUES OF PERMEABILITY
(After Terzaghi and Peck)[2:2]

Relative Permeability	Values of k (cm/sec)	Typical Soil
Very permeable	Over 1×10^{-1}	Coarse gravel
Medium permeability	1×10^{-1}–1×10^{-3}	Sand, fine sand
Low permeability	1×10^{-3}–1×10^{-5}	Silty sand, dirty sand
Very low permeability	1×10^{-5}–1×10^{-7}	Silt
Impervious	Less than 1×10^{-7}	Clay

(To convert to feet per minute, multiply above values by 2; to convert to feet per day, multiply above by 3×10^3)

Variation of k in a Soil Mass   In most soils the value of k depends on the direction in which the water is traveling. The k in the direction parallel to the bedding planes or planes of stratification is usually from 2 to 30 times that in the direction perpendicular to the bedding or stratification, because of the layers of soils with relatively low permeabilities. In soil deposits with erratic lenses of either coarse, pervious materials or fine, impervious materials, the permeability varies greatly from point to point and is extremely difficult to determine.

2:5 Compressibility and Settlement

The problem of building settlement has plagued builders for centuries. Many of the architectural masterpieces of the Middle Ages disappeared long ago because excessive settlement broke them apart. Others, such as the Leaning Tower of Pisa, became famous through their defects. But extraordinary settlements have not been limited to the Dark Ages; nearly every city of the world not founded on bedrock has its examples of buildings cracked and distorted through excessive settlement.

Until the twentieth century engineers vaguely attributed the cause of settlement to a squeezing of softer soils from beneath the structure. However, this did not explain the continuing settlement of such broad areas as the Mexico City Basin which drops at a rate of about 10 in. per year. Furthermore, samples of soil strata made in the vicinity of bad settlements did not show the bulges that might have been expected if squeezing had taken place. Samples made directly beneath the zones of greatest settlement indicated the following:

(1) Some soil strata, particularly soft clays, had decreased in thickness an amount equal to the settlement.
(2) Those soil strata that had decreased in thickness had smaller void ratios than the same strata outside the zones of settlement.

This evidence pointed toward a change in void ratio and a corresponding change in soil volume as the cause of settlement, but it remained for Karl Terzaghi to clarify the mechanics of this process of compression in his book *Erdbaumechanik* published in 1925.

Compressibility Test Terzaghi reasoned that squeezing or lateral movement of soft soil beneath a building was prevented by the strata

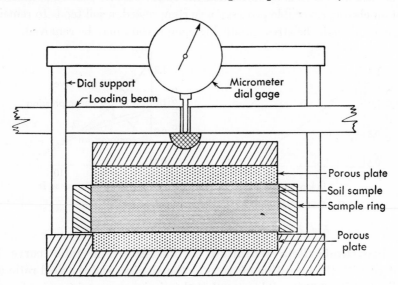

Fig. 2:5 Consolidometer.

of non-yielding soils interbedded with them. He developed a test to reproduce this for laboratory study by using a soil sample encased in a ring (to prevent lateral movement) and sandwiched between two porous plates, as shown in Fig. 2:5. In making the test, a vertical pressure or stress, $\bar{\sigma}$ (sigma), is applied to the plates in order to produce a compression of the sample. It is allowed to remain until the compression virtually ceases, and then a much larger stress is added. This is repeated for the range in stresses to which the soil is likely to be subjected under the structure. The compression of the soil is measured with a micrometer dial in order to compute the void ratio corresponding to each stress. The results are presented in the form of a *stress-void ratio* curve (or *pressure-void ratio* curve as it is often called) as shown in Fig. 2:6a.

Stress Void-Ratio Relation   The shape of the curve is concave upward, indicating a decreasing rate of compression with increasing stress. If the stress is increased to a certain point, $\bar{\sigma}_c$, and then released, the soil will not swell to its original void ratio. Instead it will increase in volume gradually along a flat, concave upward curve (Fig. 2:6b) called the *decompression* curve. If stress is again applied, the recompression of the soil will follow a flat curve that is concave downward until the stress is nearly equal to $\bar{\sigma}_c$. At this point a more rapid decrease in void ratio takes place until the recompression curve practically joins the original curve. (The original curve is often termed the *virgin* curve.) Soil compression is not an elastic, reversible process; once compressed, a soil tends to remain so, even though the stress producing compression may be removed.

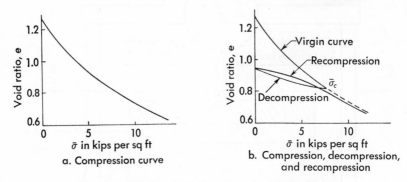

Fig. 2:6   Stress–void-ratio curves for a typical soil.

Logarithmic Representation   If the stress-void ratio curve is plotted with the logarithm of stress as the abscissa and the void ratio as ordinate (Fig. 2:7) it will be seen that the virgin compression curve forms

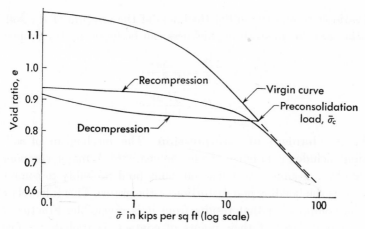

Fig. 2:7 Semilogarithmic stress–void-ratio curve.

a straight line through the greater part of its range. The logarithmic representation has become the standard form for presenting soil compression data because it affords a convenient means for expressing the compressibility of soils by comparing the slopes of their virgin curves—the steeper the slope, the more compressible the soil.

The equation of the straight-line portion of the curve is

$$\Delta e = -C_c \log_{10} \frac{\bar{\sigma}_0 + \Delta\sigma}{\bar{\sigma}_0}. \tag{2:10}$$

The term C_c is the compression index, which expresses the virgin slope.

Compression of Soil Strata The compression of a soil stratum with an initial void ratio of e_0 can be found by proportion from a sample (Fig. 2:8) with a volume of solids of 1 cu ft and a cross-sectional area of 1 sq ft. The height of the solids is 1, and the height of voids e_0. If the change in

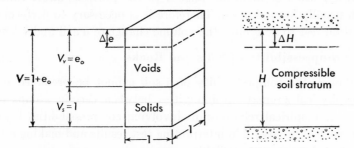

Fig. 2:8 Comparison of settlement of a soil stratum with thickness of H with change in height of soil sample whose initial height is $1 + e_0$.

void ratio is Δe and the initial thickness of the stratum of the soil is H, then the decrease in stratum thickness can be found by the proportion:

$$\frac{\Delta H}{H} = \frac{\Delta e}{1 + e_0},$$

$$\Delta H = \frac{H \, \Delta e}{1 + e_0}. \tag{2:11}$$

The Mechanism of Compression The mechanism of soil compression includes a number of phenomena.[2:3,2:4] A major component in cohesionless, organic, and micaceous soils (and probably to some extent in clays) is the bending and distortion of the grains. This is largely elastic and the compression that results from it is reversible. Fracture of the grains, particularly at their points of contact, is probably a factor in the compression of all soils. This is not reversible, and partially accounts for the decompression being less than the original compression. The electrical repulsion between particles having like charges, or surrounded by cations with like charges which holds them apart, is a major factor in clays and is probably reversible. Reorientation of the grains occurs in all soils to some degree. In order for the grains to move, the bond or attraction between points of contact of clay particles must be overcome, which is a factor in all compression but particularly important at high stresses. Such structural changes or breakdowns are not reversible and also are partially responsible for the decompression being less than the compression. The adsorbed water affects both the electrical repulsion and the attraction. Whether it has an independent effect is not known. All these phenomena are related to the physicochemical properties and the structure of the soil, which are difficult to evaluate and describe quantitatively. Most of them are related to the previous stress conditions, which usually are unknown. Therefore it is necessary to perform a consolidation test to determine the volume change of a soil under load.

2:6 Compressibility of Soils and Rocks

Although the compressibility of a soil cannot be predicted from its other physical properties, similarities between certain groups of soils and some empirical relationships involving compressibilities have been observed that are useful in interpreting test results and making estimates when test data are not available.

Low to Moderate Plasticity, Normally Consolidated Soils of low to moderate plasticity include clays, silts, organic and micaceous silts with plasticity indexes up to 30, as well as sands, gravels, and porous rocks. When they have never been subjected to stresses greater than their present overburden load, they are termed *normally loaded* and exhibit the characteristic semilogarithmic stress-void ratio curve of Fig. 2:7. The greater part of the curve is approximately straight, and the slope is expressed by the compression index, as was previously described. Terzaghi and Peck[2:5] have derived an expression for the compressibility of such clays from the work of Skempton:[2:6]

$$C_c = 0.009(\text{LL} - 10). \tag{2:12}$$

For soils of very low plasticity and porous rock, Sowers[2:7] has found the compression index to be related to the undisturbed void ratio

$$C_c = 0.75(e - a), \tag{2:13}$$

where a is a constant whose value is from 0.2 for porous rock to 0.8 for highly micaceous soils. Both relationships are approximate at the best, and considerable variations should be expected from the computed value of the compression index. Normally loaded clays can often be identified from their water content. Usually it is near the liquid limit.

The same soil remolded suffers a structural breakdown and a reduction in void ratio. It becomes somewhat less compressible, but exhibits a straight-line stress-void ratio curve on semilogarithmic coordinates.

Low to Moderate Plasticity—Preconsolidated A *preconsolidated* soil is one which has been subjected to a stress, $\bar{\sigma}_c$, which exceeds the present overburden pressure. Most undisturbed soils are preconsolidated to some degree and exhibit the characteristic stress-void ratio curve of Fig. 2:9a. Preconsolidation is produced in a number of ways. Removal of overburden by erosion or excavation leaves the soil preconsolidated. This load can be estimated if the previous overburden thickness is known. The most important and widespread cause is capillary tension arising from desiccation or drying of the soil. Stresses greater than 10,000 psf due to desiccation have been observed in arid and warm regions. The preconsolidation load caused by desiccation often decreases with increasing depth below the ground surface. The amount produced in this way cannot be predicted. A water table rising above a compressible stratum causes preconsolidation by reducing the load carried by the soil through buoyancy. The amount of the reduction is seldom very great, but it can be computed as described in Chapter 5.

   Chemical alteration produces the effect of preconsolidation by changing
the physicochemical bonds between the clay particles or by introducing
stresses by the expansion or contraction of the grains during the alteration
process. Most weathered rocks and some partially indurated rocks exhibit
preconsolidation from this source. Leaching that removes salt or high
concentrations of cations may have the same effect in some clays, especially those deposited in salt water.

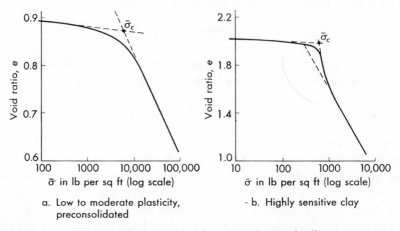

a. Low to moderate plasticity,   - b. Highly sensitive clay
**   preconsolidated**

Fig. 2:9   Stress–void-ratio curves of natural soils.

   The preconsolidation load $\bar{\sigma}_c$ can be estimated from the stress-void ratio
curve shown in Fig. 2:9a. Tangents are drawn to the initial, flat section
and to the steep straight-line portion of the curve. Their intersection
is approximately the preconsolidation load.

   Preconsolidated clays can be recognized from their water contents,
which are usually much less than their liquid limits. In heavily preconsolidated soils (particularly if desiccation is the cause) the water contents are sometimes less than the plastic limits. Their compression index
(above the preconsolidation load) can be found from the same relationships used for normally consolidated clays.

   Preconsolidation is extremely important in foundation engineering.
A soil that is inherently compressible usually will not settle appreciably
until the stress imposed by the structure exceeds the preconsolidation
load. If the natural preconsolidation load is not sufficient, it is sometimes possible to preconsolidate the soil by piling earth on the site until
the soil compresses. This is often time consuming, but the process can
be accelerated as will be described in Chapter 4.

Sensitive Clays Sensitive clays and other soils with a flocculent or highly developed skeletal structure exhibit a third characteristic curve, Fig. 2:9b. Ordinarily such soils are preconsolidated to some degree. The curve is flat up to the preconsolidation load; then it drops sharply and gradually flattens to form a straight line on semilogarithmic coordinates. It is suspected that the sharp drop in void ratio reflects a structural breakdown in which the bonds between the particles are broken and the grains rearrange themselves into a more dense orientation. The same soil badly disturbed or remolded has a straight or slightly curved stress-void ratio curve that is slightly flatter than the virgin curve at high stresses. The water content of most highly sensitive clays exceeds their liquid limit, which aids in their recognition.

2:7 Time Rate of Compression

The compression of a soil stratum does not occur suddenly. In fact it often takes place so slowly that it is difficult to believe that any settlement is taking place. Buildings in Chicago continue to settle for 50 years, and the Leaning Tower of Pisa, commenced in 1174, is still moving.

The settlement begins rapidly and becomes slower with increasing time. As shown in Fig. 2:10, it can be divided into three stages: *initial,*

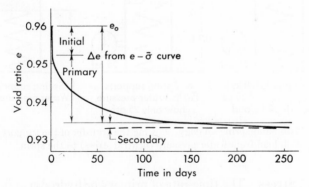

Fig. 2:10 Time-settlement curve for an increment in stress.

primary or *hydrodynamic*, and *secondary*. The sum of the initial and primary stages is the settlement computed from the laboratory stress-void ratio curve. The secondary is of importance principally in highly organic, highly micaceous, and highly sensitive soils.

Initial Consolidation   The initial stage occurs as soon as the load
is applied. It occurs largely by the compression and solution of air in
the soil voids. It also may include compression of the grains and the soil
water, although these are small. In a saturated soil the initial consolidation is usually negligible, but in partially saturated soils it is often the
largest part. (The proportion of the total void-ratio change that is initial
compression is found from an analysis of the laboratory time-settlement
data for each load increment.)

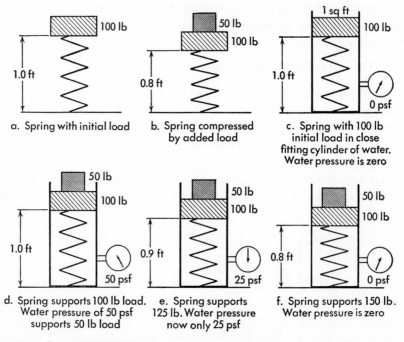

Fig. 2:11   Piston and spring analogy, showing the transfer of the support of an added
50-lb load from water pressure (neutral stress) to the spring.

Neutral Stress   The time-rate of primary or hydrodynamic compression is controlled by the escape of water from the soil voids. The water
is squeezed out by an external force applied to the soil mass. This force
increases the water pressure beyond the hydrostatic, developing a hydraulic gradient that produces flow. The mechanics of this process can
be demonstrated by the analogy of a spring, piston, and cylinder. A spring
(Fig. 2:11a) has attached to its top a piston whose cross-sectional area is

1 sq ft and whose weight is 100 lb. Under this weight the spring has a length of 1.0 ft. When an added load of 50 lb is placed on the spring (Fig. 2:11b), it compresses to a length of 0.8 ft. The compression is instantaneous as soon as the load is applied. Suppose that instead of in the open air, the piston and spring is placed in a tight-fitting cylinder (Fig. 2:11c) with the space below the piston filled with water. The spring is compressed by the weight of the piston, 100 lb, and the water is under no pressure at all.

If the 50-lb weight is now added on top of the piston (Fig. 2:11d), the spring cannot compress because the water below the piston cannot escape. The spring still supports the 100-lb piston but offers no support to the added weight. The 50 lb are supported by water pressure on the piston of 50 psf. This water pressure is *neutral stress* and is given the symbol u. If the total load of 150 lb is denoted by σ, and the actual spring load by $\bar{\sigma}$, then the following equation describes the way the total load is supported:

$$\sigma = \bar{\sigma} + u, \qquad (2:14)$$
$$150 = 100 + 50.$$

This is the most important relationship in soil mechanics and is involved in shrinkage and shear as well as consolidation. If 0.1 cu ft of water leaks out because of the pressure from beneath the piston, the spring will be compressed to a length of 0.9 ft. The spring will now support 125 lb, and the neutral stress will be reduced to 25 psf, as shown in Fig. 2:11e:

$$150 = 125 + 25.$$

When an additional 0.1 cu ft of water leaks away, the spring will carry 150 lb and the neutral stress will be zero, as in Fig. 2:11f. The spring compression is a process of transferring to the spring the 50 lb of added load that was supported initially by water pressure.

Consolidation of soil is similar to the above analogy. The resilient grain structure is represented by the spring, and the voids filled with water are represented by the cylinder. When a load is placed on the soil, the grain structure cannot immediately support it because compression cannot occur. Neutral stress therefore supports the load. As the water seeps out and the soil compresses, the grain structure assumes the load and the neutral stress becomes zero. The following sequence (Fig. 2:12) illustrates the way in which the stress transfer occurs in a soil stratum that is bounded by pervious strata above and below. The initial stress in the soil is denoted by σ_o; the added stress due to the weight of a structure

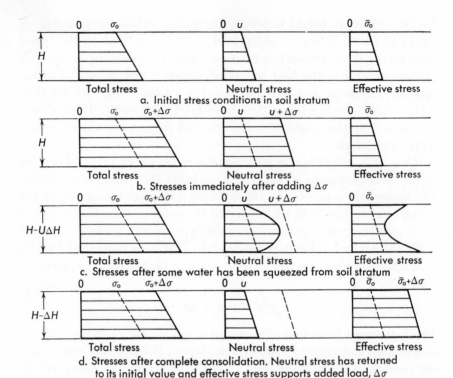

Fig. 2:12   Stresses during consolidation. The soil stratum is drained on both its top and bottom faces.

by $\Delta\sigma$; neutral stress by u, and the stress in the grain structure by $\bar{\sigma}$. The term *effective* stress is often given to the stress in the grain structure, since it is effective in producing soil compression. The relation between the stresses $\sigma = \bar{\sigma} + u$ is fundamental.

Percentage of Consolidation   The *percentage of consolidation, U,* is defined as the average percentage of the added stress $\Delta\sigma$ that is supported by increased effective stress. It represents the percentage of the total or ultimate compression that has already occurred in the stratum. The percentage of consolidation depends on several factors:

(1) The soil's permeability, which governs the rate of flow of the water.
(2) The thickness of the stratum, which influences both the volume of water that must seep out and the distance it must travel and the hydraulic gradient.
(3) The number of pervious boundaries of the stratum from which the water can leave, which influences the distance the water must travel and the gradient.

(4) The void ratio and the rate of change of void ratio with pressure, which influence both the volume of water and the way the neutral stress will decrease with a loss of water.

A mathematical analysis of the percentage of consolidation leads to the following equation:

$$U = f^* \left(\frac{t(1 + e)k}{(H/N)^2 \gamma_w a_v} \right), \qquad (2\text{:}15a)$$

$$U = f(T), \qquad (2\text{:}15b)$$

where t is time; e is the void ratio; k is the permeability; H is the stratum thickness; N is the number of horizontal pervious boundaries of the stratum (either 1 or 2); γ_w is the unit weight of water; and a_v is the rate of change of void ratio with changes in pressure, $\Delta e/\Delta \sigma$. The term T is a dimensionless ratio known as the *time factor* and is defined by the expression:

$$T = \frac{t(1 + e)k}{(H/N)^2 a_v \gamma_w}. \qquad (2\text{:}16)$$

The relation between U and T is expressed by a mathematical function that is independent of the soil characteristics or the amount of compression. Instead it depends on the variation of $\Delta \sigma$ with depth throughout the stratum and on whether the stratum is bounded by a pervious layer both top and bottom or just on one surface.

The theoretical analysis of consolidation is based on several assumptions, including a homogeneous, saturated soil, a constant value of the term $\frac{k(1 + e)}{a_v}$ during compression, and vertical movement of the water. Because of these assumptions great accuracy cannot be expected in estimates of the time rate of compression. The chart (Fig. 2:13) shows the relation of U to T for most practical problems. It is inaccurate, however, where great variations in $\Delta \sigma$ with depth occur in a stratum that is bounded by an impervious surface, either top or bottom.

The characteristics of a soil that govern its rate of consolidation may be expressed by the *coefficient of consolidation*, c_v, which is defined by

$$c_v = \frac{(1 + e)k}{\gamma_w a_v}. \qquad (2\text{:}17)$$

This coefficient varies somewhat, depending on the soil stress σ, but for most practical work it may be assumed to be a constant.

* Function of.

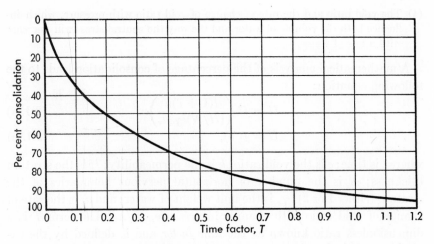

Fig. 2:13 Time-rate of consolidation for stratum drained on both faces and any distribution of stress increase or for a stratum drained on one surface and a uniform stress increase.

Example 2:1 Find the time required for 50 per cent consolidation to take place in the following soil stratum.

$k = 0.0000001$ cm/sec.

$e = 1.5$.

$a_v = 0.0003$ cm²/gm.

$\gamma_w = 1$ gm/cm³.

Thickness is 900 cm, with pervious strata top and bottom.

(1) For $U = 50\%$, $T = 0.2$.

(2) For 900 cm stratum with two pervious surfaces

$$H/2 = 900/2 = 450 \text{ cm.}$$

(3) $0.2 = \dfrac{t(1 + 1.5)0.000\ 000\ 1}{450^2 \times 0.0003 \times 1}.$

(4) $t = \dfrac{0.2 \times 203000 \times 3 \times 1}{0.001 \times 2.5} = 48.7 \times 10^6$ sec.

(5) $t = 565$ days.

Secondary Compression After the excess hydrostatic pressure has been dissipated, the compression does not cease. Instead it continues very slowly at an ever-decreasing rate indefinitely. This is *secondary compression*. This appears to be the result of a plastic readjustment of the soil grains to the new stress, of progressive fracture of the inter-particle bonds, and possibly of progressive fracture of the particles themselves.

The secondary compression can be identified on a plot of settlement as a function of logarithm of time (Fig. 2:14). The secondary appears as a straight line sloping downward or, in some cases, as a straight line followed by a second straight line with a flatter slope. The void ratio e_f corresponding to the effective end of primary consolidation can be found from the intersection of the backward projection of the secondary line with a tangent drawn to the primary curve, as indicated on Fig. 2:14. The rate of secondary compression depends on the increment of stress increase, $\Delta\sigma$, and on the characteristics of the soil. For inorganic soils of low to moderate compressibility, secondary compression is seldom important. It can be a major part of the compression of highly com-

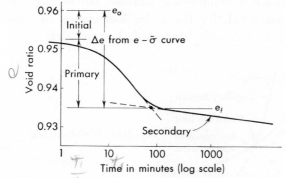

Fig. 2:14 Secondary compression; semilogarithmic time-settlement curve for an increment in stress.

pressible clays, highly micaceous soils, and organic materials. Methods for analyzing secondary compression are available but beyond the scope of this text.[2:8]

2:8 Shrinking, Swelling, and Slaking

Soils undergo volume changes that are not produced by external loads. Instead they are caused by changes in water content and in the internal stresses affected by the water.

Shrinkage Shrinkage is caused by capillary tension. When a saturated soil dries, a meniscus develops in each void at the soil surface. This produces tension in the soil water and a corresponding compression in the soil structure. This can be expressed quantitatively from equation 2:14, where the external stress σ equals zero:

$$0 = \bar{\sigma} + u,$$
$$\bar{\sigma} = -u.$$

(Since u from capillary tension is negative, then $-(-u)$ is positive and the effective stress $\bar{\sigma}$ is positive.) This compressive stress is just as effective in producing soil compression as an external load, and pressures of several thousand pounds per square foot can be produced in fine-grained soils.

Shrinkage Limit   During the shrinkage process, the voids become smaller and the potential maximum capillary tension increases. This is shown graphically on Fig. 2:15. The resistance to compression, the stress-void ratio curve, is shown also. During the drying and shrinkage process, the void ratio decreases and with it both the maximum capillary tension and the resistance to compression increase, but at different rates. The soil remains saturated, for the water loss causes an equal reduction in void ratio. A void ratio is reached, however, where the maximum

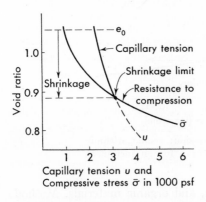

Fig. 2:15   Shrinkage limit as a function of capillary tension and resistance to compression.

tension equals the resistance. Further drying cannot produce a reduction in void ratio because the resistance exceeds the tension. At this point, known as the *shrinkage limit*, the reduction in the void ratio largely ceases. The meniscus in each void begins to retreat from the soil surface. The soil surface no longer has a damp appearance but now looks dry, and the soil mass ceases to be saturated.

The shrinkage limit is defined as the water content at the point that shrinkage ceases and the soil is no longer saturated. It can be found by drying the soil slowly, visually observing the color change, and determining the moisture at this point. It can also be found by drying a saturated soil completely. If the weight and total volume at the beginning of shrinkage are W_1 and V_1 and at the end of shrinkage (oven dried) are W_2 and V_2, then the following can be derived by assuming that there is no volume change after the shrinkage limit is reached and that the loss of weight by evaporation up to the shrinkage limit is accompanied by a corresponding loss of volume:

$$W_2 = W_s,$$
$$(V_1 - V_2)\gamma_w = W_w \text{ (lost up to shrinkage limit)},$$
$$\text{SL} = \frac{W_1 - W_2 - (V_1 - V_2)\gamma_w}{W_2} \times 100. \qquad (2:18)$$

Beyond the shrinkage limit the capillary tension can increase in the smaller voids. On the other hand the tension is released in some of the larger ones. Some soils on drying, particularly those containing fibrous organic matter and mica, may expand beyond the shrinkage limit; others may shrink further. These changes are ordinarily insignificant.

Soil shrinkage results in settlement of compressible soils. Since the capillary tension is exerted in all directions, shrinkage occurs horizontally as well as vertically, causing shrinkage cracks to form. Cracks 1 ft wide and 15 ft deep have been observed in highly compressible clays. Reoccurring shrinkage brought on by desiccation during dry weather will produce networks of shrinkage cracks in all directions and a blocky macrostructure in the soil.

Swelling Some soils not only shrink on drying but also swell when the moisture is allowed to increase. The mechanism is more complex than shrinkage and is caused by a number of different phenomena: the elastic rebound of the soil grains, the attraction of the clay minerals for water, the electrical repulsion of the clay particles and their adsorbed cations from one another, and the expansion of air trapped in the soil voids. In soils that have been precompressed by load or shrinkage, all these factors probably contribute. In soils that have never been precompressed, probably the attraction of the clay minerals for water and the electrical repulsion of the clay particles surrounded by water are major factors.

High pressures can be developed if the soil has access to water but is prevented from swelling by confinement. If precompression is the cause, the swell pressure can be nearly as great as the preconsolidation load. Where adsorption and repulsion predominate, as in clays of the montmorillonite family, pressures of several thousand pounds per square foot can develop.

Predicting Swelling and Shrinkage It is difficult to predict shrinkage and swelling quantitatively, for they depend on the character of the soil and on the moisture changes. Shrinkage can be found by merely drying the soil and computing the relation between saturated water content and volume. In general the lower the shrinkage limit, the greater the potential shrinkage of the soil. Swelling can be estimated by tests resembling consolidation. The expansion (free swell) is found by flooding the soil when it is acted upon by a constant nominal pressure (such as 100 psf). The swell pressure is found by inundating the soil and measuring the pressure required to prevent its expansion. It has been found that the shrinkage limit and the plasticity index are some indication of the potential volume change, as given in Table 2:2.

Table 2:2 VOLUME CHANGE POTENTIAL
(*Adapted from Holtz and Gibbs*[2:9])

Volume Change	Shrinkage Limit	Plasticity Index
Probably low	12 or more	0–15
Probably moderate	10–12	15–30
Probably high	0–10	30 or more

Slaking If a soil that has dried well beyond the shrinkage limit is suddenly inundated or immersed in water, it may disintegrate into a soft wet mass, a process known as *slaking*.

Two factors are involved in slaking. First, the unequal expansion of the soil as the water penetrates from the surface causes pieces of soil to flake off the mass. Second, when the soil dries beyond the shrinkage limit, some of the voids fill with air. When the dried soil is immersed, water enters these air-filled voids on all sides. The air is trapped between the meniscuses of the entering water, and its pressure builds up as water fills the void. The result is an explosion of the void and disintegration of the soil. Both the flaking and the air bubbles can be seen by placing a lump of dried clay in a glass of water.

2:9 Shear Strength and Combined Stresses

The strength of a soil is a controlling factor in the design of retaining walls, embankments, bracing for excavations, and foundations. If the soil strength is exceeded, a failure in the soil mass will occur that may endanger lives and property. Because of their three-phase composition and complicated structures, soils do not appear to have the same reactions to stress and strain as other familiar materials. Their variations of strength with time and the conditions of loading have long been a mystery to engineers—a mystery that is now being slowly solved. The problem is further complicated by the fact that soils are seldom subjected to the simple tensile or compressive stresses that are found in many engineering problems. Instead, soils stresses occur in three dimensions and combine both normal stresses (simple stresses) and shear stresses.

A stress is defined as a force per unit of area. A stress applied to a plane surface of a solid can be resolved into two components: one perpendicular (normal) to the plane known as the *normal* stress, σ (sigma), and one acting in the surface of the plane known as the *shear* stress, τ (tau), as shown in Fig. 2:16a. When the stress acting on a plane consists only of a *normal* component and $\tau = 0$, that normal stress is termed a *principal* stress, (Fig. 2:16b).

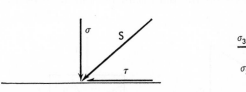

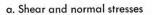

a. Shear and normal stresses   b. Principal stresses on a cube

Fig. 2:16 Shear, normal and principal stresses.

When a cube of rock or mortar is to be tested to determine its strength, it is placed in a testing machine and gradually increasing compressive forces are applied to its top and bottom faces. The compressive forces result in compressive stresses in the faces to which they are applied. These stresses are principal stresses, and the horizontal planes in which they occur are called *principal planes*. Although it is rarely done, it would be possible to introduce compressive forces on the other two pairs of cube faces. These also would result in principal stresses in the faces to which they were applied, and these faces would also be considered principal planes. It can be shown that there are three independent, perpendicular, principal stresses acting on three perpendicular, principal planes. The largest of the three principal stresses is known as the *major principal* stress and is denoted σ_1. The smallest is known as the *minor principal* stress σ_3, and the third is called the *intermediate principal* stress σ_2.

In soil mechanics, tensile stresses are comparatively rare; therefore, to avoid many negative signs, compressive stresses are considered positive. In the case of the cube of mortar in an ordinary compression test, the compressive stress applied to the top and bottom faces is σ_1, and the other two principal stresses, σ_2 and σ_3, are zero.

If an inclined plane cuts through the cube, it is possible to compute the shear and normal stresses on that plane from the three principal stresses and the laws of statics. The general case is quite complicated, for it involves the direction cosines of the plane from the principal planes. In many problems in soil mechanics, however, we are interested in stresses on planes perpendicular to the intermediate principal plane which reduces the problem to two dimensions.

The direction of an inclined plane that is perpendicular to the intermediate principal plane is defined by α (alpha), the angle the plane makes with the plane of the major principal stress, as shown in Fig. 2:17.

Shear and normal stresses on the plane can be computed by the laws

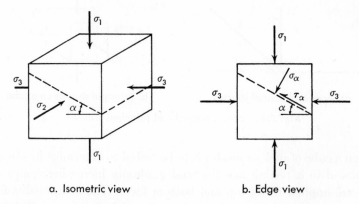

a. Isometric view   b. Edge view

Fig. 2:17   Stresses in a cube that is cut by a plane which is perpendicular to the plane of σ_2 and which makes an angle of α with the plane of σ_1.

of statics from σ_1 and σ_3. If the cube is assumed to have dimensions $1 \times 1 \times 1$, then the forces acting on the plane in the directions of σ_1 and σ_3 are respectively

$$F_1 = \sigma_1 \times \text{area},$$
$$F_1 = \sigma_1 \times 1 \times 1,$$
$$F_3 = \sigma_3 \times 1 \times 1 \tan \alpha.$$

The sum of the components of these forces normal to the plane is

$$F_n = F_1 \cos \alpha + F_3 \sin \alpha,$$
$$F_n = \sigma_1 \cos \alpha + \sigma_3 \tan \alpha \sin \alpha.$$

The sum of the components parallel to the plane is

$$F_s = \sigma_1 \sin \alpha - \sigma_3 \tan \alpha \cos \alpha.$$

The area of the plane is $1/\cos \alpha$; therefore the normal stress on the plane σ_α, is

$$\sigma_\alpha = \frac{\sigma_1 \cos \alpha + \sigma_3 \tan \alpha \sin \alpha}{1/\cos \alpha},$$

$$\sigma_\alpha = \sigma_1 \cos^2 \alpha + \sigma_3 \sin^2 \alpha,$$

$$\sigma_\alpha = \frac{\sigma_1 + \sigma_3}{2} + \frac{\sigma_1 - \sigma_3}{2} \cos 2\alpha. \qquad (2{:}19a)$$

In the same way the shear stress in the plane, τ_α, is

$$\tau_\alpha = \frac{\sigma_1 - \sigma_3}{2} \sin 2\alpha. \qquad (2{:}19b)$$

By means of the above formulas, the stresses on any inclined plane at an angle of α can be computed, or if the stresses on any two planes are known, the principal stresses can be computed.

The formulas lead to the following conclusions, which should be kept in mind in analyzing stresses:

(1) The maximum shear stress occurs when $\sin 2\alpha = 1$ or $\alpha = 45°$ or $135°$ and is equal to $\frac{\sigma_1 - \sigma_3}{2}$.

(2) The maximum normal stress occurs when $\cos 2\alpha = 1$ and $\alpha = 0$.

(3) The minimum normal stress occurs when $\cos 2\alpha = -1$ and $\alpha = 90°$ and the plane is parallel to the minor principal plane.

(4) Shear stresses are equal in magnitude on any two planes perpendicular to each other.

Mohr's Circle A German physicist, Otto Mohr, devised a graphical procedure for solving the equations for shear and normal stress on a plane perpendicular to one principal plane and making an angle α with the larger of the two other principal planes. A system of coordinate axes is established (Fig. 2:18a) where the x-distances represent normal stresses and the y-distances represent shear stresses. Compressive (positive) normal stresses are plotted to the right; tensile, to the left. Shear stresses may be plotted either upward or downward, as their sign has no meaning. The coordinates of a point (σ, τ) represent the combination of shear and normal stress on a plane regardless of the plane's orientation.

On this diagram are plotted the coordinates of σ_1 and σ_3 (Fig. 2:18b). Both lie on the σ axis, since the shear stresses on the principal planes are zero. Through these points a circle is drawn whose center is also on the σ axis (Fig. 2:18c). The center of this circle is at the point $\left(\frac{\sigma_1 + \sigma_3}{2}, 0\right)$

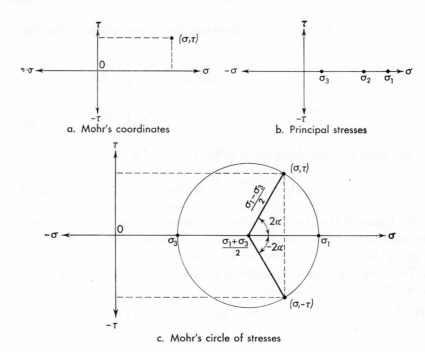

c. Mohr's circle of stresses

Fig. 2:18   Mohr's coordinates and Mohr's circle of stresses.

and its radius is equal to $\dfrac{\sigma_1 - \sigma_3}{2}$. A radius is drawn at an angle of 2α measured counterclockwise from the σ axis. The x-coordinate of a point on the circle at the end of the radius is

$$\frac{\sigma_1 + \sigma_3}{2} + \frac{\sigma_1 - \sigma_3}{2} \cos 2\alpha,$$

which is σ on a plane that is inclined at an angle of α with the major principal plane. The y-coordinate of the point is

$$\frac{\sigma_1 - \sigma_3}{2} \sin 2\alpha,$$

which is τ on the same plane. Therefore the circle represents the possible stress conditions on any plane perpendicular to the intermediate principal plane. The stresses on a particular plane at angle α can be found from the construction. From this construction it can be shown that maximum τ occurs on a plane with an angle of $2\alpha = 90°$ and is equal to $\dfrac{\sigma_1 - \sigma_3}{2}$, or half the difference between the major and minor principal stresses. Also the shear stresses on two planes perpendicular to each other are equal.

The same construction can be applied to stresses on a plane that is perpendicular to the major principal plane, by using σ_2 and σ_3, or to a plane perpendicular to the minor principal plane, by using σ_1 and σ_2. Since the circle is symmetrical about the x-axis, ordinarily only the top half of the circle is plotted. The bottom half can be plotted, using -2α (measured clockwise from the axis) and negative values for the shear stress.

Mohr's circle of stresses was derived by the laws of statics and applies regardless of the material involved. Although the discussion was limited to stresses acting on the faces of cubes, it applies equally well to the infinitesimal cube we call a point.

Example 2:2 Given: $\sigma_1 = 10$ kg/cm² and $\sigma_3 = 2$ kg/cm²
Find: σ and τ on a plane making an angle of 30° with the major principal plane.
(1) Plot σ_1 and σ_3 on the σ-axis (Fig. 2:19a).

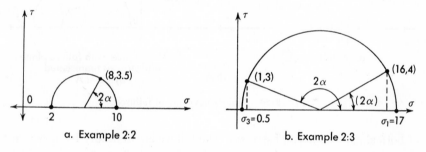

Fig. 2:19 Computing stresses with Mohr's circle.

(2) Draw circle through points with center on axis.
(3) Construct radius with $2\alpha = 60°$.
(4) Scale σ and τ from diagram.
   $\sigma = 8$ kg/cm²; $\tau = 3.5$ kg/cm².

Example 2:3 Given: The normal and shear stresses on a plane are 16 psf and 4 psf, respectively; normal and shear stresses on a second plane are 1 psf and 3 psf, respectively. Compute the major and minor principal stresses and find the angle between the two planes.
(1) Plot the stress coordinates of both planes (Fig. 2:19b).
(2) Draw circle with center on axis through two points. (Center at intersection of perpendicular bisector of a line joining two points, with the σ-axis.)
(3) σ_1 and σ_3 may be scaled directly from diagram.
   $\sigma_1 = 17$ psf; $\sigma_3 = 0.5$ psf.

(4) The 2α of each plane is found from the diagram. The angle between the planes is $\frac{1}{2}(2\alpha_1 - 2\alpha_2) = 65°$.

2:10   Mohr's Theory of Rupture

Otto Mohr also contributed to engineering science a theory of the failure of materials that represents more nearly the true stresses involved than do the theories involving simple stresses alone. The theory has been found to apply particularly well to soils and to materials such as concrete and stone.

Mohr reasoned that yield or failure within a material was not caused by normal stresses alone reaching a certain maximum or yield point, or by shear stresses alone reaching a maximum, but by critical combinations

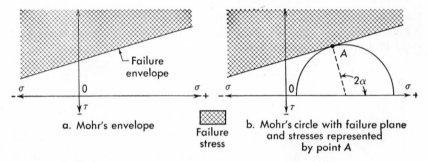

Fig. 2:20   Mohr's envelope of failure.

of both shear and normal stresses. The failure is essentially by shear, but the critical shear stress is governed by the normal stress acting on the potential surface of failure.

The critical combinations of shear and normal stress, when plotted on the σ, τ coordinates form a line known as *Mohr's envelope of rupture* (Fig. 2:20a). Failure will occur if for a given value of σ the shear stress exceeds that shown by the envelope.

If the stresses on any two planes through a point are known, the stresses can be found on any other planes by means of Mohr's circle. Since the circle represents *all* possible combinations of shear and normal stress at that point, failure will occur on the plane represented by the point of intersection with the envelope (Fig. 2:20b).

Example 2:4   A cylinder of soil cement has applied to it a minor principal stress of zero and a slowly increasing major principal stress. If the rupture envelope passes through (0,4000) at a slope of 20° upward to the right, compute: (a) the maximum value of axial load when failure occurs, (b) shear and normal stress on failure plane, and (c) the angle of failure plane.

(1) At $\sigma_1 = \sigma_3 = 0$, Mohr's circle is a point. As σ_1 increases slightly, the circle enlarges (Fig. 2:21b).

(2) At the instant the circle through $(0,0)$ $(\sigma_1,0)$ touches the envelope, failure will occur on the plane through the cylinder corresponding to the point of tangency (Fig. 2:21b).

(3) From Mohr's diagram, $\sigma_1 = 11,500$ at failure.

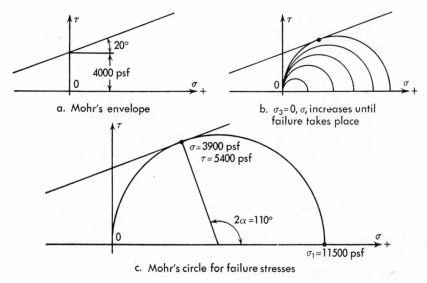

a. Mohr's envelope

b. $\sigma_3 = 0$, σ, increases until failure takes place

c. Mohr's circle for failure stresses

Fig. 2:21   Stresses during compression test of soil cement.

(4) $\tau = 5400$ and $\sigma = 3900$ on the failure plane. It is found that $2\alpha = 110°$; so, the failure plane makes an angle of 55° with σ_3 or an angle of 35° with the axis of the cylinder (Fig. 2:21c).

NOTE: The normal and shear stresses on the *failure* plane are usually designated p and s, respectively. The difference between the principal stresses, $\sigma_1 - \sigma_3$, at failure is termed q_r, the compressive strength.

2:11   Methods of Making Shear Tests

Because of the complex nature of the shearing resistance of soils, many methods of testing have been tried with varying success. The principal shear tests in use today are *direct, ring or double direct,* and *triaxial.* Of these, triaxial testing gives the most consistent and reliable results with varying soils.

Direct Shear Test[2:10]   One of the earliest methods for testing soil strength, used extensively today, is direct shear. A sample of soil is placed in a rectangular box (Fig. 2:22a) the top half of which can slide over the bottom half. The lid of the box is free to move vertically, and to it is applied the *normal load, P*. A *shearing force, S*, is applied to the top half of the box, shearing the sample along line x—x. In practice, the top and bottom of the box may be either porous plates to permit changes in the water content of the sample or projecting vanes to help develop a uniform distribution of stress on the failure surface. The test utilizes a relatively thin sample which consolidates rapidly under load (when such consolidation is required). The sample preparation and test operation are simple in most soils, which makes the test attractive for routine work.

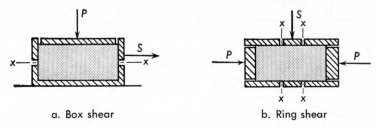

a. Box shear   b. Ring shear

Fig. 2:22   Direct shear tests; shear planes marked x-x.

Inherent shortcomings limit the reliability of the test results. First there is an unequal distribution of stresses over the shear surface; the stress is more at the edges and less at the center. The result is progressive failure. In materials with highly developed structures, such as flocculent clays and cemented or very loose cohesionless soils, the strength indicated by the test will often be too low. Second the soil is forced to shear on a predetermined plane which is not necessarily the weakest one. The strength given by the test, therefore, may be too high. Finally it is difficult to control drainage or changes in water content during the test, which limits its usefulness in wet soils.

Ring Shear   The ring shear is a double-direct shear test. A cylindrical sample is supported laterally by a close-fitting metal tube (Fig. 2:22b). Normal pressures are applied to the sample by pistons on the ends. A section of the tube is forced downward, shearing the soil on two surfaces, x—x. This equipment makes it possible to control sample water content changes more closely than in the single direct shear, and in addition small-diameter samples can be used. It suffers from the same limitations of non-uniform stress distribution and a forced failure plane as does the direct shear test.

Triaxial Shear Test[2:11]   The most reliable shear test is the triaxial direct stress (Fig. 2:23). A cylindrical sample is used with a diameter of 1.4 in., 2.8 in., or more and a length of at least twice the diameter. The sample is encased in a rubber membrane, with rigid caps or pistons on both ends. It is placed inside a closed chamber and subjected to a con-

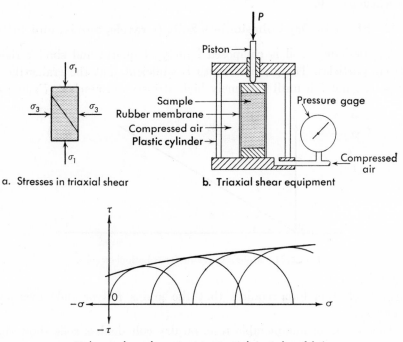

a. Stresses in triaxial shear   b. Triaxial shear equipment

c. Mohr envelope drawn tangent to Mohr's circles of failure

Fig. 2:23   Triaxial shear test.

fining pressure σ_3 on all sides by air or water pressure. An axial stress σ_1 is applied to the end of the sample by a piston. Either the axial stress can be increased or the confining pressure decreased until the sample fails in shear along a diagonal plane or a number of planes. The Mohr circles of failure stresses for a series of such tests, using different values for σ_3, are plotted, and the Mohr envelope drawn tangent to them (Fig. 2:23c).

The important advantages of the method are the relatively uniform stress distribution on the failure plane and the freedom of the soil to fail on the weakest surface. Furthermore, water can be drained from the soil or forced through the soil during the test to simulate actual conditions in the ground. Sample preparation is simple, and small-diameter cylindrical samples can be used. The chief disadvantage is the elaborate equipment required, including sample membranes, compressed air or water pressure equipment, the triaxial cell itself, and auxiliary devices to measure the volume change of the soil during testing.

A special case of the triaxial shear is the *unconfined compression test,* in which $\sigma_3 = 0$.

2:12   Shear in Dry Cohesionless Soils (Gravels, Sands, and Silts)

A cohesionless soil is composed largely of quartz and similar rigid, strong particles. The grain strength is sufficient that the grains themselves do not fail until extremely high stresses are reached. Failure of

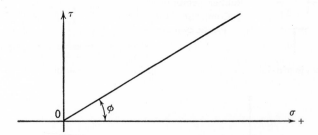

Fig. 2:24   Mohr's envelope for cohesionless soils.

such a soil therefore requires that the grains roll or slide over one another.

The results of innumerable tests on dry cohesionless soils show that the shear stress of failure, termed the *shear strength*, s, is nearly proportional to the normal effective stress on the failure surface, $\bar{p}$. (Note that the letters s and $\bar{p}$ are used for the limiting values of τ and $\bar{\sigma}$.) The Mohr envelope for the test is approximately a straight line through the origin (Fig. 2:24) which makes an angle of ϕ with the σ-axis. The equation for soil strength is given by

$$s = \bar{p} \tan \phi. \tag{2:20}$$

The angle ϕ is termed the *angle of internal friction*. It is analogous to the angle of friction between two sliding bodies whose ϕ is the angle of sliding friction and $\tan \phi$ the coefficient of friction. The angle of the failure plane can be found graphically from the Mohr's circle of failure or analytically from the geometry of the Mohr's circle:

$$\alpha = 45 + \frac{\phi}{2}. \tag{2:21}$$

Factors Influencing ϕ in Cohesionless Soils The resistance of the grains to rolling and sliding is more complex than simple friction. The sliding resistance of the grains is determined by the effective stress, the coefficient of friction between the minerals, the surface roughness, and the angle of contact between the grains. These in turn depend on the grain shape and the soil structure as reflected in the relative density. The resistance to rolling depends on the particle shape, the gradation, and the relative density. As a result the angle of internal friction is greater than the angle of friction between the minerals, and it varies with grain shape, gradation, and relative density. The Mohr envelope is not always perfectly straight nor does it always pass through the origin because the resistance to rolling is present even with no confinement. At very high stresses the envelope may be curved concave downward owing to fracture of some of the grains. Typical values of the angle of internal friction are given in Table 2:3.

Table 2:3 ANGLE OF INTERNAL FRICTION OF COHESIONLESS SOILS COMPOSED LARGELY OF QUARTZ

Description	Angle of Internal Friction	
	D_d less than 20	D_d over 70
Rounded, uniform	29	35
Rounded, well-graded	32	38
Angular, uniform	35	43
Angular, well-graded	37	45

Volume Changes with Shear As the shear stress increases to the point of failure, volume changes take place in the soil. In dense materials the grains are so closely packed that they must climb over one another in order to allow failure to take place. Consequently there is a swelling of dense sand as it fails by shear (Fig. 2:25a).

In loose sands, shearing results in a volume decrease. Particles of sand, lying unstably atop one another, fall into the large voids as shear continues and the volume of voids becomes smaller (Fig. 2:25b).

If shearing is continued beyond the point of failure, both loose and dense sands tend to approach the same intermediate density, often termed the *critical density*. If a soil's void ratio is higher than its void ratio at the critical density, it is termed *loose* and is often unstable under strain and vibration; if a soil is more dense than the critical, it is termed *dense* and tends to be stable. In many soils the critical density corresponds to a relative density of 50 per cent.

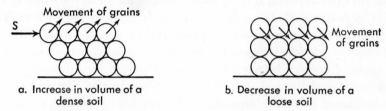

a. Increase in volume of a   b. Decrease in volume of a
   dense soil   loose soil

Fig. 2:25   Volume changes that accompany shear in cohesionless soils.

2:13   Shear in Wet Cohesionless Soils

As stated earlier, the total stress applied to a soil is sustained by grain structure stress which is $\bar{\sigma}$ (*effective stress*) and by *neutral* or *water stress*, u. So, at any time the stresses can be represented by the relation

$$\sigma = \bar{\sigma} + u. \tag{2:14}$$

Since shearing resistance is a friction phenomenon, it depends on grain structure stress; therefore at failure the equation for shearing strength of moist sand must be written:

$$s = \bar{p} \tan \phi, \tag{2:20}$$
$$s = (p - u) \tan \phi, \tag{2:22}$$

where $\bar{p}$ is the *effective normal stress* at failure. Failure to recognize this relationship has resulted in many misconceptions of the variation of internal friction with moisture. Experiments have shown ϕ to be almost unchanged by moisture—the real change occurs in the effective stresses that produce friction and shearing resistance.

Hydrostatic Neutral Stress   Many cases of hydrostatic neutral stress exist in nature, largely owing to the water table and its fluctuations. In a dry sand the vertical normal stress is caused by the unit weight of the sand itself; so, at a depth z the resistance to horizontal shear is given by:

$$\bar{\sigma} = \sigma = \gamma z, \tag{2:23a}$$
$$s = \gamma z \tan \phi. \tag{2:23b}$$

If the water table rises through this soil, the total unit weight of the soil increases to γ_s, the saturated unit weight, but now

$$\bar{\sigma} = \gamma_s z - u, \tag{2:23c}$$
$$s = (\gamma_s z - u) \tan \phi. \tag{2:23d}$$

If u is sufficiently large, the shear strength may be reduced to a negligible amount. Landslides are often caused by neutral stress that builds up until the soil shear strength is incapable of sustaining the applied loads. A shear failure can result and large masses of soil can be placed in motion under such circumstances.

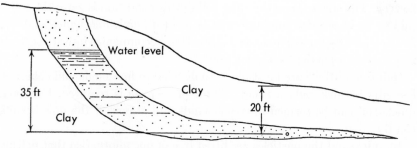

Fig. 2:26   Hydrostatic neutral stress in a hillside (Example 2:5).

Example 2:5   (Fig. 2:26)

Given: Clay γ_s = 110 lb/cu ft. Compute shear strength of sand at point x.
(1) σ = 20 × 110 = 2200 psf.
(2) u = 35 × 62.4 = 2180 psf.
(3) $\bar{\sigma}$ = 20 psf.
(4) s = 20 tan ϕ (practically zero).

Neutral Stress from Moving Water   High neutral stress is often caused by moving water, particularly in fine-grained soils. High heads are required to produce movement of the water through such soils. Since head of water at any point is a measure of water pressure or neutral stress, high head means lowered effective stress. If the dimensions of a soil stratum, its permeability, and the rate of flow through it are known, it is possible to compute the head h at any point and the neutral stress.

Example 2:6   (Fig. 2:27)

Given: Water flowing upward through sand at a rate of 0.0015 cm³/sec. Compute effective stress at x. Cross-sectional area = 3 cm², k = 0.001 cm/sec, γ = 1.9 gm/cm³.

(1) σ_x = 5 cm × 1.9 gm/cm³ + 1 gm/cm²
    = 10.5 gm/cm².

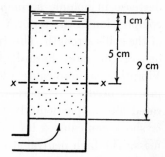

(2) $Q = kiA$; $i = \dfrac{0.0015}{3 \times 0.001}$ = 0.5.

(3) h_x = 6 + 5i = 6 + 2.5 = 8.5 cm;
    u = 8.5 cm × 1 gm/cm³ = 8.5 gm/cm².
(4) $\bar{\sigma}_x$ = 10.5 − 8.5 = 2 gm/cm².

Fig. 2:27   Neutral stress from upward seepage.

The neutral stress causes a corresponding reduction in soil strength. If the soil has a low angle of internal friction due to rounded grains and low density, the strength under conditions of upward seepage can be very low.

If the water in Example 2:6 flows upward at a rate of 0.0027 cm^3 per sec the neutral stress will be 10.5 gm per cm^2 and the effective stress will be zero. The shear strength of the soil in this condition is zero; the soil is said to be in a *quick* condition and is termed *quicksand*. Quicksand is a state caused by excessive neutral stress that accompanies upward seepage rather than a particular type of soil.

Quick conditions are most likely to develop in fine sands and cohesionless silts because only a small volume of seepage is required. However, quicksand can be formed in coarse sands and gravels if the flow is sufficiently great.

In quicksand the particles are lifted free of one another so that neither friction nor interlocking is effective. The soil behaves like a heavy viscous liquid. A man will sink into quicksand, but will eventually float because the soil is more dense than the human body.

Neutral Stress through Volume Change As a cohesionless soil is sheared, its volume changes; if the soil is saturated, the volume change must be accompanied by a change in the distribution of water in the voids. If shear and the change in volume occur so slowly that the movement of water requires negligible head, there will be only insignificant changes in neutral stress. Quick shear, however, requires rapid changes in water content that develop tremendous neutral stresses. This is particularly important in the very fine-grained soils of low permeability.

In dense soils expansion accompanies shear. The expanding voids produce tension in the water—a negative neutral stress that increases the effective stress and the shear strength tremendously. In loose sands, a decrease in volume accompanies shear. The contracting voids produce compression in the water, positive neutral stresses, and a temporary loss of the soil's strength. This is known as a *temporary quick condition* and is one of the most hazardous phenomena in underground construction. Vibration can also cause a loose soil to become more compact and in the process produce temporary large neutral stresses. Honeycombed, saturated silts are particularly dangerous. Slight vibrations, water movement, or shock can cause a breakdown of structure at one point in such a soil mass. The high neutral stress that results produces low or zero strength at that point and induces failure at adjacent points. The process is a chain reaction. An entire mass of soil may break down almost instantaneously with the least provocation and flow like water, since its shear strength is almost zero. The movement stops when the excess water drains away; then the soil becomes dense and hard. Some soils are particularly unstable because the difference between their loose and dense states is small. They can become alternately "quick" and hard with little apparent cause. There is no sure remedy for a temporary quick condition. Extreme caution must be exercised in construction work involving loose, saturated soils to prevent changes in volume or structure that can result in devastating soil flow.

Neutral Stress from Capillary Tension Capillary tension can be the cause of negative neutral stress that increases soil shear strength. Moist sand owes its ability to pack and maintain a shape to capillary tension in thin water films between the grains. The small meniscus radii develop high tensile stresses in the moisture wedges that hold the grains in rigid contact (Fig. 2:28).

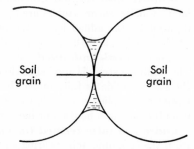

Fig. 2:28 Neutral stress from capillary tension producing compression between soil grains.

Fine sand and silt above the ground water table within the zone of capillary rise owe their strength to the capillary tension and the resulting effective stresses in the soil structure. Frequently, deep excavations can be made in such soils with very steep side slopes because of this strength. If the soil should dry out completely or should become inundated, the capillary tension will be destroyed and the strength reduced. Many failures can be traced to such a loss of strength from a reduction in capillary tension.

A sample of saturated fine sand or silt will hold its shape when subjected to an unconfined compression test because capillary tension produces a positive effective σ_3. If loose, it will finally collapse when the load causes a reduction in the volume of the voids and a buildup of neutral stress. If dense, it will expand and develop even greater capillary tension.

2:14 Shear Strength of Saturated Cohesive Soils[2:3,2:11]

Shear in a saturated cohesive soil (a clay) is more complex than in a sand or gravel. Like the cohesionless soil, the clay is made up of discrete particles which must slide or rotate for shear to take place. However, there are a number of significant differences. First the soil is relatively compressible; therefore, when a load is applied to the saturated clay, it is initially supported by neutral stress and is not transmitted to the soil structure. Second the permeability of the clay is so low that the neutral stresses produced by the load are dissipated very slowly. Therefore it may be months or even decades before the soil structure feels the stress increase. Third there are significant forces developed between the particles of clay by their mutual attraction and repulsion.

Rate of Loading   Because of the slow changes in the neutral stress and the corresponding slow changes in effective stress, the strength of clays is defined in terms of neutral stress dissipation. Three basic conditions are defined:[2;13]

Drained (also termed Consolidated-Drained or Slow) Shear: The confining and the shear stresses are applied so slowly that the neutral stress is not changed by the added loads; the applied stress produces an equal increase in effective stress; and the soil consolidates fully.

Consolidated-Undrained (also termed Consolidated-Quick) Shear: The confining stress is applied so slowly that the neutral stress is not changed and the soil consolidates fully under the increased effective stress. The shear stress, however, is applied so quickly that neutral stress carries all this change and there is no further consolidation or increase in effective stress.

Undrained (also termed Unconsolidated-Undrained, or Quick) Shear: Both the confining and shearing stresses are applied so rapidly that the neutral stress carries all the added load.

Drained Shear   In drained shear, there is no neutral stress change and the increase in load produces a corresponding increase in effective stress. The increased stress causes the soil to consolidate, reducing the void ratio and the water content. As a result the interparticle attractive or bond forces increase and in direct proportion to the effective stress increase. The Mohr envelope (Fig. 2:29), therefore, is a straight line through the origin similar to that for cohesionless soils.

The angle of the Mohr envelope is termed the *angle of shear resistance* or *apparent internal friction* and is denoted ϕ_D or ϕ_{CD}. Typical values lie between 20° and 35°. The higher angles are usually associated with clays having plasticity indexes of 5 to 10, while the lower values are for clays having plasticity indexes of from 50 to 100. This is a verification of the effect of particle repulsion and adsorbed water on the interparticle bonds, for the high PI indicates high adsorption and repulsion, large interparticle spacing, and correspondingly less interparticle attraction.

When a clay has been preconsolidated to a stress of $\bar{\sigma}_c$ and then unloaded, the particles do not return to their original spacing and previously higher void ratio. As a result the interparticle attractive force is not reduced and the strength at stresses less than the preconsolidation load is no longer proportional to the effective confining pressure but is somewhat higher (Fig. 2:29).

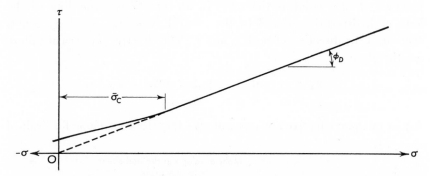

Fig. 2:29 Mohr's envelope for saturated clay in drained (consolidated-drained or slow) shear.

The strength above the preconsolidation load is given by the expression

$$s = \bar{p} \tan \phi_D. \qquad (2:24a)$$

Below the preconsolidation load the strength must be obtained directly from the Mohr diagram. This curved portion of the envelope can be approximated by a straight line having the equation

$$s = c' + \bar{p} \tan \phi' \qquad (2:24b)$$

In this expression c' is the intercept on the τ axis and ϕ' is the angle that the straight line makes with the σ axis.

The drained shear condition represents the strength of the soil developed by a long-term stress change. However, it can be used for any problem involving shear in saturated clays by determining the effective stress at failure from the total and neutral stress. It is particularly useful in analyses involving complex changes in loading and water pressure. The drained shear test is time consuming; however, the Mohr envelope for this condition can usually be approximated from the consolidated-undrained test results.

Consolidated-Undrained Shear   In consolidated-undrained shear, the soil consolidates completely under the confining stress σ_3, with a corresponding reduction in void ratio and water content. The axial load is then increased suddenly by an amount $\Delta\sigma_1$ without further changes in void ratio or water content until failure occurs. The total major principal stress at failure is $\sigma_1 = \sigma_3 + \Delta\sigma_1$, and the total minor principal stress is σ_3. Since no drainage or consolidation occurs from the added load $\Delta\sigma_1$, it is supported entirely by neutral stress, or $u = \Delta\sigma_1$. Water pressure at any point is the same in all directions, according to the laws of hydrostatics; therefore the neutral stress produced by $\Delta\sigma_1$ is exerted in the direction of both σ_1 and σ_3. The effective stresses at failure are therefore

$$\bar{\sigma}_1 = \sigma_1 - u = \sigma_3 + \Delta\sigma_1 - \Delta\sigma_1 = \sigma_3,$$
$$\bar{\sigma}_3 = \sigma_3 - u = \sigma_3 - \Delta\sigma_1.$$

A plot of these effective stresses will give the Mohr envelope for drained

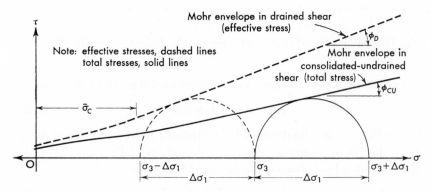

Fig. 2:30 Mohr's envelope and stresses for saturated clay in consolidated-undrained (consolidated-quick) shear.

shear. However, if the total stresses are plotted (Fig. 2:30), a different envelope will be produced because the circles are shifted horizontally to the right by $\Delta\sigma_1$. The apparent Mohr envelope of total stresses will also be a straight line through the origin above the preconsolidation load and will have an apparent angle of shear resistance, ϕ_{CU}, which is about half of ϕ_D. The equation for shear strength above the preconsolidation load is

$$s = p \tan \phi_{CU}. \tag{2:25}$$

A consolidated-undrained test is frequently employed to obtain ϕ_D, using a plot of effective rather than total stresses. The test is less time consuming than the drained, and the computed effective envelope is approximately the same as that obtained in drained shear. Measurements of neutral stress can be made in the soil during the test to aid in plotting the effective envelope, but these require considerable skill and complex apparatus.

Consolidated-undrained shear represents a clay soil that has been fully consolidated by the weight of a structure which is later subjected to a sudden increase in stress by the construction of an addition or by an abnormal live load. It is frequently employed in the analysis of embankment foundations where construction lasts for more than a year.

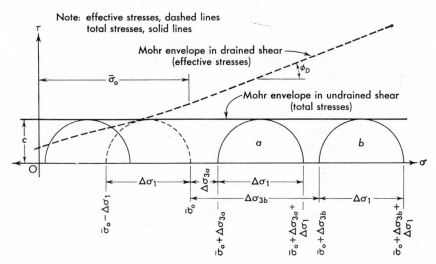

Fig. 2:31 Mohr's envelope and stresses for saturated clay in undrained (unconsolidated undrained or quick) shear.

Undrained Shear In undrained shear, both the confining and shear stresses are applied so rapidly that no consolidation takes place. The soil void ratio and water content remain unchanged, and neutral stress supports all the added loads. The soil initially supported an overburden pressure, $\bar{\sigma}_0$ (or a preconsolidation load $\bar{\sigma}_c$), under which it consolidated to establish its void ratio, water content, and interparticle spacing. The soil strength resulting from this initial effective stress can be obtained from $\bar{\sigma}_0$, using the Mohr envelope of drained shear shown in Fig. 2:31. An increased confining pressure, $\Delta\sigma_3$, is supported by neutral stress, and the void ratio, interparticle spacing, and resulting soil strength remain unchanged. An increased axial load, $\Delta\sigma_1$, also is supported by neutral stress, and likewise produces no change in void ratio or water content. The stress conditions during loading are tabulated below.

Loading	Total Stress	Neutral Stress	Effective Stress
Overburden	$\sigma_1 = \bar\sigma_o$	$u = 0$	$\bar\sigma_1 = \bar\sigma_o$
	$\sigma_3 = \bar\sigma_o{}^*$	$u = 0$	$\bar\sigma_3 = \bar\sigma_o{}^*$
Added confining stress, $\Delta\sigma_3$	$\sigma_1 = \bar\sigma_o + \Delta\sigma_3$	$u = \Delta\sigma_3$	$\bar\sigma_1 = \bar\sigma_o$
	$\sigma_3 = \bar\sigma_o + \Delta\sigma_3$	$u = \Delta\sigma_3$	$\bar\sigma_3 = \bar\sigma_o$
Added axial load, $\Delta\sigma_1$	$\sigma_1 = \bar\sigma_o + \Delta\sigma_3 + \Delta\sigma_1$	$u = \Delta\sigma_1 + \Delta\sigma_3$	$\bar\sigma_1 = \bar\sigma_o$
	$\sigma_3 = \bar\sigma_o + \Delta\sigma_3$	$u = \Delta\sigma_1 + \Delta\sigma_3$	$\bar\sigma_3 = \bar\sigma_o - \Delta\sigma_1$

* In many cases the minor principal stress from the overburden load will be less than the major principal stress, but this does not alter the neutral stress effects described in the table.

The effective minor principal stress is independent of the added confining stress σ_3, and therefore the effective major principal stress at failure and the strength depend only on the original overburden stress $\bar\sigma_o$ and the effective (drained shear) envelope. A plot of the total stresses, the solid lines on Fig. 2:31, shows a series of Mohr circles. All have the same diameter (since they are in reality the same circle), and the resulting envelope of total stresses is a horizontal straight line. As can be seen from the diagram, the intercept of the envelope on the τ-axis is approximately equal to the shear strength of the soil in its original condition, consolidated by the overburden stress, $\bar\sigma_o$. The intercept is denoted c and is called the *cohesion* of the soil. The strength of the soil under undrained conditions can be expressed by the equation

$$s = c. \tag{2:26a}$$

The apparent angle of friction, ϕ_U, is zero. However, the angle of the failure plane α is determined by equation 2:21, using ϕ_D, and is not 45° as might be assumed with $\phi_U = 0$.

The undrained strength represents the existing strength of a natural soil. Since most construction proceeds rapidly compared with the rate of clay consolidation, undrained strength is used in most problems of design. Even where construction is so slow that some strength increase will develop, the undrained strength is frequently used because it is the minimum strength and therefore conservative. Caution must be exercised in using the undrained shear in the analysis of problems where the final stress is less than the original overburden load, such as the design of excavation bracing or in the study of landslides. For short-term conditions where the soil does not have sufficient time to expand, the undrained strength applies, but for long-term conditions, the soil becomes weaker and the use of undrained strength is unsafe.

The undrained strength depends on the original overburden stress, $\bar{\sigma}_o$ or $\bar{\sigma}_c$, and on the drained Mohr envelope. In a compressible soil such as a clay the overburden stress is related to the void ratio by the stress-void ratio curve. As a result the undrained strength of a saturated clay increases with decreasing void ratio and also decreasing water content. For normally consolidated clays, a graph of the logarithm of undrained strength plotted as a function of either water content or void ratio is approximately a straight line.

Unconfined Compression Test of Saturated Clay Since the undrained strength is the same regardless of the confining pressure, the strength can be determined with zero confining pressure. The strength is given by

$$s = \frac{1}{2} q_u = c, \qquad (2\!:\!26\mathrm{b})$$

where q_u, the unconfined compressive strength, is equal to σ_1 at failure when $\sigma_3 = 0$.

Sensitivity If a sample of undisturbed saturated clay is completely remolded without changing its water content, and then tested, it will be found that the undrained strength has been reduced. This is caused by a breakdown in the soil structure and a loss of the interparticle attractive forces and bonds. In clays with a dispersed structure, the loss is small, but in clays with a highly flocculent structure or soils with a well-developed skeletal structure, the loss in strength can be large. The ratio of the undisturbed to the remolded strength is defined as the *sensitivity*, S_t:

$$S_t = \frac{c \ (\text{undisturbed})}{c \ (\text{remolded})} = \frac{q_u \ \text{undisturbed}}{q_u \ \text{remolded}}. \qquad (2\!:\!27)$$

Table 2:4 TYPICAL VALUES OF SENSITIVITY

Clays of medium plasticity, normally consolidated	2–8
Highly flocculent, marine clays	10–80
Clays of low to medium plasticity, overconsolidated	1–4
Fissured clays, clays with sand seams	0.5–2

Clays with Fissures Some clays in nature develop cracks or fissures from desiccation, high overburden stresses which produce local fracture, or physicochemical alteration and weathering. Often the fissures appear to be closed, but they still remain as planes of weakness and paths of seepage. The strength of such clays is dependent on the orientation of the cracks and fissures and on the effect of changing stress and water percolation on the clay along the fissures. Tests of the intact clay between the fissures are misleading; large enough samples must be used so that the fissures are included. Drained tests are best, since the fissures permit more rapid dissipation of neutral stress than in ordinary clays.

2:15   Shear of Partially Saturated Cohesive Soils[2:3,2:12,2:14]

Shear of partially saturated cohesive soils involves the same forces as for saturated cohesive soils. However, the neutral stress in the soil pores is a complex combination of capillary tension and gas pressure which depends on the degree of saturation and the size of the voids. The effective

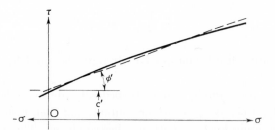

Fig. 2:32   Mohr's envelope of total stresses for partially saturated clay.

stresses are difficult if not impossible to determine in partially saturated soils, and so the envelope of total stresses is usually employed to express test results (Fig. 2:32). The Mohr envelope is ordinarily curved, with an intercept on the τ-axis and with a decreasing slope at increasing normal stresses. The intercept is probably the combined result of capillary tension in the voids and interparticle bonds from preconsolidation. The initially steep slope results from soil consolidation under the increasing confining pressure and is comparable to the drained shear of a saturated clay. As the soil consolidates under increasing pressure, however, the degree of saturation increases, capillary tension decreases, and positive pore pressures eventually develop. This is comparable to undrained shear and results in the Mohr envelope approaching a horizontal asymptote. The strength for any confining pressure is read directly from the envelope. For convenience the curved envelope is often approximated by a straight line having the equation

$$s = c' + p \tan \phi',* \qquad (2\!:\!28)$$

where c' is the intercept on the τ-axis and ϕ (or sometimes ϕ') is the *angle of shear resistance*. More than one straight line can be used to approximate any given curved envelope, depending on which part of the envelope is of most importance in that particular case. Therefore c' and ϕ' should be considered to be empirical constants and not properties of the soil. The approximate angle of the failure plane, α, can be found graphically or by equation 2:21.

Partially saturated clays often become saturated from high rainfall or a rising ground water table. Therefore the strength of a partially saturated clay should not be used in analyzing practical problems unless the soil remains in that condition. Frequently partially saturated clays

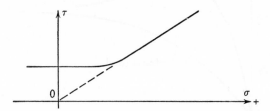

Fig. 2:33   Mohr's envelope for a cemented soil.

are first soaked in water and then tested as saturated clays to obtain data for design.

2:16   Shear Strength of Cemented Soils

Soils with a cemented skeletal structure, including many soft rocks and partially weathered rocks, consist of rigid grains bound together with a cementing agent. The strength depends on the distribution and strength of the cementing agent, the friction between the soil grains, and the strength of the grains themselves. The Mohr envelope of effective stress (Fig. 2:33) is ordinarily complex. At low stresses the strength is governed by that of the cementing agent, which often is constant, independent of the confining stress. At higher stresses the friction of the grains governs, and the envelope slope increases. At very high stresses the grains themselves fracture and the envelope sometimes flattens.

For use in analysis, the envelope is approximated by a straight line

* This is the same form of equation as 2:24b.

having the same equation as that for the partially saturated cohesive soil. The only difference is that effective rather than total stresses are employed for the cemented soils.

2:17 Stress and Strain in Soils

The relation between stress and strain in soils is similar to that found in many other engineering materials. In the course of making shear tests and unconfined compression tests, the deformations accompanying different stresses are recorded and from these data stress-strain curves can be plotted. The ratio of a change in stress to the change in strain producing it is the modulus of elasticity, E. It is proportional to the slope of the stress-strain curve. Although it is not a constant for most soils, it

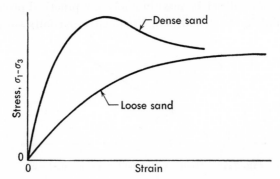

Fig. 2:34   Stress strain in loose and dense cohesionless soils.

is as much a constant as the modulus of elasticity of concrete and should be used with about the same degree of caution.

Stress–Strain in Cohesionless Soils   Typical stress–strain curves for a sand in both the loose and dense states are shown in Fig. 2:34. The relationship for dense sands shows a relatively high initial modulus of elasticity that decreases as the stress increases. The curve for loose sand shows a similar trend, but the curvature is more uniform from zero stress to failure. Tests made with different values for the minor principal stress indicate that the modulus of elasticity increases as σ_3 increases for both loose and dense sands.

Since the modulus of elasticity of cohesionless soils varies widely with the amount of compressive stress, with the density, and with the minor principal stress, values of E for design purposes must be obtained under the same conditions that will exist in the soil mass. The value of E that is ordinarily required is the average E for the first one-third of the stress-strain curve. Computations involving E for cohesionless soils are approximate at best.

Stress–Strain in Cohesive Soils   The relation of strain to stress in undisturbed cohesive soils (Fig. 2:35) more closely resembles that for some metals. The curve is very straight for the greater part of its length and usually does not begin to flatten until the failure stress is approached. Failure of the soil occurs rapidly and along a well-defined failure plane. The modulus of elasticity is nearly a constant, and it is often as high as 200,000 psf. Remolded clays such as compacted fill soils or badly disturbed samples have gradually flattening stress–strain curves that resemble those for sands. The values of the modulus of elasticity for such

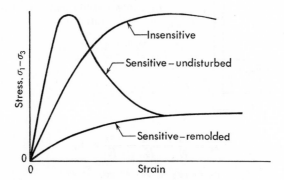

Fig. 2:35   Stress strain in sensitive and insensitive
cohesive soils.

soils are considerably lower than for the undisturbed clays. Failure in remolded soils takes place along many parallel and intersecting planes, thus giving a soil sample the appearance of bulging like a barrel.

Poisson's Ratio   When an axial stress is applied to a prism of soil, the soil decreases in height in the axial direction and expands or bulges in the lateral direction (Fig. 2:36). The ratio of the lateral strain, ϵ_2 or ϵ_3, to the axial strain is Poisson's ratio ν:

$$\nu = -\frac{\epsilon_2}{\epsilon_1} \quad \text{or} \quad -\frac{\epsilon_3}{\epsilon_1}. \tag{2:29}$$

(The minus sign is introduced because the sign of ϵ_1 is negative and of ϵ_2 or ϵ_3, positive.)

Poisson's ratio can be determined by measuring the axial and lateral strains during triaxial tests, but the instrumentation is complex. It also can be determined by loading the soil axially and measuring the confining stress required to prevent any lateral expansion. The ratio of the lateral stress to the axial stress is a measure of Poisson's ratio as shown below.

The strain in the lateral direction of σ_3 is the algebraic sum of the strains caused by σ_1, σ_2, and σ_3. In the triaxial test, σ_2 and σ_3 are equal, and if any lateral expansion is prevented, $\epsilon_3 = 0$.

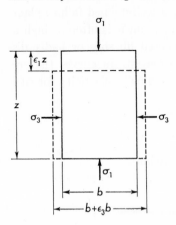

Fig. 2:36   Strain under axial load; Poisson's ratio.

$$\epsilon_3 = \frac{\sigma_3}{E} - \frac{\nu\sigma_2}{E} - \frac{\nu\sigma_1}{E} = 0,$$

$$\sigma_3 = \nu\sigma_2 + \nu\sigma_1 = \nu\sigma_3 + \nu\sigma_1,$$

$$\nu\sigma_1 = \sigma_3 - \nu\sigma_3,$$

$$\frac{\sigma_3}{\sigma_1} = \frac{\nu}{1 - \nu}. \tag{2:30a}$$

$$\nu = \frac{\sigma_3}{\sigma_1 + \sigma_3}. \tag{2:30b}$$

The Poisson's ratio for saturated clay in undrained loading approaches 0.5. For saturated clay with drained loading and for sands, values of from 0.2 to 0.4 have been observed. With small changes in stress, the values for loose sand and clays in drained loading are probably close to zero.

REFERENCES

2:1   A. Hazen, "Water Supply," *American Civil Engineers Handbook*, John Wiley & Sons, Inc., New York, 1930.

2:2   K. Terzaghi and R. B. Peck, *Soil Mechanics in Engineering Practice*, John Wiley & Sons, Inc., New York, 1948.

2:3   T. W. Lambe, "The Engineering Behavior of Compacted Clay," *Journal of the Soil Mechanics Division, Proceedings, ASCE*, Vol. 84, SM 2, May, 1958.

2:4   T. K. Tan, "Discussion on Structure Mechanics of Clay," *Proceedings, Fourth International Conference on Soil Mechanics and Foundation Engineering*, Vol. 3, London, 1957, p. 87.

2:5   Reference 2:2, p. 66.

2:6   A. W. Skempton, "Notes on the Compressibility of Clays," *Quarterly Journal of Geological Society*, Vol. 100, London, 1944, p. 119.

2:7   G. F. Sowers, "Soil and Foundation Problems in the Southern Piedmont Region," *Proceedings, ASCE*, Vol. 80, Separate 416, 1953.

2:8   G. F. Sowers, "Shallow Foundations," *Foundation Engineering*, McGraw-Hill Book Co., Inc., New York, 1961.

2:9   W. G. Holtz and H. J. Gibbs, "Engineering Properties of Expansive Clays," *Transactions, ASCE*, Vol. 120, 1956.

2:10 *Symposium on Direct Shear Testing of Soils*, ASTM Special Technical Publication 131, American Society for Testing Materials, Philadelphia, 1953.

2:11 A. W. Bishop and D. J. Henkel, *The Measurement of Soil Properties in the Triaxial Shear Test*, Edward Arnold, Ltd., London, 1957.

2:12 G. A. Leonards, "Strength Characteristics of Compacted Clays," *Transactions*, ASCE, Vol. 119, 1956.

2:13 *Triaxial Shear Research and Pressure Distribution Studies*, U.S. Waterways Experiment Station, Vicksburg, 1947.

2:14 H. B. Seed and C. K. Chan, "Structure and Strength Characteristics of Compacted Clays," *Journal of the Soil Mechanics and Foundations Division, Proceedings*, ASCE, Vol. 85, SM 5, October, 1959.

Suggestions for Additional Study

1. References 2:3, 2:6, 2:10, 2:11, 2:12, 2:14.

2. D. W. Taylor, *Research on the Consolidation of Clays*, Massachusetts Institute of Technology, Cambridge, 1942.

3. *Proceedings of Third International Conference on Soil Mechanics and Foundation Engineering*, Vol. 1, Zurich, 1953.

4. *Proceedings of Fourth International Conference on Soil Mechanics and Foundation Engineering*, Vol. 1, London, 1957.

5. *Proceedings Research Conference on Shear Strength of Cohesive Soils*, ASCE, 1960.

6. T. W. Lambe, *Soil Testing for Engineers*, John Wiley & Sons, Inc., New York, 1951.

7. R. H. Karol, *Engineering Properties of Soils*, Prentice-Hall, Inc., Englewood Cliffs, N.J., 1955.

8. R. W. Dawson, *Laboratory Manual of Soil Mechanics*, Pitman Publishing Corp., New York, 1960.

PROBLEMS

2:1 a. Compute the maximum capillary tension in grams per square centimeter and pounds per square foot in a tube 0.001 mm in diameter.

b. Compute the height of capillary rise in the tube in feet.

2:2 Compute the capillary tension in pounds per square foot and the theoretical height of capillary rise in feet in a soil whose D_{10} is 0.002 mm if the effective pore diameter is about $\frac{1}{5}D_{10}$.

2:3 Compute the height of capillary rise in feet in a sand whose D_{10} is 0.2 mm if the effective pore diameter is $\frac{1}{5}D_{10}$.

2:4 A sample of soil in a permeability test is 5 cm in diameter and 12 cm long. The head difference is 25 cm and the flow is 1.5 cm³ in 5 min. Compute coefficient of permeability in centimeters per second and feet per the minute.

2:5 Given a block of soil 12 cm long and 6 sq cm in cross-section. The water level at one end of the block is 20 cm above a fixed plane and at the other end is 3 cm above the same plane. The flow rate is 2 cm³ in 1.5 min. Compute the soil permeability in feet per minute.

2:6 A canal and a river run parallel, an average of 150 ft apart. The elevation of water in the canal is El. 618 and in the river El. 595. A stratum of sand intersects both the river and the canal below their water levels. The sand is 5 ft thick and is sandwiched between strata of impervious clay. Compute the seepage loss from the canal in cubic feet per second per mile if the sand's permeability is 0.063 cm per sec.

2:7 A wood crib filled with earth serves as a temporary cofferdam across a river to lower the water level in a construction site. The water level upstream is 20 ft above the rock stream bed and downstream is 5 ft above the stream bed. The cofferdam is 200 ft long across the river and is 30 ft wide upstream to downstream. It is filled with well-graded, silty, sandy gravel having a coefficient of permeability of 0.0005 cm per sec. Estimate the seepage through the cofferdam in gallons per hour (the unit in which construction pumps are rated). *Hint:* Assume that the average cross-section of the water flowing through the cofferdam is the average of the intake area (20 × 200) and the outlet (5 × 200).

2:8 The stress void-ratio curve for a saturated clay is shown on Fig. 2:7. Compute the compression index C_c. Find the change in void ratio from the curve if the stress increases from 1000 to 10,000 psf. Find the change in void ratio from the curve if the stress changes from 10,000 to 100,000 psf. Recompute the change in void ratio in both cases, using equation 2:10, and compare with the values found directly from the curve. Explain the differences.

2:9 A consolidation test had the following results:

σ	e	σ	e
250 psf	0.755	4,000 psf	0.740
500	0.754	8,000	0.724
1000	0.753	16,000	0.704
2000	0.750	32,000	0.684

a. Plot the stress void-ratio curves on semilog coordinates.

b. Compute the compression index.

c. If the initial soil stress is 1400 psf and the soil stratum is 8 ft thick, how high can the stress become before the ultimate settlement is ¾ in.?

2:10 A consolidation test on a sample of soil yields the following void ratios for 100 per cent consolidation:

σ	e	σ	e
100 psf	1.85	16,000 psf	1.22
500	1.82	32,000	1.05
1000	1.77	10,000	1.10
2000	1.68	2,000	1.20
4000	1.56	500	1.28
8000	1.39	100	1.38

a. Plot the stress void-ratio curves on both arithmetic and semilog coordinates.

b. Compute the compression index, C_c.

c. Find the change in void ratio when the soil stress is raised from 1650 psf to 2700 psf.

d. If the soil stratum in (c) is initially 6.8 ft thick, compute its settlement.

e. If the soil has a coefficient of consolidation of 0.02 sq ft per day and the stratum in (d) is drained on both sides, compute the time required for 25, 50, and 75 per cent consolidation.

2:11 A soil has a compression index, C_c, of 0.27. Its void ratio at a stress of 2600 psf is 1.04, and its permeability is 3.5×10^{-8} cm per sec.

a. Compute the change in void ratio if the soil stress is increased to 3900 psf.

b. Compute the settlement in (a) if the soil stratum is 16 ft thick.

c. Find the time required for 25, 50, 75, and 90 per cent of settlement in (b) to occur.

2:12 Given a major principal stress of 8 kg per cm² and a minor principal stress of 1 kg per cm²; draw the Mohr's circle. Find the maximum shear stress and the normal and shear stresses on a plane that makes an angle of 60° with the major principal plane. 350° psf, 2800 psf, 3050 psf

2:13 Given a major principal stress of 12,000 psf and a minor principal stress of 3000 psf; draw the Mohr's circle. Find the maximum shear stress and the normal and shear stresses on a plane that makes an angle of 60° with the minor principal plane. 4500, 9700 psf, 3900 psf

2:14 The normal stresses on two perpendicular planes are 18 and 3 kg per cm² and the shear stresses are 6 kg per cm². Find the major and minor principal stresses graphically. 20.1 kg/cm² 0.9 kg/cm²

2:15 Given a major principal stress of 4 kip per sq ft and a minor principal stress of 1 kip per sq ft, find the maximum shear stress and the angle of the plane on which it acts.

2:16 The shear and normal stresses on one plane are respectively 2000 psf and 7000 psf, and on a second plane, 4000 psf and 3000 psf.

a. Find the principal stresses.

b. Find the shear and normal stresses on a plane making an angle of 50° with the major principal plane.

2:17 Given the normal stresses on two perpendicular planes as 3500 psf and 1200 psf, the shear stresses on each as 2300 psf, draw Mohr's circle.

a. Can tension occur on any plane with this stress condition?

b. Find the principal stresses.

c. What are the shear and normal stresses on a plane making an angle of 74° with the direction of the major principal stress?

2:18 Given a major principal stress of 7500 psf, find the minimum value of the minor principal stress to limit shear stresses to 3200 psf.

2:19 A cylinder of concrete is tested in the ordinary manner and is found to have a "compressive" strength of 3450 psi. The failure plane makes an angle of 63° with the major principal plane.

a. Draw Mohr's circle for the concrete at failure. (The minor principal stress is zero.)

b. Draw the Mohr rupture envelope, assuming it to be a straight line.

c. Find the "compressive" strength (difference between the principal stresses) if the minor principal stress is 1000 psi.

2:20 Given ϕ of a sand, derive the algebraic relation between ϕ and α.

2:21 Given ϕ of a sand, derive the algebraic expression for the ratio of the major principal stress to the minor principal stress when failure in the sand occurs.

2:22 A sample of sand subjected to a triaxial shear test failed when the minor principal stress was 3200 psf and the major principal stress was 11,500 psf. Draw Mohr's circle, and find ϕ and α.

2:23 A sample of sand in a direct shear test fails when the normal stress is 6 kip per sq ft and the shear stress is 4 kip per sq ft. Find the angle of internal friction and the principal stresses at failure.

2:24 Given the following stress conditions in a dense, angular, well-graded sand:

Plane A	Plane B
Shear stress 1 kip/sq ft	1 kip/sq ft
Normal stress 3.5	2.2

Will failure occur?

2:25 A cylindrical sample of saturated rock flour composed of extremely fine-grained bulky particles is subjected to an unconfined compression test. The minor principal stress is developed by capillary tension in soil pores that have an effective diameter of 0.00075 mm. The angle the failure plane makes with the minor principal stress is 65°.

a. Draw Mohr's circles for both total and effective stresses.

b. Find ϕ and the compressive stress necessary to produce failure.

2:26 A soil stratum 30 ft thick overlies a bed of shale. The water table is 15 ft above the surface of the shale and the height of capillary rise is 10 ft. The soil has a void ratio of 0.35 and a specific gravity of solids of 2.65. Draw diagrams showing the total, neutral, and effective vertical stresses in the deposit. (Remember that above the water table the neutral stress is negative, which denotes tension.)

2:27 A thin seam of sand lies inclined at an angle of 30° and intersects the base of a cliff. The drainage of the sand is stopped by accumulated talus. The sand is overlaid by clay 50 ft thick and 3 ft of topsoil. The ground surface slopes at 30° and there is a deep vertical crack extending through the clay 60 ft from the face of the cliff. The clay and topsoil weigh 110 lb per cu ft and the angle of internal friction of the sand is 40°. How high must the water rise in the sand before the block of clay slides upon the sand layer?

2:28 A steel sheet piling cofferdam, 20 × 40 ft in plan is driven 10 ft below the bed of a river in order to construct the foundation for a bridge. The soil in the river bottom consists of 10 ft of sand underlain by 5 ft of coarse gravel. The river level is 15 ft above the elevation of the sand. The sand weighs 130 lb per cu ft saturated. To what level can the water in the cofferdam be lowered before a quick condition develops in the sand? What will be the upward flow at that time if the sand has a permeability coefficient of 0.03 cm per sec? Assume that the head in the gravel stratum is the same as the river level.

2:29 A saturated clay in consolidated-undrained shear had a ϕ_{cu} of 12°. Find the approximate value of ϕ_D graphically.

2:30 A saturated clay in drained shear was found to have a ϕ_D of 25°. Find the approximate value of ϕ_{cu} and the approximate unconfined compressive strength if the overburden pressure is 1200 psf.

2:31 Derive by means of Mohr's circle the relation between the major and minor principal stresses when given c from a quick shear test of a saturated clay.

2:32 Given the following data from an unconfined compression test of saturated clay:

Stress (psf)	Strain
0	0
2000	0.0035
4000	0.0080
6000	0.0170
7000	0.0270
8000	0.0650

a. Plot the stress–strain curve.

b. Find the shear strength, c.

c. Find the average modulus of elasticity for 40 per cent of the failure stress.

3... SOILS and SOIL DEPOSITS

A knowledge of the geology of soil deposits is vital to the soils engineer because he must either fit the structure to the existing conditions or employ the deposits as a source of raw materials for construction. Likewise, knowledge of the geology of the underlying rock is necessary. The rock in some localities is the source of the soil, and in other areas the structure of the rock has a profound influence on the behavior of the soil above. In many projects both soil and rock are involved in the design of the structure (particularly deep foundations and tunnels) and both furnish raw materials for construction.

Natural soils are principally the products of rock weathering—silica and clay minerals, plus varying amounts of mica, feldspar, iron oxide, calcium carbonate, and ferromagnesian minerals. Organic matter is sometimes present in either the colloidal or fibrous form. Man-made soils are principally wastes, either the heterogeneous rubbish and garbage from cities or the more uniform and voluminous by-products of industrial processes, such as slag and sludge.

These materials accumulate in many different forms of deposits with different arrangements of composition and particle size.

The products of weathering that remain in the place they were formed are termed *residual soils*. In some gently rolling regions great deposits of residual soils accumulate, but in most cases gravity and erosion by ice, wind, and water move the products of weathering to form new deposits of *transported soils*. During the transportation process the particles of weathered rock are mixed with others of different origin; they may be ground up or decomposed still further; and they are usually sorted according to grain size before finally being deposited. The newly formed soil deposit is again subject to weathering, especially when the soil particles find themselves in a completely different environment from that in which they were formed. This *secondary weathering* produces a characteristic *soil profile* that is of particular interest to agriculturalists and to highway and airfield engineers who must deal with the uppermost portions of soil deposits.

To reduce the work of evaluating soils, different soil descriptive terms and classification systems have been developed. These supplement the traditional soil names that have some general meaning for the layman but which are too indefinite for the engineer.

3:1 Residual Soils

Residual soils are found wherever the rate of rock weathering exceeds the rate at which the products of weathering are removed by gravity and erosion. Most residual deposits are relatively thin and irregular, but in gently rolling areas where the rocks have little resistance and in warm, humid regions where the weathering agencies are particularly severe, the deposits of residual soils are sometimes as much as 100 ft deep.

Residual Soils from Igneous and Metamorphic Rock Many parts of the world, particularly the roots of mountains, are formed of granites, gneisses, schists, basalts, and similar rocks that were at one time heated to a plastic condition. They vary greatly in their resistance to weathering; granites tend to be very durable, whereas schists that are high in feldspar and mica and porous volcanic rocks weather rapidly. Extensive deposits of residual soils formed from these rocks are found in the Appalachian Piedmont region and in scattered areas in Texas, Idaho, and other western states.

The soils vary from coarse gravelly quartz sands to very fine-grained accumulations of quartz, mica, and clay minerals, depending on the composition of the original rock. The deposits are extremely erratic in composition and in extent. The minerals in metamorphic rocks tend to be arranged in narrow bands that resemble strata, and those bands are often twisted and distorted from plastic flow and faulting. The residual soils from such rocks may retain the same distorted and folded bands as differences in texture and composition. Such soils are termed *saprolites*. There is no sharp line of demarcation between soil and rock. The degree of weathering becomes less with increasing depth until eventually sound rock is reached. Within the mass of unweathered rock there sometimes are pockets of weathered material, and within the soil are often lenses and

pinnacles of only partially weathered rock. At one building site in the
Southeastern United States the depth to sound rock varied from 5 to
70 ft in a distance of only 200 ft, seams of unweathered rock alternated
with soft residual soils, and over ten different changes in composition
and texture occurred in each foot of depth. An example of such variability
is shown in Fig. 3:1. Because of their erratic variability and their high
mica and clay mineral contents, residual soils require careful study and
close control when used for structural support and for construction.

Fig. 3:1   Banding in a residual soil derived from the decomposition of
gneiss.

Residual Soils from Limestones   Limestones (and dolomites) are
sedimentary rocks composed largely of calcium and magnesium carbonates. These minerals are dissolved by water that contains small
amounts of carbon dioxide, and the insoluble impurities remain behind
as residual soil. These impurities are largely chert (gravel and sand sizes),
clay, and iron oxide, and they usually comprise from 2 to 10 per cent
of the original rock.

The soils derived from these impurities are clays and sandy, gravelly
clays that frequently are reddish from the iron oxides they contain.
The boundary between the soil and rock is sharp, but it is usually very
irregular. Water percolating through cracks and fissures in the limestone
causes a saw-tooth or slotted profile to develop at the rock surface, and

solution channels, cavities, and even large caverns to form at greater depths, as shown in Fig. 3:2.

Percolating water erodes the soil and carries it into the rock fissures and cavities, creating new cavities in the soil immediately above the rock. The roofs of the soil cavities ravel or even fall, which enlarges the openings and partially fills them with a wet, pasty soil. Eventually the ground surface subsides to form a saucer-shaped depression known as a *sink* or even an open hole termed a *sink hole*. The collapse of a large cavity in the rock also can produce sinks and sink holes. A characteristic pock-

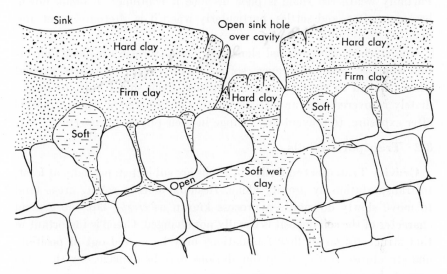

Fig. 3:2   Cross-section of a residual soil with sink and cavity development in limestone terrain.

marked landscape develops from advanced underground solution, which aids in its recognition.

Limestone soils are usually good sources of mixed materials for earth construction. They furnish good support for structures, provided there are no open cavities or active erosion into fissures in the rock below.

Residual Soils from Sandstones   Sandstones are cemented sands and weathering reconverts them to the original soil. The deposits of residual sandstone soil are usually thin and grade into sound rock with increasing depth without a definite boundary between soil and rock. Weathered sandstone soils ordinarily are excellent sources of sand and silty sand fill materials and are good foundations for structures.

Residual Soils from Shales Shales are formed by the consolidation, partial cementing, and chemical alteration of clays. Weathering converts them back to clay, which frequently is different from the original soil. The deposit is often very thick but irregular, with lenses of more resistant shale surrounded by completely weathered materials. Weathered shale usually provides good structural support if it is level-bedded; however, if it is tilted, it will tend to slide on the bedding planes. Completely weathered shale that shows no evidence of its original structure can be a source of clay for construction (provided its plasticity is not too high). Partially weathered shale is poor because it continues to break down, becomes softer, and settles, particularly when it is alternately wet and dry.

Undisturbed, unweathered shales ordinarily furnish excellent foundation support. Some, however, soften rapidly, whereas others expand when exposed to air and surface moisture. Such shales must be immediately recovered with an airtight coating of bitumen or cement mortar after exposure, to prevent any change in their physical properties.

3:2 Transported Soils

Gravity Transported Soils All soils are subjected, partially at least, to transportation by gravity alone. Residual soils in rolling areas tend to move slowly downhill—a process known as *creep*—but the general character of the soil deposit is usually not changed. Creep is important in that structures on shallow foundations may be moved out of position, and structures on deep, rigid foundations may be damaged by the pressure of the moving mass of soil.

A *talus* is an accumulation of fallen rock and rock debris at the bases of steep rock slopes and faces. It is composed of irregular, coarse particles and is very likely to be in an unstable condition. It is often a good source of broken rock and coarse-grained soil for construction.

Mud flows take place when loose, sandy, residual soils on relatively flat slopes become saturated. The soils flow like water and then come to rest in a more dense condition. The deposits are characterized by their heterogeneous composition and irregular surface topography.

River Deposits (**Alluvium**) Running water is one of the most active agents for soil transportation. As a transporting agent, water serves to mix soils from several different sources and then sorts and deposits them according to grain size. Small soil particles are lifted by the turbulence of the moving water and are carried downstream with little physical change, while the larger particles of sand, gravel, and even boulders are rolled along the stream bed to become ground down and rounded by abrasion.

The ability of running water to move solid particles is a function of the velocity and rate of flow. The total volume of particles that can be carried by a single cubic foot of water is proportional to the velocity squared. The volume of the largest particle that can be moved is proportional to the sixth power of the velocity. Therefore, during periods of high discharge, rivers carry tremendous volumes of coarse and fine particles; in periods of low flow, only small quantities of fine particles may be transported. If the stream velocity increases, such as where steeper portions of its channel are reached or when rainfall swells the flow, the river erodes its channel until its ability to transport materials is satisfied. If the stream velocity decreases because of flatter slopes or decreased flow, some of the transported particles are deposited, with the largest particles dropped first.

Streams in arid regions are characterized by flash floods and prolonged periods of little or no flow. Tremendous quantities of small boulders, gravel, and sand may be carried during periods of high water, but the volume of material transported in dry weather is negligible. The deposits formed in the steep portions of such a river fill the channel to great depths and also form narrow *terraces* of gravel and sand parallel to the low-water channel. Both shift and change during every flood season. At the point the river enters flat country, its velocity is sharply checked, and some of its load is deposited in the form of a flat, triangular mass termed an *alluvial fan*. As the fan builds up, the river shifts its course to build a succession of these masses. After it enters a flat valley, the river continues to drop its load and soon chokes its channels with the deposited solids. Ultimately it overflows and seeks a new course, leaving behind sinuous, erratic deposits of sand, gravel, and boulders. All are good sources of cohesionless soils for construction.

Streams in humid regions are characterized by floods and sustained dry-weather flow. The particles carried by such streams are likely to be finer than those carried by streams in arid regions because the flood velocities tend to be smaller and because the greater degree of weathering in humid regions tends to produce a larger proportion of fines. The deposits in the steeper portions of streams in humid regions are similar to those formed by steep streams in arid regions but are smaller and less likely to shift during every period of high water. Where the rivers enter flat valleys they tend to form alluvial fans that are ordinarily broad and flat and composed largely of sands and fine gravels.

River deposits in flat valleys in humid regions are very important because valleys are often the sites of highways, railroads, airfields, industrial plants, and large cities. During periods of low flow, the stream is confined in its channels and deposition is balanced by erosion. During flood periods, however, it overflows its banks and floods the valley to form immense lakes and broad, flat sheets of slowly moving water. The velocity in the overflow areas is so much smaller than in the channel that deposition takes place along the banks of the channel, forming natural levees. The broad overflow areas act as settling basins in which the fine particles are deposited out of the slowly moving water. As the flood subsides, still finer particles are deposited until evaporation reduces the remaining

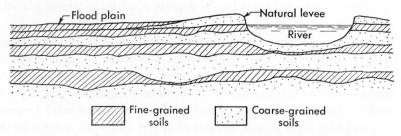

Fig. 3:3 Cross-section of a flood-plain deposit in a humid region.

puddles to dust. Flood-plain deposits (Fig. 3:3) consist of broad, flat, thin strata of very fine sands and clays with occasional elongated lenses of sand that formed in temporary channels or sloughs.

The foundation capacity of flood-plain deposits is often limited, depending on the relative thickness and compressibility of the clay strata, and construction is often complicated by high ground water. The old river channels and the inside of bends are good sources of sand and gravel, and the plains are sources of sand, silt, and clay for construction.

Lake (Lacustrine) Deposits Geologically, lakes are temporary basins of water supplied by rivers, springs, and the outflow from glaciers. They act as giant desilting basins in which the greater portion of the suspended matter carried by the streams that feed them is deposited.

Streams in arid regions carry great quantities of suspended, coarse sands during periods of high discharge. These are deposited at the point the stream enters the lake and form a *delta*. Deltas are characterized by

uniform grain size and by bedding at angles of about 30°. The finer
suspended particles are carried out into deeper water where they settle
out to form horizontal, thin strata of alternately coarse, then fine-grained
particles. Lakes in arid regions soon fill with soil and become nothing
more than shallow ponds that dry out in the hot summer sun. If they
have no outlets, they are salty or alkaline, depending on the dissolved
matter in the inflowing streams. The resulting deposits consist of thin
strata of fine sands, silts, and sometimes clays that may be partially
cemented with borax, gypsum, or calcium carbonate. At the edges of the
deposits are thick, uniform beds of sand that represent the former deltas.

Lakes in humid regions also accumulate deltas at the mouths of the
inflowing streams, but the deposits are likely to be finer-grained than
those of arid regions. The finer particles are carried out into deeper water
where the silt particles and the coarser clays are slowly deposited. During

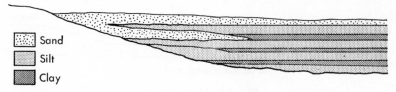

Fig. 3:4 Cross-section of a lake deposit in a humid region.

periods of low flow when there is little turbulence and when slight changes
in the water may produce flocculation, the colloidal clays are deposited.
The result is alternate thin strata of silt and clay. As the lake fills up and
becomes shallow, plant life around the edges increases. Rotting vegetable
matter produces organic colloids that are deposited with the silts and
clays to form organic soils. Microscopic organisms called *diatoms* contribute their silica skeletons, and other organisms add their calcium
carbonate shells to the deposit. Finally the lake chokes up with vegetation
so thick and matted that only incomplete decomposition can take place.
The result is a covering of fibrous organic matter known as *peat*, and at
that stage the lake has become a swamp or bog. Lake deposits (Fig. 3:4)
consist of alternate thin strata of silt and clay overlaid by organic silts
and clays and finally topped with a stratum of peat. Thick beds of sand,
the former deltas, are found at the edges of the deposit.

The remains of old river channels in regions of meandering streams
are termed *oxbow lakes*. They are long, river-shaped lakes and develop

the characteristic deposits of humid regions. Often, however, the lakes and their deposits are covered by a veneer of flood-plain silts and clays which obscures the former lakes completely.

Lake deposits ordinarily make poor foundations because the soils are likely to be weak and compressible. The deltas sometimes provide good structural support, and they are sources of uniform sand for construction.

Marine Deposits   Marine soils include two groups: offshore deposits and shore deposits. The offshore conditions are similar to those in lakes in that deposition takes place in relatively still water below the zone of wave action. The degree of flocculation may be considerably greater because of the salt water, and calcium carbonate in the form of shells or microscopic particles may accumulate. Offshore deposits consist of horizontal strata of silt and clay that frequently have a highly flocculent structure. Occasional strata of shells or calcareous sands, silts, and clays termed *marls* may be formed that are partially cemented.

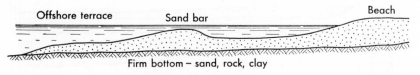

Fig. 3:5   Shore deposits.

The shore deposits are highly complex, owing to the mixing and transporting activities of the many different shore currents and wave action. Materials brought to the sea by rivers and washed from the sea by wave action are swept along the shore by the shore currents, to be deposited in the form of *spits* or *bars* in areas where deep water or wide bays reduce the current velocity. These materials are reworked by the waves to form the offshore bar at the line of breakers and the beach itself (Fig. 3:5). The deposits continually move along the shore as *littoral drift*. The drift accumulates behind structures that extend out from the shore, leaving the shore beyond starved for sand and subject to accelerated erosion. Spits, bars, and the beach are composed of coarser soil particles—sands, fine gravels, and shell fragments—which are uniform at any one point but which may vary considerably in size throughout the deposit. The coarser particles of sand and fine gravel may be subrounded to rounded, but the finer sand grains are usually subangular. Irregular beds of broken shells are often a part of beach deposits.

On many coastlines the spits or bars form barriers that eventually close off the beach from the sea and create shore lagoons. In some cases the lagoons are permanent lakes that rise and fall with the tide but in others they may be flat tidal marshes. Lagoon deposits are similar to the deposits in shallow lakes. The clay deposits are likely to be thick and have a highly developed flocculent structure. They often contain thick lenses of sand or shells that are washed into them during large storms. Marine sands and gravels and the cemented strata provide excellent foundation support and are good sources of cohesionless materials for construction. The clays are ordinarily weak and highly compressible and capable of supporting only light loads. They are too wet for use in construction.

Wind Deposits Wind is a highly selective agent of particle transportation. Particles coarser than 0.05 mm, such as sand, are rolled along by the wind or may be lifted a few feet from the ground during violent wind storms only to be deposited a short distance away. Sand deposits formed by wind action are known as *dunes*. They form in desert regions where mechanical weathering produces an abundance of coarse particles and along lake or sea shores where the sands have been concentrated in beaches or bars by wave action. The most important characteristic of sand dunes is their continual migration in the direction of the prevailing wind—a migration that man is often powerless to halt. The moving sands cover highways, railroads, farmlands, and even towns, and efforts to stop them with sand "fences" or by attempting to cover them with protective coverings of vegetation have met with only sporadic success. Dunes take the form of irregular hills or ridges with flat slopes on their windward sides and slopes equal to the angle of repose to the leeward. They are usually composed of relatively uniform rounded to subrounded particles of sand sizes and are a good source of such materials.

Wind has the ability to lift and transport particles that are smaller than fine sand. Wind erosion is largely limited to dry silts of the arid regions, however, since cohesive or moist soils resist wind erosion.

Wind-blown silt may be carried for many miles before being deposited. Thick beds of wind-blown silt ordinarily accumulate in the semiarid grasslands that border the arid regions. The deposits build up slowly; therefore the grass growth keeps pace with the deposition. The result is high vertical porosity and vertical cleavage combined with an extremely loose structure. Such soils are termed *loess*. Most loess soils are hard because of deposits of calcium carbonate and iron oxide that line the former rootholes, but they become soft and mushy when saturated. Loess deposits are characterized by their uniform grain size, their yellow-brown color, and their pronounced vertical cleavage. Stream banks, gullies, and cuts in loess assume nearly vertical slopes because of the cleavage and because the high vertical permeability permits rapid saturation from rainfall and consequent sloughing of the soil on vertical planes. Loess may be altered by weathering in humid regions, particularly if the soil grains consist of feldspars that were broken up by mechanical weathering alone. Such a soil is termed *loess loam* and it lacks the characteristic uniformity, high void ratio, and cleavage of true loess.

Loess provides good foundation support if it does not become saturated. It can be a source of fine-grained soil for construction if its structure can be broken down before use.

Volcanic ash may be grouped with wind-transported soils. It consists of small fragments of igneous rock blown out by the superheated steam and gasses of the volcano. Fresh volcanic ash is a lightweight sand or sandy gravel. The deposits may be stratified or may be well-graded mixtures. Volcanic ash soaks up water readily and decomposes rapidly. When partially decomposed and then dried, it cements to form a soft rock known as *tuff*. Complete decomposition of the ash results in the formation of highly plastic clays with extremely high void ratios and high compressibilities. Although thick deposits of such clays are uncommon, the extreme settlement of structures built on them, such as in Mexico City, makes them worthy of attention.

Cemented volcanic ash makes a good foundation. It is sometimes used as a construction material, but it tends to break down chemically and physically.

Glacial Deposits Ice, in the form of the glaciers which plowed up great portions of North America and Europe, has been a very active agent of both weathering and transportation. The expanding ice sheets planed off hill tops, ground up rock, and mixed the materials together as they pushed their way southward. Some of the materials were directly deposited by the moving ice, while the remainder were transported by water flowing from the ice to be deposited in the lakes along the face of the ice sheets or transported in the rivers flowing away from the ice.

The direct deposits of the glacier are usually termed *moraines*. They are composed of *glacial till*, which is a term applied to the heterogeneous mixtures of particles, ranging from boulders to clay, that the ice accumulated in its travels. *Terminal moraines* are irregular, low hills or ridges pushed up by the bulldozing action of the ice sheet. These mark the outermost limit of the glacier's travel, for they were left behind as the ice retreated. A *ground moraine* or *till plain* is the irregular veneer of till left on the areas once covered by the glacier. The upper surface of the ground moraine is undulating but rather level over broad areas; its thickness varies considerably, however, depending on the preglacial topography of the area. *Drumlins* are elongated low hills of till that point in the direction of the ice travel. They occur in areas of ground moraines and possibly represent deposits of soil that accumulated in crevasses in the ice.

The water-laid deposits of glaciers resemble those derived from mountain streams except that both the volume of water and the load of solids were considerably greater. *Eskers* are the remains of rivers that flowed in tunnels beneath the ice. When the ice retreated, the river bed materials formed sinuous ridges of coarse sands and gravels that resemble a crooked railroad embankment. *Kames* are terraces of coarse sand and gravel deposited in valleys along the margins of the ice sheets. Rivers flowing out of the edge of the ice sheet broke through the terminal moraine to deposit great quantities of sand and gravel in irregular, flat beds termed *outwash plains*. In many areas the glacial streams flowed into large lakes that formed in depressions left by the retreating ice. The deposits in these lakes are similar to those formed in other lakes except that they are more extensive. Great deltas of sand formed at the mouths of the rivers, and thick beds of silt and clay formed in the still, deep waters beyond the shores. Occasional boulders and gravel found in the clays are believed to have been dropped by floating pieces of ice as they melted. The silts and clays often formed in thin alternate strata which represent seasonal variations in the rate of ice melting and the resulting stream flow. The coarser particles were deposited in summer, during periods of high discharge, and the clays in winter. Such deposits are known as *varved clays* when the individual strata are more than $\frac{1}{8}$ in. thick and as *laminated clays* when the strata are thinner.

Glacial sands, gravels, and till usually make good foundations. They are also good sources of construction materials. The glacial clays are only moderately strong and are often compressible. They often are problems in foundation design and usually are too wet to be used as construction materials.

3:3 The Soil Profile

From the ground surface down to a depth of several feet every soil deposit develops a characteristic profile due to surface weathering and to leaching of soluble minerals by the moving soil moisture. The profile ultimately formed depends on the nature of the original deposit and on the environment, including topography, climate, and vegetation. It is of particular interest to the agronomist, who finds that the soil fertility and workability are related to its profile; and to the engineer, who uses the uppermost strata for the support of small structures or as materials for construction.

Cool and Temperate Humid Region Profile In cool and temperate regions with humid climates there is an abundant growth of vegetation and an accumulation of dead leaves, plants, and other organic debris. The slow decomposition of these materials and the secretion of plant roots create weak acids which accelerate the weathering. The prevailing soil-moisture movement is downward to the water table, and this creates a profile with three distinct layers or *horizons:* A, B, and C.

The A-horizon is characterized by the chemical alteration of the soil materials in an acid, reducing environment. Clays of the kaolinite family, soluble carbonates, and semisolid reduced iron minerals are likely to be produced. These are leached downward by the soil moisture, leaving the A-horizon deficient in them but rich in silica. As a result the lower part, designated the A_2-*horizon*, is usually very sandy and light-colored. The upper part, designated A_1, is dark-colored from its content of organic matter and has a spongy texture. The A_2-horizon is frequently a source of sandy soils in regions underlain by clays.

The leached materials accumulate in the B-horizon below. It is thicker than the A and contains a greater concentration of clay minerals, iron, and carbonates than does the original soil. The top part, B_1, is frequently partially cemented, and is deeply colored. The B_2 is rich in clay and soluble carbonates. The B_3 again suffers from downward leaching and is lighter colored. The B-horizon is the best source of clays in regions where they are scarce.

Below is the C-horizon, which is the unweathered parent material. When an unrelated stratum of different soil underlies the other materials, it is sometimes called the *D-horizon*.

Hot, Humid Region Profiles In hot, humid regions the upper parts of the soil deposit are also subject to wetting, drying, and leaching, but the rapid decay of organic matter produces little or no organic accumulation or organic acids. Bases form from the soil weathering, which make the silica somewhat soluble and which render the iron oxides and the hydrous aluminum silicates less soluble. The silica leaches downward, leaving the surface zone rich in iron oxides, aluminum oxides, and clay minerals. These become cemented and hard and develop a strong red color from the highly oxidized iron. This process is *laterization* and the soils are called *laterites*. They are strong, relatively incompressible, but often rather porous, with a blocky or crumby macrostructure. They usually make good sources of soil for construction, but some forms are softened if inundated.

Dry Region Profile In dry regions there is little or no organic matter. Any moisture movement is predominantly upward because of surface evaporation. This results in the accumulation of soluble materials such as carbonates near the surface and in the partial cementing of the soil. Such soils are hard and incompressible when dry but somewhat softer when inundated. They usually make satisfactory sources of construction materials.

Pedology Pedology is the study of the soil profile and its development from different parent materials and in different environments.

The pedologist classifies soils in a manner similar to the way a biologist classifies plants or animals—according to their origin and development. Each soil name denotes a particular parent material and a particular development of profile. These are further subdivided by the texture of the A-horizon. The soil is named for the location in which it was first identified, and this is followed by its textural description, such as the Congaree silt-loam or the Norfolk sand. Publications of the U.S. Department of Agriculture describe these in more detail.[3:1,3:2,3:3]

Agriculturalists have found pedology useful in correlating soil drainage, fertility, and land management, and therefore most pedological studies have been made with this purpose in mind. Soil engineers, however, have found that the soil profile is also related to the soil's capabilities for surface construction. Empirical correlations between soil excavation, drainage, compaction, and even road design have proved helpful in appraising conditions for engineering work.[3:4,3:5]

3:4 Ground Water

Water is one of the most important factors of soil strength, compressibility, and volume change. Although water is present in all soils, the term *ground water* is reserved for the continuous body of underground water in the soil voids that is free to move under the influence of gravity. The *water table* is the upper surface of a body of ground water. It is defined by the level of water in an open hole in the ground and is the level at which the pressure in the water is zero. Ground water is not a static body with a level surface as the name *ground water table* implies. Instead it is a moving stream with a sloping surface that takes many shapes, depending on the structure of the soils and rocks through which it flows.

The elevation of the water table at any one point is not constant. Water is supplied to the moving stream by percolation from the ground surface and it leaves the ground by evaporation and by seepage into rivers, lakes, and the ocean. When the rate of intake exceeds the rate of loss, as it does during wet weather, the water table rises; and when the intake decreases, as in dry weather, or when the loss increases because of pumping for water supply or because of drainage, the water table falls.

Aquafers Aquafers are relatively pervious soil and rock strata that

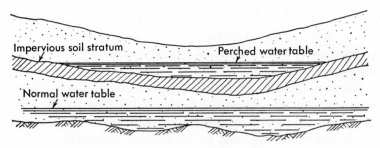

Fig. 3:6 Perched water table.

contain ground water. They are similar to the lake basins and river channels that contain surface water. The most familiar aquafer is a stratum of relatively pervious soil in which the ground water level rises and falls with the weather and with pumpage. The water table slopes in the same direction as the ground surface, but the slopes are more gentle and uniform. In soils that consist of alternate strata of pervious and impervious soils the ground water pattern becomes more complex. A sagging, impervious stratum creates a basin that may hold a small quantity of ground water perched above the general water table. *Perched water tables* (Fig. 3:6) occur rather frequently but are ordinarily of limited extent. They may be drained by drilling a hole through the impervious basin, allowing the water to seep downward. When an aquafer is confined between two impervious strata, it is capable of carrying water under pressure. When it does, the elevation of zero pressure is above the upper surface of the water, and the ground water is said to be under *artesian* pressure. Artesian pressures are usually developed by sloping aquafers (Fig. 3:7) where the point at which the water enters the confined previous stratum is higher than the point at which the pressure is measured. When a hole is drilled into an artesian aquafer, the water rises to the elevation of zero pressure. If this level is above the ground surface, a flowing artesian well results. Artesian aquafers may be local structures existing over an area of a few acres, or they may be continuous over large areas like the vast artesian sandstones in North and South Dakota. They are often troublesome to engineers because of the reduction of soil strength by neutral stress. Excavations that extend close to strata that are under artesian pressure may be damaged from *bottom blowouts*. The water pressure, which formerly was balanced by the weight of the

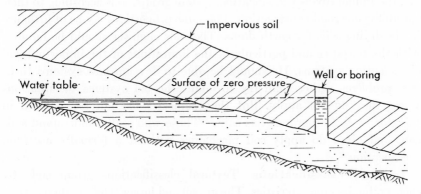

Fig. 3:7 Artesian water table.

overlying soil, causes the remaining soil to burst upward into the excavation, or if the soil is sand, it will create a "quicksand" condition.

Springs and Swamps When the ground water table intersects the ground surface on a hillside, a *spring* is formed, water trickles down the ground surface, and the soil may be softened by the added water and also by the seepage pressures. This may be corrected by intercepting the water with drains before it reaches the surface. The intersection of the water table and a level ground surface produces a *swamp*. During periods of wet weather and high water table the swamp may be partially covered with water, while during dry weather it may be relatively dry and firm. The upward seepage of water in some swamps produces a semiquick condition that is most pronounced during periods of a rising water table. Swamps are difficult to correct because they ordinarily occur in low areas in which there is no place to drain the excess water.

3:5 Soil Classification

A soil classification system is an arrangement of different soils into groups having similar properties. The purpose is to make it possible to estimate soil properties or capabilities by association with soils of the same class whose properties are known, and to provide the engineer with an accurate method of soil description. However, there are so many different soil properties of interest to engineers and so many different combinations of these properties in any natural soil deposit that any universal system of classification seems impractical. Instead the groups or classes are based on those properties which are most important in that particular phase of engineering for which the classification was developed. For example, the Public Roads Classification System groups soils according to their suitability for road construction. The same properties may be of little use in classifying soils for earth dams. The soils engineer should be familiar with the purposes and particularly the limitations of the important soil classification systems. He should be able to develop new systems to fit new problems rather than try to adapt the old systems to situations where they do not apply. But the engineer must not lose himself in this, for as A. Casagrande has said, "Those who really understand soils can, and often do apply soil mechanics without a formally accepted classification."[3:6]

Textural Classifications Textural classifications group soils by their grain-size characteristics. The gravel and larger sizes are disregarded and the particles finer than 2 mm in diameter are divided into three groups: sand sizes, silt sizes, and clay sizes. The soils are then grouped by the percentage of each of these three components.[3:6]

Textural classification was developed by agricultural engineers who found that grain size was an indication of the workability of topsoils. A number of different textural classification schemes have been employed in engineering work, but they have been superseded by the more complete engineering classification systems described below.

Bureau of Public Roads Classification System The Public Roads Classification is one of the oldest systems of grouping soils for an engineering purpose. Since its introduction in 1929 it has undergone many revisions and modifications and is widely used for evaluating soils for highway subgrade and embankment construction. The modification proposed in 1945 is termed the *Revised Bureau of Public Roads, Highway Research Board,* or *AASHO* (American Association of State Highway Officials)

Table 3:1 REVISED BUREAU OF PUBLIC ROADS CLASSIFICATION[37]

Group	Sub-group	Per Cent Passing U.S. Sieve 10	40	200	Character of Fraction Passing No. 40 Sieve — Liquid Limit	Plasticity Index	Group Index No.	Soil Description	Subgrade Rating
A-1			50 max	25 max		6 max	0	Well-graded gravel or sand; may include fines	Excellent to Good
	A-1-a	50 max	50 max	15 max		6 max	0	Largely gravel but can include sand and fines	
	A-1-b		50 max	25 max		6 max	0	Gravelly sand or graded sand; may include fines	
A-2*				35 max	40 max	10 max	0 to 4	Sands and gravels with excessive fines	
	A-2-4			35 max	40 max	10 max	0	Sands, gravels with low-plasticity silt fines	
	A-2-5			35 max	41 min	10 max	0	Sands, gravels with elastic silt fines	
	A-2-6			35 max	40 max	11 min	4 max	Sands, gravels with clay fines	
	A-2-7			35 max	41 min	11 min	4 max	Sands, gravels with highly plastic clay fines	
A-3			51 min	10 max		Nonplastic	0	Fine sands	Fair to Poor
A-4				36 min	40 max	10 max	8 max	Low-compressibility silts	
A-5				36 min	41 min	10 max	12 max	High-compressibility silts, micaceous silts	
A-6				36 min	40 max	11 min	16 max	Low-to-medium-compressibility clays	
A-7				36 min	41 min	11 min	20 max	High-compressibility clays	
	A-7-5			36 min	41 min	11 min†	20 max	High-compressibility silty clays	
	A-7-6			36 min	41 min	11 min†	20 max	High-compressibility, high-volume-change clays	
A-8								Peat, highly organic soils	Unsatisfactory

* Group A-2 includes all soils having 35 per cent or less passing a No. 200 sieve that cannot be classed as A-1 or A-3.

† Plasticity index of A-7-5 subgroup is equal to or less than LL-30. Plasticity index of A-7-6 subgroup is greater than LL-30.

System.[3:7] This system divides all soils into three categories: granular, with 35 per cent or less by weight passing a No. 200 sieve (finer than 0.074 mm); silt-clay, with more than 35 per cent passing the No. 200 sieve; and organic soils. The first two categories are subdivided further, depending on their gradation and plasticity characteristics, as shown in Table 3:1. The symbols A–1 through A–8 are given to the classes which loosely indicate a decreasing quality for highway construction with increasing number. Some of the classes are subdivided, to indicate differences in plasticity, but the subdivisions are not an essential part of the system. The classification is supplemented by the *Group Index*, or GI:

$$GI = 0.2a + 0.005ac + 0.01bd, \tag{3:1}$$

where a = percentage passing the No. 200 sieve greater than 35 and not exceeding 75; expressed as a whole number (0 to 40)

   b = percentage passing No. 200 sieve greater than 15 and not exceeding 55; expressed as a whole number (0 to 40)

   c = that portion of the liquid limit greater than 40 and not exceeding 60; expressed as a whole number (0 to 20)

   d = that portion of the plasticity index greater than 10 and not exceeding 30; expressed as a whole number (0 to 20)

The value of the GI ranges from 0 to 20, with the low numbers indicating higher quality than the high numbers. The number is placed in parentheses following the class, such as A–2(0) or A–5(9).

Since the same basic symbols have been used for all the versions of the Public Roads System, the engineer should always note which he is using. The presence of the GI number, however, denotes the 1945 revision.

Unified Soil Classification System   The Unified Soil Classification[3:8] is an outgrowth of the Airfield Classification (AC) system developed by A. Casagrande[3:6] as a rapid method for identifying and grouping soils for military construction. The soils are first divided into coarse-grained and fine-grained classes. The coarse-grained soils have over 50 per cent by weight coarser than 0.074 mm (No. 200 sieve). They are given the symbol G if more than half of the coarse particles by weight are coarser than 4.76 mm (No. 4 sieve) and S if more than half are finer. The G or S is followed by a second letter that describes the gradation: W, well-graded with little or no fines; P, poorly graded, uniform, or gap-graded with little or no fines; M, containing silt or silt and sand; and C, containing clay or sand and clay. The fine-grained soils (over half finer than 0.074 mm) are

Table 3:2 UNIFIED SOIL CLASSIFICATION
(After U.S. Waterways Experiment Station)

Major Division		Group Symbol	Laboratory Classification Criteria		Soil Description
			Finer than 200 Sieve %	Supplementary Requirements	
Coarse-grained (over 50% by weight coarser than No. 200 sieve)	Gravelly soils (over half of coarse fraction larger than No. 4)	GW	0–5*	D_{60}/D_{10} greater than 4, $D_{30}^2/(D_{60} \times D_{10})$ between 1 & 3	Well-graded gravels, sandy gravels
		GP	0–5*	Not meeting above gradation for GW	Gap-graded or uniform gravels, sandy gravels
		GM	12 or more*	PI less than 4 or below A-line	Silty gravels, silty sandy gravels
		GC	12 or more*	PI over 7 and above A-line	Clayey gravels, clayey sandy gravels
	Sandy soils (over half of coarse fraction finer than No. 4)	SW	0–5*	D_{60}/D_{10} greater than 4, $D_{30}^2/(D_{60} \times D_{10})$ between 1 & 3	Well-graded sands, gravelly sands
		SP	0–5*	Not meeting above gradation requirements	Gap-graded or uniform sands, gravelly sands
		SM	12 or more*	PI less than 4 or below A-line	Silty sands, silty gravelly sands
		SC	12 or more*	PI over 7 and above A-line	Clayey sands, clayey gravelly sands
Fine-grained (over 50% by weight finer than No. 200 sieve)	Low compressibility (liquid limit less than 50)	ML	Plasticity chart		Silts, very fine sands, silty or clayey fine sands, micaceous silts
		CL		Plasticity chart	Low plasticity clays, sandy or silty clays
		OL		Plasticity chart, organic odor or color	Organic silts and clays of low plasticity
	High compressibility (liquid limit more than 50)	MH	Plasticity chart		Micaceous silts, diatomaceous silts, volcanic ash
		CH		Plasticity chart	Highly plastic clays and sandy clays
		OH		Plasticity chart, organic odor or color	Organic silts and clays of high plasticity
Soils with fibrous organic matter		Pt		Fibrous organic matter; will char, burn, or glow	Peat, sandy peats, and clayey peat

* For soils having 5 to 12 per cent passing the No. 200 sieve, use a dual symbol such as GW-GC.

divided into three groups: C, clays; M, silts and silty clays; and O, organic silts and clays. These symbols are followed by a second letter denoting the liquid limit or relative compressibility: L, a liquid limit less than 50; and H, a liquid limit exceeding 50.

The Casagrande plasticity chart (Fig. 3:8) is the basis for dividing the fine-grained soils. It also aids in comparing different soils. For example, clays having a similar geologic origin will usually plot in a narrow band parallel to the dividing line (often called the A-line) between the C and M-O soils. The different symbols, the soils they represent, and the classi-

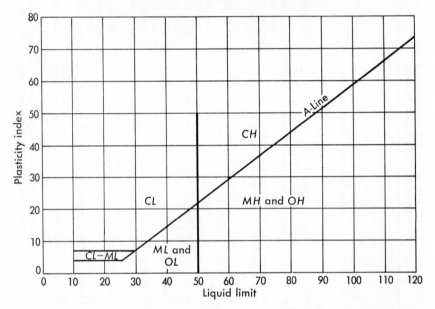

Fig. 3:8 Plasticity chart for the classification of fine-grained soils. Tests made on fraction finer than No. 40 sieve. (After A. Casagrande[3:6] and the U.S. Waterways Experiment Station.[3:8])

fication criteria are given on Table 3:3. For border-line soils a dual classi-fication is sometimes given, such as GW-GC. To the symbols should be added a description giving information on the grain shape, composition, color, macrostructure, and the soil strength or density in the ground.

The original AC system differs from the Unified in the grouping of the coarse-grained soils: the division between coarse and fine is 0.1 mm; the symbol M is replaced by F; and all the coarse-grained subdivisions, W, C, P, and F, have slightly different meanings. For most practical purposes, however, the systems are the same.

The Unified System has proved very useful in classifying soils for many different purposes such as highway and airfield construction, earth dams, embankments, and even for foundations. It is frequently supplemented by tables showing the typical properties of each group, such as the drainage characteristics, and as such is a valuable guide for design and construction. The system is simple. Many soils can be grouped visually and only tests for grain size and plasticity are necessary for accurate classification. It must be kept in mind, however, that no classification is a substitute for tests of the soil's physical properties and engineering analysis of the results.

Highway Department Systems[3:9] Several state highway departments have developed classification systems that are adapted to the soils which they regularly encounter. Most of these systems are based on empirical correlations between soil performance in highway construction and some simple laboratory tests such as grain size, plasticity, shrinkage, expansion, and density after compaction. Within the state for which they were developed, they can be a valuable guide to the selection of materials for highway work.

Civil Aeronautics (CAA) System The CAA system classifies soils according to their suitability for airfield subgrades.[3:7] The soils are divided into groups E–1 to E–14 on the basis of grain size and plasticity, similar to the Public Roads system. Other tests are used to aid in the classification but are not essential.

3:6 Soil Identification and Description

The different soil classification schemes, while useful for grouping soils for a particular purpose, may be useless or misleading in other applications. In many fields, such as foundation engineering, there are so many significant soil properties that any scheme of soil classification would be very awkward. Instead an accurate description of the significant soil properties can convey the necessary information without the restrictions of a definite classification scheme. The following soil properties are of significance in most soil problems and therefore form the basis of a complete soil description. They are also a required supplement to the Unified Classification.

(1) Shear strength (cohesive soils)
(2) Density (cohesionless soils)
(3) Compressibility
(4) Permeability

(5) Color
(6) Composition (grain size, shape, plasticity, mineralogy)
(7) Structure of soil

For a precise description many of these properties must be determined by laboratory tests. An experienced soils engineer, however, can estimate most of these by careful field observation and examination of small samples of the soil.

Soil Strength   Shear strength is a fundamental property of undisturbed cohesive soils, a knowledge of which is necessary in solving many

Table 3:3   SOIL STRENGTH

Term	Unconfined Compressive Strength (After Terzaghi and Peck)[3:10]	Field Test (After Cooling, Skempton, and Glossop)[3:11]
Very soft	0–0.5 kips per sq ft	Squeezes between fingers when fist is closed
Soft	0.5–1.0	Easily molded by fingers
Firm	1.0–2.0	Molded by strong pressure of fingers
Stiff	2.0–3.0	Dented by strong pressure of fingers
Very stiff	3.0–4.0	Dented only slightly by finger pressure
Hard	4.0 or more	Dented only slightly by pencil point

(A method of estimating strength from sampling operations is given in Table 10:4.)

problems. It is ordinarily defined in terms of unconfined compressive strength but may be estimated from the pressure required to squeeze an undisturbed sample between the fingers. If the soil is *brittle* (fails suddenly with little strain), *elastic* (rubbery), *friable* (crumbles easily), or *sensitive* (loses strength on remolding), these terms should be included in the description.

Density   Density is as important for cohesionless soils as strength is for cohesive. It can be found by comparing the soil's actual void ratio with the range in void ratio from loose to dense for that soil. It may be estimated from the ease with which a reinforcing rod penetrates the soil, or from Table 10:3.

Table 3:4   SOIL DENSITY

Term	Relative Density	Field Test
Loose	0–50%	Easily penetrated with ½-in. reinforcing rod pushed by hand
Firm	50–70	Easily penetrated with ½-in. reinforcing rod driven with 5-lb hammer
Dense	70–90	Penetrated a foot with ½-in. reinforcing rod driven with 5-lb hammer
Very dense	90–100	Penetrated only a few inches with ½-in. reinforcing rod driven with 5-lb hammer

Compressibility Compressibility is determined by direct laboratory tests or is estimated from the liquid limit and void ratio.

Table 3:5 COMPRESSIBILITY

Term	Compression Index	Liquid Limit (Approx.)
Slight or low compressibility	0–0.19	0–30
Moderate or intermediate	0.20–0.39	31–50
High compressibility	0.40 and over	51 and over

Permeability Permeability is determined by direct laboratory and field tests or may be estimated from Table 2:1.

Color Color, while not an important physical property in itself, is an indication of more important properties. For example, yellow and red hues indicate that a soil has undergone severe weathering, for the colors are iron oxides. A dark greenish brown is often an indication of organic matter. A change in color encountered during excavation often means a different soil stratum with different properties has been uncovered. Color is usually the easiest property of a soil for persons untrained in soil mechanics to identify; therefore a practical method of describing a certain soil to workers is by color. Soil color is described visually with the aid of the Munsel color charts.[3:12]

Composition Composition includes the grain size, gradation, grain shape, minerology (of the coarser grains), and plasticity. Two groups of soils are recognized: predominantly coarse-grained (over 0.074 mm) and predominantly fine-grained (less than 0.074 mm), as in the Unified Classification. The coarse-grained soils are described primarily on the basis of the grain size, the fine-grained primarily on the basis of their plasticity. The amount of coarse or fine component required to predominate is not fixed, for it depends on the soil structure: If the coarse-grained particles can make contact with one another, the soil behaves essentially as a coarse-grained material; if they cannot touch but are separated by the fines, the fines predominate. The Unified Classification arbitrarily defines predominate grain size at over 50 per cent by weight. However, in soils containing clay minerals, the fines may predominate even though they comprise considerably less than 50 per cent by weight of the soil. Therefore no fixed point can be established, and the engineer must exercise his judgment.

The sizes of particles as defined by ASTM–ASCE and their visual identification are given in Table 3:6.

Table 3:6 GRAIN SIZE IDENTIFICATION

Name	Size Limits	Familiar Example
Boulder	12 in. (305 mm) or more	Larger than basketball
Cobbles	3 in. (76 mm)–12 in. (305 mm)	Grapefruit
Coarse gravel	¾ in. (19 mm)–3 in. (76 mm)	Orange or lemon
Fine gravel	4.76 mm (No. 4 Sieve)–¾ in. (19 mm)	Grape or pea
Coarse sand	2 mm (No. 10 Sieve)–4.76 mm (No. 4 Sieve)	Rocksalt
Medium sand	0.42 mm (No. 40 Sieve)–2 mm (No. 10 Sieve)	Sugar, table salt
Fine sand	0.074 mm (No. 200 Sieve)–0.42 mm (No. 40 Sieve)	Powdered sugar
Fines	Less than 0.074 mm (No. 200 Sieve)	

NOTE: Particles finer than fine sand cannot be discerned with the naked eye at a distance of 8 in. (20 cm).

Gradation is estimated by the same criterion as for the Unified Classification (Table 3:2). A smooth grain-size curve and a uniformity coefficient of more than 6 for sands or 4 for gravels denotes a *well-graded* soil. An irregular gradation denotes *gap-graded*. A uniformity coefficient less than the above limits indicates a *uniform* soil. The term *poorly graded* is sometimes applied to either uniform or gap graded soils.

Grain shapes are identified as angular to well-rounded, as shown in Fig. 1:7. In addition, elongated or platey particles can be identified.

The mineral composition of the grains can often be determined by a microscopic examination. The carbonates are easily identified by a strong acid, which causes them to effervesce.

The fines are described on the basis of the Casagrande plasticity chart (Fig. 3:8). Soils above the A-line are clays and those below, silts. Soils that plot near the A-line are given a double designation: If the PI is less than 10 per cent above the A-line, the soil is described as a silty clay; if it is less than 33 per cent below the A-line, it is a clayey silt. A soil should not be termed a silty clay if its liquid limit is above 60, however.

Silts and clays can be identified in the field by the shaking test. A pat of wet soil (consistency of soft putty) is shaken in the hand. If it becomes soft and glossy with shaking or tapping the hand and then becomes hard, dull, and forms cracks when the pat is squeezed between the fingers, it has a *reaction to shaking*, or *dilatancy*. A rapid reaction indicates a non-plastic silt; a slow reaction means an organic silt, slightly clayey silt, or possibly a non-plastic silt with a very high liquid limit (over 100). No reaction indicates a clay or silty clay. (To be decisive the test should be made at different water contents.)

The toughness of the thread that forms when the soil is rolled at the plastic limit also helps identify the fines. Inability to form a thread or a very weak thread indicates an inorganic silt of very low plasticity (ML). A weak spongy thread indicates an organic silt or an inorganic silt having a high liquid limit but low plasticity (MH). A firm thread indicates a low-plasticity clay (CL), while a tough, rigid thread indicates a highly plastic clay (CH).

Plasticity is determined by the plasticity index or can be estimated from the strength of an air-dried sample. The sample is prepared by first removing all particles coarser than a No. 40 sieve and then molding a cube at the consistency of stiff putty, adding water if necessary. The cube is dried in air or sunlight and then crushed between the fingers.

Table 3:7 PLASTICITY

Term	PI	Dry Strength	Field Test
Non-plastic	0–3	Very low	Falls apart easily
Slightly plastic	4–8	Slight	Easily crushed with fingers
Medium plastic	9–30	Medium	Difficult to crush
Highly plastic	31 or more	High	Impossible to crush with fingers

Organic soils can be identified by their odor, which is intensified by heating, and their color, which is usually black, brown, dark green, or blue-black. However, some inorganic soils are black from certain iron, titanium, and ferromagnesian minerals. Organic matter can also be identified by oxidizing the soil with hydrogen peroxide and noting the loss in dry weight. It also can be identified by the loss of weight on ignition, provided no carbonate minerals and no adsorbed water or water of crystallization are present.

Soils containing fibrous organic matter are identified visually or by their loss of weight on ignition. A weight loss (organic content) of 80 per cent or more denotes *peat*. If less fibrous organic matter is present, the soils are described as peaty sand or peaty clay, as the case may be.

In forming the description, a predominately coarse-grained soil is termed either a *gravel* or a *sand*, depending on which component appears to be the more abundant. The less abundant component and the fines (either silt or clay) are used as modifiers, with the least important component first. For example, a soil with 30 per cent fines (silt), 45 per cent gravel, and 25 per cent sand would be described as sandy, silty gravel. The grain shapes and sizes precede the component to which they apply. A predominately fine-grained soil would be considered either silt or clay and the coarse components would be used as modifiers, with the least important first. For example, a soil with 70 per cent fines (clay), 20 per cent sand, and 10 per cent gravel would be described as gravelly, sandy clay.

Describing Soil Structures The structure of the soil must be determined by careful observation. The following descriptive terms may be used:

> Homogeneous (uniform properties)
> Stratified (alternate layers of different soils)
> Laminated (repeating alternate layers less than $\frac{1}{8}$ in. thick)
> Banded (alternate layers in residual soils)

It is important to recognize defects in a soil structure. The following are often observed:

> Slickensides (former failure planes)
> Rootholes
> Fissures (cracks, from shrinkage, frost)
> Weathering (irregular discoloration)

Writing a Soil Description The soil should be described in essentially the order of the significant properties given previously. As many of the properties as are of interest should be included. Examples might be:

(1) Hard, moderately compressible, blue-gray, medium-plastic clay.
(2) Dense, well-graded, clayey, sandy, well-rounded gravel.
(3) Loose, brown, uniform, angular, fine sand.
(4) Firm, black, slightly compressible silt and clay; laminated.
(5) Loose, compressible, brown, micaceous, sandy silt; banded.

3:7 Soil Names

In addition to standardized terms used to describe soils, there are many names that have been given to soils and soil deposits. Many of these names, such as *gumbo* and *buckshot*, have originated through association with other more familiar objects and have essentially a local meaning. Others, such as *silt* and *clay*, have been applied to soils having such wide ranges in characteristics that the names often have no definite meaning. In some cases a soil name that is associated with soils of certain characteristics in one region refers to soils of completely different characteristics in other regions. The soil names defined below are often encountered in engineering literature.[3:13]

Adobe refers to sandy clays of medium plasticity found in the semiarid regions of the southwestern United States. These soils have been used for centuries for making sun-dried brick. The name is also applied to some highly plastic clays of the West.

Bentonite is a highly plastic clay resulting from the decomposition of volcanic ash. It may be hard when dry but swells considerably when wet.

Buckshot is applied to clays of the southern and southwestern United States that crack into small, hard, relatively uniform sized lumps on drying.

Bull's liver is inorganic silt of very low plasticity. In a saturated condition it quakes like jelly from shock or vibration and often becomes quick and flows like a fluid.

Caliche is a silt or sand of the semiarid areas of the southwestern United States that is cemented with calcium carbonate. The calcium carbonate is deposited by the evaporation of ground water brought to the ground surface by capillary action.

Clay is applied to any soil capable of remaining in the plastic state through a relatively wide range in water contents. As a soil name, the term *clay* has been badly abused. In some parts of the United States clay means a non-plastic silt; in other parts it is used to designate micaceous silts of low plasticity. Engineers should use the word clay in the restricted meaning given by Casagrande's plasticity chart (Fig. 3:8).

Diatomaceous earths are silts containing large amounts of diatoms—the silaceous skeletons of minute marine or fresh water organisms.

Fill is any man-made soil deposit. Fills may consist of soils that are free of organic matter and that are carefully compacted to form an extremely dense, incompressible mass, or they may be heterogeneous accumulations of rubbish and debris.

Fuller's earths are soils having the ability to absorb fats or dyes. They are usually highly plastic, sedimentary clays.

Gravel means a soil composed largely of particles from 4.76 mm to 3 in. in diameter. In some parts of the United States the term *gravel* is restricted to rounded gravel.

Gumbo is a fine-grained, highly plastic clay of the Mississippi Valley. It has a sticky, greasy feel and forms large shrinkage cracks on drying.

Hardpan is a term that should be avoided by the engineer. Originally it was applied only to a soil horizon which had become rocklike because of the accumulation of cementing minerals. True hardpan is relatively impervious and does not soften upon exposure to air or water. Unfortunately the term is also applied to any hard or highly consolidated soil stratum that is excessively difficult to excavate. Many lawsuits have centered about the meaning of hardpan because of its ambiguity. The name implies a condition rather than a type of soil.

Kaolin is a white or pink clay of low plasticity. It is composed largely of minerals of the kaolinite family.

Laterites are residual soils formed in tropical regions. The cementing action of iron oxides and hydrated aluminum oxides makes dry laterites extremely hard.

Loam is a surface soil that may be described as a sandy silt of low plasticity or a silty sand that is well suited to tilling. It applies to soils within the uppermost horizons and should not be used to describe deep deposits of parent materials.

Loess is a deposit of relatively uniform, wind-blown silt. It has a loose structure, with numerous rootholes that produce vertical cleavage and high vertical permeability. It consists of angular to subrounded quartz and feldspar particles cemented with calcium carbonate or iron oxide. Upon saturation it becomes soft and compressible because of the loss of cementing. Loess altered by weathering in a humid climate often becomes more dense and somewhat plastic. It is known as *loess loam. Swamp loess* is water-deposited loess. It does not have the loose structure or vertical cleavage of loess.

Marl is a water-deposited sand, silt or clay containing calcium carbonate. Marls are often light to dark gray or greenish in color and sometimes contain colloidal organic matter.

Muck or mud is extremely soft, slimy silt or organic silt found on river and lake bottoms. The terms indicate an extremely soft consistency rather than any particular type of soil. Muck implies organic matter.

Muskeg is peat found in northwest Canada. The bogs in which the peat forms are often termed *muskegs.*

Peat is fibrous, partially decomposed organic matter or a soil containing large amounts of fibrous organic matter. Peats are dark brown or black, loose (void ratio may be 3 or 4), and extremely compressible. When dried they will float. Peat bogs often emit quantities of inflammable methane gas.

Quicksand is a condition and not a soil. Gravels, sands, and silts become "quick" when an upward flow of ground water takes place to such extent that the particles are lifted.

Rock flour is extremely fine-grained silt formed by the grinding action of glaciers.

Sand is a soil composed largely of particles from 0.074 mm to 4.76 mm in diameter. *Dirty sand* means a slightly silty or slightly clayey sand.

Silt is any fine-grained soil of low plasticity. Often it is applied to fine sands. In some parts of the United States the term *silt* is applied only to organic silts. Casagrande's plasticity chart may be used to differentiate between silt and clay.

Stone is sometimes used to designate angular gravel. It is more properly applied to gravel manufactured by crushing rock.

Till is a mixture of sand, gravel, silt, and clay produced by the plowing action of galciers. The name *boulder clay* is often given such soils, particularly in Canada and England.

Topsoils are surface soils that support plant life. They usually contain considerable organic matter.

Tuff is the name applied to deposits of volcanic ash. In humid climates or in areas in which the ash falls into bodies of water, the tuff becomes cemented into a soft, porous rock.

Tundra is the thick mat of moss and shrubby vegetation that covers a gray, clayey subsoil in arctic regions. The deeper soil is permanently frozen, while the surface soil freezes and thaws seasonally. (See Art. 4:6)

Varved clays are sedimentary deposits consisting of alternate thin layers of silt and clay. Ordinarily each pair of silt and clay layers is from $\frac{1}{8}$ in. to $\frac{1}{2}$ in. thick. They are the result of deposition in lakes during periods of alternately high and low water in the inflowing streams and are often formed in glacial lakes.

REFERENCES

3:1 "Soils of the United States," *Atlas of American Agriculture*, Part III, U.S. Dept. of Agriculture, Washington, 1935.

3:2 *Soils and Man*, Yearbook of American Agriculture, U.S. Dept. of Agriculture, 1938.

3:3 *Soil Survey Manual*, Handbook 18, U.S. Dept. of Agriculture, Washington, 1951.

3:4 "Glossary of Pedologic and Landform Terminology," *Special Report 25*, Highway Research Board, Washington, 1957.

3:5 "Engineering Use of Agricultural Soil Maps," *Bulletin 22*, Highway Research Board, Washington, 1949.

3:6 A. Casagrande, "Classification and Identification of Soils," *Transactions*, ASCE, 1948, p. 901.

3:7 "Classification of Highway Subgrade Materials," *Proceedings, Highway Research Board*, Washington, 1945.

3:8 *Unified Soil Classification System*, Technical Memorandum 3–357, U.S. Waterways Experiment Station, Vicksburg, 1953.

3:9 W. F. Abercrombie, "A System of Soil Classification," *Proceedings, Highway Research Board*, Vol. 33, 1954, p. 509.

3:10 K. Terzaghi and R. B. Peck, *Soil Mechanics in Engineering Practice*, John Wiley & Sons, Inc., New York, 1948, p. 31.

3:11 L. F. Cooling, A. W. Skempton, and R. Glossop, *Discussion*, of Reference 3:6.

3:12 *Munsell Soil Color Charts*, Munsell Color Company, Inc., Baltimore, 1954.

3:13 W. L. Stokes and D. J. Varnes, *Glossary of Selected Geologic Terms*, Colorado Scientific Society Proceedings, Volume 16, Denver, 1955.

Suggestions for Additional Study

1. References 3:1, 3:2, 3:6.
2. *PCA Soil Primer*, Portland Cement Association, Chicago, 1950.
3. D. P. Krynine and W. R. Judd, *Principles of Engineering Geology and Geotechnics*, McGraw-Hill Book Co., Inc., New York, 1957.
4. R. F. Leggett, *Geology and Engineering*, McGraw-Hill Book Co., Inc., New York, 1939.
5. D. S. Jenkins, D. J. Belcher, L. E. Gregg, and K. B. Woods, "The Origin, Distribution and Airphoto Identification of U.S. Soils," U.S. Department of Commerce, CAA Technical Development Report 52, 1946.
6. D. M. Burmister, "Identification and Classification of Soils," *Symposium on Identification and Classification of Soils*, ASTM Special Publication 113, Philadelphia, 1951.

PROBLEMS

3:1 Prepare a log of the soils you might expect when making an excavation in the following deposits:
(1) Flood plain of a flat river in Mississippi.
(2) Coastal swamp in North Carolina.
(3) Edge of swampy lake in the glaciated portion of Michigan.
(4) A dried-up lake bed in Nevada.
(5) Sand dune in Indiana.
(6) Prairie in North Dakota.
(7) River valley in Connecticut.
(8) Coastal plain of Texas.

3:2 Classify the following soils according to the Revised Public Roads System and find the GI number: *Ans.*

[handwritten annotations:]

G, I No.

1 A-6(8)   5 A-3(0)
2 A-4(3)   6 A-5(8)
3 A-7-6 (20)   7 A-1-b(0)
4 A-1 (0)   8 A-2-4(0)

Soil No.	Per Cent Passing		Characteristics of −40 Fraction	
	No. 40	No. 200	LL	PI
1	95	57	37	18
2	72	48	31	4
3	100	97	73	45
4	18	0		
5	63	8		
6	97	65	50	6
7	45	18	14	3
8	70	30	17	5

3:3 The following data were obtained by mechanical analysis and plasticity tests of soil samples. (Percentages finer than given size noted.) *Calculate by A method*

Size	Sample 1	Sample 2	Sample 3	Sample 4	Sample 5	Sample 6
No. 10	—	—	—	—	—	100
20	86%	98%	93%	99%	98%	
40	72	85	79	94	95	86
60	60	72	68	89	92	
100	45	56	56	82	86	
200	35	42	42	76	83	12
0.05 mm	33	41	41	74	82	
0.01 mm	21	20	11	38	57	0
0.002 mm	10	8	4	23	36	
LL	19	44	30	40	67	NP
PI	0	0	0	12	27	NP

Plot the grain size curve.   *Ans. 1-SM   4-ML*
a. Classify each using the Unified System.   *2-SM*
b. Classify each using Revised Public Roads System.

3:4 a. Describe visually a sample of soil you have secured from an excavation or highway cut.

b. Estimate the soil classification according to the Revised Public Roads System and the Unified System.

4... SEEPAGE, DRAINAGE
and FROST ACTION

The district representative of a nation-wide manufacturing concern purchased what appeared to be an ideal site for a warehouse and distribution center. It was in a small valley close to a railroad and an arterial highway. After construction began, however, it was found that a high ground water table hampered work, and ground water flowing into some of the footing excavations made concreting impossible. The first contractor quit the job in despair, and another contractor, who tried to take over the work, finally lost his business. The manufacturing concern had no alternative but to drop the entire project, abandon the property, and purchase a new site. The cause of all this trouble was uncontrolled ground water—a difficulty that the businessman untrained in engineering could scarcely have recognized, and a difficulty that might have been corrected by proper seepage control.

Water is the ingredient of soils that tends to fluctuate with time and the season; as it changes, the soil's strength or volume may change correspondingly. Control of the water content, control of the movement of water, and prevention of the damage caused by the movement of water in soils are important aspects of soils engineering. They present problems in making excavations, constructing roads and airports, designing earth dams and levees, and building safe foundations.

The energy possessed by a particle of water is in three forms: *potential energy*, owing to its height; *pressure energy*, owing to the pressure; and *kinetic energy*, owing to its velocity. (In the flow of water through soils, the velocities are so low that the kinetic energy is practically zero.) Energy in water is usually expressed as *head*—a linear dimension such as feet that actually means foot-pound per pound. Since energy is only relative, head must always be expressed with relation to some fixed point, usually an arbitrary datum plane. The head possessed by water in soils is manifested by the height, h, to which water will rise in a small tube or standpipe above the fixed datum plane, as shown in Fig. 4:1a. This height to which water rises is often termed the *piezometric level* and it is a measure of the total energy of the water.

If at two different points within a continuous mass of water there are different amounts of energy, then there will be movement of the water particles toward the points of lesser energy, and the difference in head (energy) is used up in the work of moving the water. Darcy's law expresses the head loss, Δh, required to move water through soil at a rate Q, a

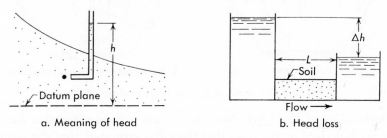

a. Meaning of head   b. Head loss

Fig. 4:1 Head and head loss.

distance of L, by the formula

$$\Delta h = \frac{QL}{kA}, \tag{4:1}$$

which is simply formula 2:8 rewritten (Fig. 4:1b). Of course this implies laminar flow, which is ordinarily the case in all soils except coarse gravels.

4:1 Saturated Flow, The Flow Net

The flow of water through saturated soil can be represented pictorially by *flow lines* (Fig. 4:2a), which are the paths taken by the moving particles of water. Water tends to follow the shortest path from point to point but at the same time makes only smooth curves when it changes direction. The flow lines, therefore, are curved, somewhat parallel lines, like loosely stretched bundles of rubber bands, that extend from points of greater head to points of lesser head. In many cases the curves are segments of ellipses or parabolas.

The different amounts of energy or head can be represented on the same picture by *equipotential lines* (Fig. 4:2b), which are lines that indicate points having equal heads. The equipotential lines can be thought of as contours of equal energy; the flow lines cross them at right angles, since the water moves from higher energy levels to lower energy levels along paths of maximum energy gradient in the same way water flows down a hillside from higher levels to lower levels, following the steepest paths.

The pattern of flow and equipotential lines is termed the *flow net*, and it is a powerful tool for the solution of seepage problems.

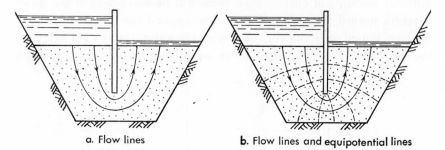

a. Flow lines   b. Flow lines and equipotential lines

Fig. 4:2   Flow net of seepage beneath sheet piling.

Derivation of the Flow Net   The mathematical expression for the flow net is derived on the basis that the soil is saturated, that the volume of water in the voids remains the same during seepage, and that the coefficient of permeability is the same at all points and in any direction at any point. The basic equation of seepage, Darcy's law (equation 2:8), is resolved into x- and y-components:

$$Q_x = ki_x A_x,$$
$$Q_y = ki_y A_y,$$
$$i = \frac{\Delta h}{\Delta L} = \frac{dh}{dL}.$$

The seepage velocity v is the rate of seepage divided by the area of flow, and so the equations can be rewritten:

$$v = \frac{Q}{A},$$
$$v_x = k\frac{\partial h}{\partial x},$$
$$v_y = k\frac{\partial h}{\partial y}.$$

The flow through a small element of soil having the dimensions of dx, dy, and 1 is shown in Fig. 4:3a and is expressed as follows:

In: $v_x \, dy + v_y \, dx.$

Out: $\left(v_x + \dfrac{\partial v_x}{\partial x} \, dx\right) dy + \left(v_y + \dfrac{\partial v_y}{\partial y} \, dy\right) dx.$

If the volume of water in the voids remains constant, then the flow *in*

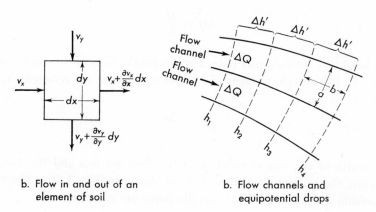

b. Flow in and out of an   b. Flow channels and
   element of soil   equipotential drops

Fig. 4:3 Meaning of the flow net.

equals the flow *out;* so, equating the above expressions and collecting terms,

$$\frac{\partial v_x}{\partial x} + \frac{\partial v_y}{\partial y} = 0.$$

By substituting the equations for velocity, the relation becomes

$$\frac{\partial^2 h}{\partial x^2} + \frac{\partial^2 h}{\partial y^2} = 0. \qquad (4:2)$$

This is the Laplace equation of mathematical physics which describes the energy loss through a resistive medium. It represents two sets of lines, each set containing an infinite number of parallel curves and with each curve of one set intersecting each curve of the other at right angles, as shown in Fig. 4:3b. The *equipotential lines* comprise one set and the *flow lines* the other, and the entire pattern is the *flow net.*

Flow Net Construction The two-dimensional flow net derived above is a useful representation of the seepage patterns through earth dams, into large excavations, and below retaining walls and masonry structures. Unfortunately the Laplace equation can be integrated mathematically for only a few very simple conditions, and in practice the flow net must be obtained by other methods.

The graphical procedure of Forcheimer is simple and is applicable to any problem of steady flow in two dimensions. The space between any pair of flow lines is a *flow channel*. If a certain number of flow channels, N_f, is selected so that the flow through each, ΔQ, is the same, then

$$\Delta Q = \frac{Q}{N_f}.$$

The head loss between any pair of equipotential lines is the *equipotential drop* $\Delta h'$. If a certain number of equipotential drops are selected, N_D, so that all are equal,

$$\Delta h' = \frac{\Delta h}{N_D}.$$

The width of any one element of such a flow net is a and the distance between the equipotential lines is b, as shown in Fig. 4:3b. (The third dimension is 1.) The gradient and discharge are given by

$$i = \frac{\Delta h'}{b} = \frac{\Delta h/N_D}{b},$$

$$\Delta Q = k \left(\frac{\Delta h/N_D}{b}\right) a.$$

The total discharge for the net, whose third dimension is 1, is expressed by

$$Q = \Delta Q N_f = k \, \Delta h \left(\frac{a}{b}\right) \frac{N_f}{N_D}. \tag{4:3a}$$

The ratio of (a/b) is fixed by the ratio of N_f/N_D and is the same throughout the net. If N_f and N_D are selected so that $a = b$, the equation for discharge (for a unit dimension perpendicular to the flow net) is

$$Q = k \, \Delta h \, \frac{N_f}{N_D}. \tag{4:3b}$$

This is termed a *square net* because all the intersections between the sides are at right angles and the average length and width are equal. However, it should be noted that the term *square* is used in a descriptive sense because the opposite sides of the figure are not necessarily equal and they are seldom straight lines.

The first step in constructing a flow net is to make a scale drawing (Fig. 4:4a) showing the soil mass, the pervious boundaries through which water enters and leaves the soil, and the impervious boundaries that confine the flow. Second, two to four flow lines are sketched, entering and leaving at right angles to the pervious boundaries and approximately parallel to the impervious boundaries (Fig. 4:4b). Third, equipotential lines are drawn at right angles to the flow lines (Fig. 4:4c) so that the length and width of each figure will be equal. Of course this will be impossible on the first attempt because the positions of the flow lines were only

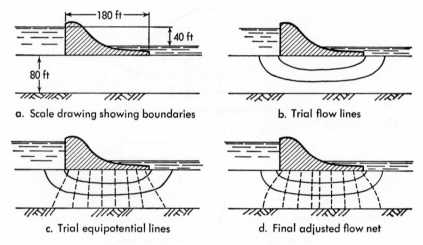

a. Scale drawing showing boundaries   b. Trial flow lines

c. Trial equipotential lines   d. Final adjusted flow net

Fig. 4:4 Steps in constructing a flow net.

guessed, but the resulting net will guide the second attempt. Fourth, the flow lines and equipotential lines are readjusted so that all the intersections are at right angles and the length and width of each figure are equal (Fig. 4:4d). Between one pair of equipotential lines the figures may work out to be rectangles. However, each rectangle should have the same ratio of a/b. The resulting equipotential drop is a fraction of the others.

The quantity of seepage is computed by equation 4:3b, using the values of N_f and N_D found by the graphical trial and revision. This is multiplied by the third dimension, perpendicular to the plane of the flow net, to get the total seepage.

Much practice is necessary to develop skill in drawing flow nets, and many cycles of trial and revision are required for an accurate solution.

Example 4:1 Compute the quantity of seepage under the dam in Fig. 4:4 if $k = 0.0003$ fpm and the level of water upstream is 60 ft above the base of the dam and downstream is 20 ft above the base of the dam. The length of the dam (perpendicular to the direction of seepage) is 850 ft.

(1) From the flow net $N_f = 3$ and $N_D = 9.5$.

(2) Q per foot $= 0.0003 \times \dfrac{3}{9.5}$ (60 − 20),

Q per foot $= 0.0038$ cu ft per min.

(3) $Q = 0.0038 \times 850 = 3.2$ cfm.

Flow Net with Free Surface In some cases, such as the flow of water through earth dams (Fig. 4:5a), one boundary flow line may be a free

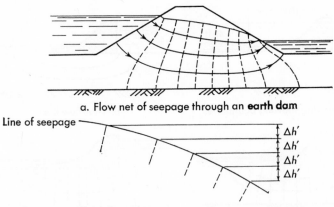

a. Flow net of seepage through an **earth dam**

b. Intersections of equipotential lines with line of seepage (uppermost flow line)

Fig. 4:5   Flow net with a free surface.

water surface that is not fixed by any solid, impervious mass. This is analogous to the free water surface in open channel flow and is a more difficult problem to solve with the flow net. The upper boundary flow line is called the *line of seepage*. It must satisfy all the requirements of any flow line, and in addition its intersections with the equipotential lines must be vertically spaced a distance equal to $\Delta h'$ (Fig. 4:5b). Considerable juggling is necessary to construct such a net correctly, but in many practical problems even a rough net will be sufficiently accurate.

A comprehensive paper describing methods of constructing flow nets with free surfaces and for constructing nets in soils whose permeability is not the same in all directions or at all points has been presented by A. Casagrande.[4:1]

4:2   Seepage Effects and Their Control

Uncontrolled seepage results in two types of trouble: Too much seepage causes excessively wet excavations or a loss of water through dams; excessive water pressure causes heave or loss in strength of the soil and failure. Control of seepage is complicated by the fact that correction at one point can aggravate the conditions at another.

Neutral Stress   The water pressure in still water can be found from the law of hydrostatics:

$$\Delta u = \gamma_w \, \Delta z. \tag{2:6}$$

When the water is moving, no matter how slowly, this no longer applies, and the pressure must be computed from the flow net. The total head h

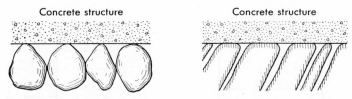

a. Soil against a concrete structure   b. Rock against a concrete structure

Fig. 4:6   Uplift and contact with a structure.

at any point is given by the equipotential line. If the elevation of that point is z, then the pressure head is $h - z$. The water pressure is

$$u = \gamma_w(h - z). \tag{4:4a}$$

The pressure is the same in all directions at any one point but not necessarily the same at different points all at the same level.

Uplift on a Structure   When a structure rests on a soil, a part of the structure is in contact with the soil grains while the remainder bridges over the voids, as shown in Fig. 4:6a. The actual area in contact with the soil grains is infinitesimal; and so, with a neutral stress of u, the uplift force U of the water on the base of the structure is given by

$$U = uA = \gamma_w(h - z)A. \tag{4:4b}$$

In this expression A is the total area in contact with the soil. When the structure is in contact with rock, the area on which the water pressure acts is smaller, as shown in Fig. 4:6b. Based on the meager data available, the uplift area for concrete on sound rock is 0.5 to 0.75 times the total area and for concrete on fissured rock is 0.75 to 1 times the total area.

When the uplift on the base of a structure exceeds the downward force, owing to the weight of the structure and the loads it carries, the structure will rise or heave. In one case the empty concrete sedimentation basin for a sewage treatment plant under construction rose with the rising water table following a period of rain. Basement floors heave or even blow up as if they were blasted when subjected to excessive uplift.

Heave and Boiling in a Soil   Uplift develops within a soil mass in a way similar to the way in which it occurs between soil and a structure. The actual points of contact between soil grains have an extremely small area, and so the uplift force is approximately equal to the water pressure multiplied by the total area. If the uplift force U over an area A exceeds

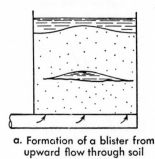

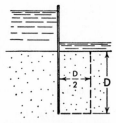

a. Formation of a blister from
upward flow through soil

b. Width of critical zone for
boiling (after Terzaghi)

Fig. 4:7   Development of heave and boiling.

the downward force P, then the soil will heave and failure will result. At the point of failure

$$P = U \qquad \text{and} \qquad \frac{P}{A} = \frac{U}{A},$$

$$\sigma = u.$$

If the area is sufficiently great, any excess water pressure will force the overlying mass of soil and water to rise, a process called *heave*. The soil expands with a decrease in void ratio, and in some cases a blister of water forms within the soil mass (Fig. 4:7a). The roof of the blister falls to its bottom and by this process, termed *roofing*, the blister rises to the surface. The soil surface bulges upward and then appears to explode as the blister reaches the top. Finally the soil seethes and bubbles in a *boil* as if it were cooking. Heave can occur in any soil, but roofing and boiling are limited to cohesionless materials. (See Example 2:6; p. 67.)

Heave without boiling results in an increase in void ratio, a decrease in strength, and a great increase in compressibility.

Boiling destroys the soil structure and reduces the strength of a cohesionless soil to zero—the quicksand condition described in Chapter 2. (Since $\sigma = u$, then $\bar{\sigma} = \sigma - u = 0$ and the soil has no strength.)

Terzaghi[4:2] has stated that heaving ordinarily will not take place unless the instability occurs over a width of $D/2$, where D is the depth of soil above the level of instability (Fig. 4:7b). The average neutral stress over different widths $D/2$ for different assumed depths D can be computed from a flow net. Where the average neutral stress equals or exceeds the stress because of the weight of the overlying soil and water, there is a possibility of heave or boiling. It must be remembered that stability computations are approximate at best, and that a large safety factor should be used to be certain that boiling will not occur.

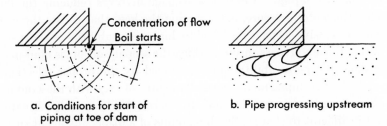

a. Conditions for start of piping at toe of dam

b. Pipe progressing upstream

Fig. 4:8 Piping beneath a masonry dam on a sand foundation.

Piping and Seepage Erosion If the soil within the zone of boiling is washed away by the flowing water, an open pit will be created. This causes a concentration of flow into the pit and an increase in the hydraulic gradient because the seepage path is shortened. Consequently the boiling is even more fierce and the pit becomes deeper, working its way upstream at an increasing speed toward the source of the water, as shown in Fig. 4:8. An opening or *pipe* is developed in the soil, and the process of continued backward erosion is called *piping*.

Piping also begins from very localized boiling or concentrations of seepage, as shown in Fig. 4:8a. When the upward hydraulic gradient approaches 1 at the soil surface, a small surface boil can form, and if the soil is carried away, a pit will develop. This pit works its way upstream, becoming larger and moving faster as the seepage path is shortened.

If the seepage is horizontal, toward the sloping face of an excavation or downstream face of an earth dam or downward into an improperly protected drain or leaking sewer, piping sometimes will develop from very small gradients. Extensive cavities have been created where cohesive strata support the remainder of the soil mass across the opening. In one situation erosion of fine sand through a ½-in. crack in a bulkhead created a cavity 5 ft deep beneath a concrete pavement which was not discovered until a loaded truck broke through into the crater below.

When the pipe approaches the source of water, there is a sudden break-through and a rush of water through the pipe, which enlarges it. One such pipe, a few inches in diameter through an earth dam, was enlarged to 10 ft in a few minutes after a breakthrough. Finally the enlarged hole collapses from lack of support, destroying part of the soil mass.

Cohesionless soils, particularly fine sands and silts, are most susceptible to piping failures. Clays resist piping because the interparticle bonds help prevent the particles from washing away; however, they are not immune.

Control of Seepage   Control of seepage involves reducing the flow, reducing the water pressure, or increasing the load that resists the water pressure. Excessive seepage is caused by high permeabilities or short seep-age paths. If the soil mass through which the seepage occurs is man-made, like a dam, the permeability can be reduced by the proper selection of materials. For example, mixing a small amount of clay with the sand used for constructing a levee can reduce the permeability greatly. A natural deposit is difficult to change. Small amounts of a dispersing agent such as sodium tetraphosphate mixed in the surface of a flocculent structure clay, or injection of clay, chemicals, or cement into the voids of a coarse-grained soil, can reduce the permeability, but at considerable expense.

The seepage path can be lengthened, which will reduce the quantity of seepage and also reduce the water pressure at the downstream end of the flow. An impervious core in an earth dam (Fig. 4:9a) and an impervious cutoff trench in a pervious foundation for a dam can increase the path greatly. A complete cutoff (Fig. 4:9b) that extends to a deeper impervious stratum is more effective than the partial cutoff (Fig. 4:9a). Cutoffs are constructed of an impervious soil or steel sheet piling, depending on avail-ability of materials and ease of construction. An impervious blanket of clay upstream (Fig. 4:9c) is also useful but must not be used downstream because it will increase the uplift.

Excessive water pressure can be controlled by drainage that short-cir-cuits the flow and bleeds off the excess neutral stress at a point where it can do no harm. The *trench drain, blanket drain,* and *toe drain* (Fig. 4:9c) are used separately or in combination in earth dams to reduce neutral stresses in the downstream part of the embankment. Relief holes (Fig. 4:9d) reduce uplift on masonry dams. Relief wells (Fig. 4:9e) are used to reduce pressures in confined seams or pockets. Drainage has the disadvantage of shortening the seepage path and increasing the flow, but this can be corrected as previously described. It is essential that the drainage system be properly designed to avoid seepage erosion, as will be described in Art. 4:5.

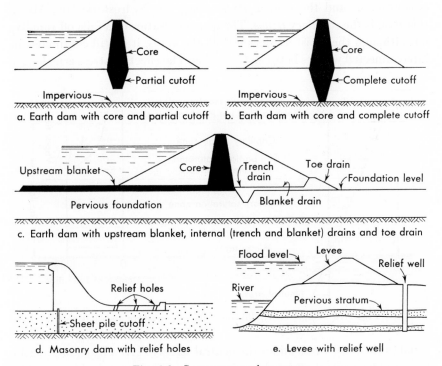

a. Earth dam with core and partial cutoff   b. Earth dam with core and complete cutoff

c. Earth dam with upstream blanket, internal (trench and blanket) drains and toe drain

d. Masonry dam with relief holes   e. Levee with relief well

Fig. 4:9   Seepage control measures.

4:3   Capillary Moisture and Flow

Above the free water surface or water table the movement of moisture is more complex. The soil is saturated to the height of capillary rise but above that level the degree of saturation is less. Gravity and fluid friction still act on the soil moisture but the capillary forces are even more important. These include surface tension and the physicochemical bonds between water and soil. These forces are tensile and result in negative neutral stresses. The tension increases with decreasing temperature and with a decreasing degree of saturation. In the zone of partial saturation water also exists in the vapor phase. The vapor pressure decreases with decreasing temperature.

Capillary Equilibrium As described in Art. 2:2, moisture rises above the free water surface as a result of capillary tension. When equilibrium is established, the soil moisture is distributed approximately as shown in Fig. 4:10. In the capillary zone the soil is saturated. The moisture is continuous and the neutral stress obeys the hydrostatic law. Above this zone is the *capillary fringe*. The degree of saturation falls off rapidly, but although the moisture does not fill the voids, it is still continuous in interconnected wedges between the grains. The effective stress is no longer

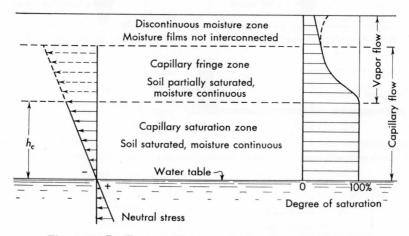

Fig. 4:10 Capillary equilibrium and soil-moisture distribution.

equal to the total stress minus the neutral stress as given by equation 2:14 because the neutral stress does not act over the entire void area. The degree of saturation becomes less with increasing height above the free surface until the moisture wedges are no longer interconnected. There is still neutral stress in the upper zone of *discontinuous moisture*, but it no longer follows the hydrostatic distribution. Each moisture wedge develops a different stress, depending on its radius, and although the stress can be very high, it acts over only a small fraction of the void.

Vapor Movement Moisture movement in the vapor phase occurs both in the fringe and discontinuous moisture zones. The difference in vapor pressures required to produce the flow can come about in a number of ways. Evaporation at the soil surface reduces the pressure and induces

an upward movement. A sudden drop in temperature at the ground surface will also reduce the pressure and induce upward movement, while
a sudden rise in temperature at the surface will produce a downward
movement.

Capillary Flow Capillary flow takes place in the zone of saturation
and in the capillary fringe. Loss of water by evaporation from the surface
will reduce the degree of saturation, increase the tension, and create an
upward flow. In arid regions there is a continuous upward movement of
moisture toward the surface and therefore equilibrium is never established. Construction of a building or a pavement on the soil will reduce
evaporation; the degree of saturation will then increase until equilibrium
is established. Such an increase in moisture beneath buildings and pavements is a serious source of trouble because it can cause weakening of the
soil or expansion and heave, as described in Art. 2:8. Rainfall will increase
the amount of moisture at the soil surface and thus reduce the capillary
tension. Downward flow will be induced until equilibrium is again established. Temperature differences create differences in capillary tension and
capillary flow, a phenomenon termed *thermal osmosis*. A sharp drop in
ground surface temperature will produce increased capillary tension and
upward seepage until equilibrium is re-established by the reduction in
capillary tension from the increased degree of saturation. Construction
work in the fall season is often troubled by an increase in soil moisture
brought on by the continually decreasing temperature. Moisture migrates
toward cold-storage warehouses and away from sources of heat such as
furnaces and kilns by the same mechanism.

4:4 Drainage

Drainage ordinarily means removal of water from the soil. It has two
objectives: prevention of seepage out of the soil, such as into an excavation where it would be a nuisance or a hazard; and improvement of the
soil properties such as an increase in strength or a reduction in compressibility. Drainage is also employed to reduce water pressure in the soil.
Usually this is accompanied by removal of water, but in fine-grained soils
it can be effective even though little or no water is lost.

Forces Involved in Drainage A number of forces are involved in the
ease with which water drains from the soil. First is the resistance to seepage, as indicated by the permeability coefficient. Second is the effect of
the drainage on the soil structure. If the soil is relatively incompressible,
the water lost will be replaced by air in the voids. If the soil is compres-

sible, the water loss can be accompanied by consolidation and the soil will remain saturated. Third are the forces that restrain the water: capillarity and adsorption. Both the resistance to flow and the capillary retention become greater with decreasing grain size. Coarse-grained soils, such as gravel and coarse sand, drain rapidly and air replaces the water in the voids. Fine-grained soils that have low permeability and very high capillary retention drain very slowly and may lose only as much water as the consolidation will permit.

In order to remove water from the soil, the force producing drainage must be greater than the retentivity and the resistance to flow. *Gravity* is the force most often employed: Water moves from the soil into the drain under the influence of its own weight. This method is cheap and reliable but not strong enough in fine-grained soils. A *vacuum* can be used to add atmospheric pressure to the head produced by gravity. With its aid, finer soils such as silty sands can be drained. A direct electric current will induce a flow of water in the soil toward a negative electrode. This principle of *electro-osmosis* can be used to induce drainage of low-permeability soils such as silts.

Evaporation is ordinarily not considered a drainage method but it does cause a loss of water. It is a slow but powerful force that can drain even clays. *Consolidation* produced by a load on the soil mass is essentially a drainage process that is effective in compressible materials.

Drainage and Soil Type   The ease of draining a soil and the forces that are effective in producing drainage can be estimated from laboratory tests for permeability, consolidation, and shrinkage. The grain-size distribution offers some indication of drainage properties, as shown in Fig. 4:11. Table 4:1 gives the drainage potential for the Unified Soil Classification.

Table 4:1   DRAINAGE POTENTIALITIES, UNIFIED SOIL CLASSIFICATION[4:13]

Soil Class	Drainage Characteristics	Soil Class	Drainage Characteristics
GW	Excellent	ML	Fair to poor
GP	Excellent	CL	Impervious
GM	Fair to impervious	OL	Poor
GC	Poor to impervious	MH	Fair to poor
SW	Excellent	CH	Impervious
SP	Excellent	OH	Impervious
SM	Fair to impervious	Pt	Fair to poor
SC	Poor to impervious		

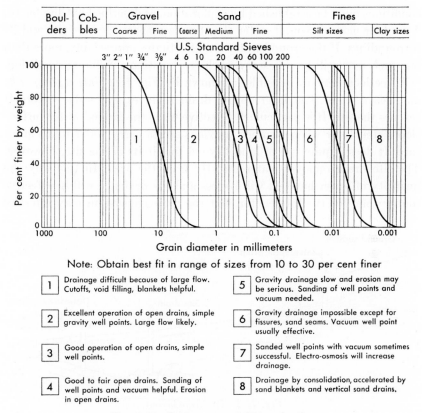

Fig. 4:11 Drainage capabilities of soils.

4:5 Drainage Design

The design of a drainage system depends on the drainage characteristics of the soil, the length of time the system must operate, and the position of ground water. For temporary drains installed during construction, minimum interference with work and maximum effectiveness in a short time are essential. For permanent drains, long-term effectiveness and minimum maintenance are essential.

Drainage Layout The position of the drainage system depends on the initial seepage pattern and the pattern that is to be established. If the drainage is installed in a dam, for example, the position of the water before and after drainage can be established by flow nets. If the drainage is for a building site, a highway, or an airfield, the initial ground water conditions must be established by exploration, as described in Chapter 10. A contour map of ground water elevation is prepared for the site and its surroundings. If the ground water level fluctuates appreciably, more than one such map will be necessary, each representing a different condition.

Three locations are possible, as shown by Fig. 4:12: *intercepting*, *site*, and *downstream*. The intercepting drain removes the water before it reaches the site. It is particularly effective when the ground water surface slopes steeply or when confined pervious strata carry water under pressure. It does require use of land beyond the limits of the site, however. The site drain removes water directly from the area. In this way the quantity of water handled will be less and the drainage will be effective sooner than for the interceptor, but the drainage system may interfere

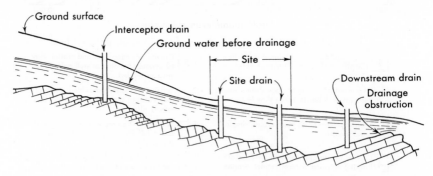

Fig. 4:12   Drainage layout.

with the work at the site. The downstream drain enables the water to leave the site more rapidly. It is most effective when an underground obstruction tends to dam up the ground water. In some cases one location is sufficient; in others, all three will be employed.

Filters, Conduits, Disposal   A complete drain consists of three components: the filter, the conduit or collector, and the disposal system. The filter is essential for continued efficiency of the drain and to prevent seepage erosion when the hydraulic gradients are high. A *filter* or *protective filter* is *any* porous material whose openings are small enough to prevent movement of the soil into the drain and which is sufficiently pervious to offer little resistance to seepage. Extensive experiments have shown that it is not necessary for a filter to screen out all the particles in the soil. Instead the filter openings need restrain only the coarsest 15 per cent, or the D_{85}, of the soil.[4:3] These coarser particles, D_{85} and larger, will collect over the filter opening as shown in Fig. 4:13a. Their voids will create smaller openings to trap even smaller particles of soil. Therefore the diameter of the openings in the filter must be less than D_{85} of the soil. If the filter is a metal screen or holes in a perforated pipe, this limit fixes the finest soil that can be filtered by any given opening, or it establishes the largest opening that can be used with a given soil. Frequently a soil is employed as a filter. This means that the effective diameter of its voids must be less than D_{85} of the soil being filtered. Since the effective pore diameter is about $\frac{1}{5}D_{15}$, then

$$D_{15(\text{filter})} \leqq 5D_{85(\text{soil})} \qquad (4:5a)$$

If the filter is to provide free drainage, it must be much more pervious

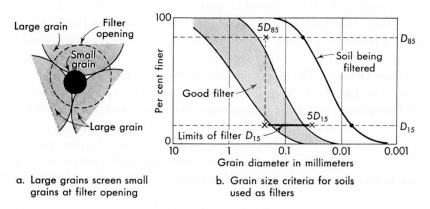

a. Large grains screen small grains at filter opening

b. Grain size criteria for soils used as filters

Fig. 4:13 Protective filter.

than the soil. Since the permeability coefficient varies as the square of the grain size, then a ratio of permeabilities of over 20 to 1 can be secured by

$$D_{15(\text{filter})} \geqq 5D_{15(\text{soil})}. \qquad (4:5b)$$

These criteria (Fig. 4:13b) are the basis for filter design.[4:3] In general the filter soil should be well within these limits, and its grain-size curve should be parallel to or flatter than the soil. If the soil being filtered is very fine-grained, more than one filter layer will be required. The final filter layer is designed to fit between the openings in the conduit and the next finer filter. For many silty and clayey soils a well-graded concrete sand makes a satisfactory filter. A coarser pea-gravel second filter is then needed for the first.

The filter thickness is not critical; for small heads a few inches is sufficient, while in dams where the heads are great, 2 to 10 ft are commonly used.

The drain conduit collects water from the filter and carries it away. The simplest is a ditch or pipe designed like any other hydraulic conduit. Ordinarily the conduit is several times larger than its hydraulics dictate to allow for silting. Typical collecting perforations in conduits are $5/16$ to $3/8$ in. in diameter and require a filter with a maximum size of $1/2$ in. A *French conduit* is made of coarse gravel or crushed rock; where the amount of water is small, it can be cheap and effective. It is not, however, a substitute for a filter, and if employed as one, it will soon clog.

The disposal system removes the water from the area. If possible, gravity is used because it is permanent and foolproof. However, the topography may make this impossible, particularly during wet weather when the drain is needed most. Pumping will remove the water faster, but the cost of power over a long period will be appreciable, and maintenance is often uncertain.

Open Drains The oldest method of draining excavations, roads, and similar projects is the open drain—either a ditch or a sump. A *sump* is a shallow pit into which the ground water flows by gravity. A *ditch* may be merely an elongated sump. Both are very effective in sands and gravels. Sumps and ditches are cheap; they can be constructed easily with unskilled labor or with simple equipment, and ordinarily gasoline construction pumps are suitable for pumping the water out of them. Boiling and piping sometimes commence in sumps and ditches, particularly if the soil is fine sand of low permeability; therefore they must be carefully watched on important and hazardous projects. Boils can be prevented by placing filter layers on the sides and bottoms of sumps, but this will increase the cost of construction.

Closed Drains When seepage erosion or piping is troublesome or where a permanent drain is desired, perforated pipe or open-jointed tile can be laid in the ditches and the ditch backfilled with a filter material. It is important that the pipe be surrounded by one or two filter layers, as required, to prevent soil from clogging the openings. The pipe should be laid in straight lines. Drains in silty soils should have an opening every 50 to 100 ft through which a fire hose can be inserted to flush out the pipe occasionally. Manholes should be provided at changes in direction and at intervals of 300 or 400 ft along straight sections.

Blanket Drains Continuous drainage blankets are sometimes provided beneath dams and basement floor slabs to reduce uplift pressures and beneath pavements to prevent capillary flow upward. The blanket consists of a filter layer in contact with the soil and a coarser collector layer which also serves as a second filter. The latter is placed in contact with the underside of a masonry dam or basement floor, or is sandwiched between two filter layers in the base of an earth dam. Water is removed from the collector by conduits.

Deep Wells Deep wells, such as are used for water supply, are occasionally employed in temporary drainage. Diameters of 12 to 24 in. with spacings of 25 to 100 ft and depths of 100 ft or more have been used, depending on the size of the area to be unwatered and the amount the water table is to be lowered. They are also used in coarse soils and porous rock where the quantities of water drained are large.

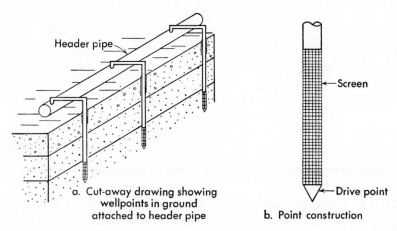

a. Cut-away drawing showing wellpoints in ground attached to header pipe

b. Point construction

Fig. 4:14 Wellpoint installation and construction.

Horizontal Wells Horizontal wells, about 3 in. in diameter and over 100 ft long, have been found useful in draining hillsides. The wells are installed by drilling into the hill at a slight upward angle to intercept water-bearing strata. The hole is then lined with a slotted or perforated pipe to keep it open and to carry the water out.[4:5]

Wellpoints Wellpoints are small diameter wells that are driven or jetted into the soil. Usually they are placed in straight lines along the sides of the area to be drained and are connected at their upper ends to a horizontal suction pipe called the *header*, as shown in Fig. 4:14a. Depending on the type of soil to be drained, one or two wellpoints are usually installed for each 8 ft of header. The header terminates in a self-priming pump specially designed for wellpoint work, and one pump is ordinarily used for each 50 to 100 points.[4:6]

Many different types of points have been devised (Fig. 4:14b). The drivepoint consists of a length of heavy-gauge, 2-in. pipe. To its lower end is attached a perforated section 2 to 4 ft long covered with a wire-gauze screen terminating in a conical steel tip. Points designed to be jetted into the soil are equipped with special valves at their lower ends. During jetting water is pumped into the well point and is directed out of the tip by the valve. This washes a hole in the soil allowing the wellpoint to sink into position. When the wellpoint is connected to the suction header, the valve changes and the wellpoint takes in water through the gauze screen at its lower end.

It has been found that the effectiveness of the points in fine-grained

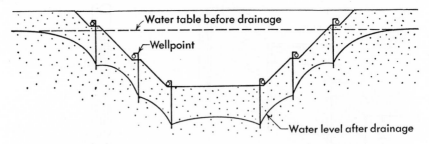

Fig. 4:15   Multiple-stage wellpoint system for draining deep excavations.

soils is increased by sealing the point into the uppermost soil strata with a plug of clay and maintaining a vacuum on the header at all times, even when little water is removed from the soil. With a vacuum applied within the soil mass, the atmospheric pressure tends to force the water out of coarser soils and to reduce the neutral stresses and decrease the void ratio of finer soil. Pumping units designed for wellpoint work usually include vacuum pumps.

Since wellpoints are operated by suction, the maximum vertical distance from the pump intake to the water level at the points is from 20 to 25 ft. If excavations extend more than 20 ft below the water table, they must be unwatered in two or more stages as shown in Fig. 4:15. The first stage consists of a row of points that are set in the ground and placed in operation as soon as the ground water table is reached. Excavation is resumed as soon as the water table is lowered by the first points. A second row of points is then placed when the excavation again reaches the ground water table. Excavations as deep as 50 ft below the original water table have been made by using from three to four lift stages of points.

Wellpoints have proved very successful for draining soils of high and medium permeability, such as coarse sands and clean fine sands, and vacuum wellpoints have been used with some success in soils of low permeability, such as silty sands and sandy silts. Their success depends to a large extent on the experience and skill of the persons making the installation.[4:6][4:7]

Electro-osmosis If a direct current is passed through a soil of low permeability, the rate of drainage is increased greatly.[4:7] Wellpoints serve as the negative electrodes, and steel rods driven into the soil midway between the wells form the positive electrodes. From 20 to 30 amp of electric current are used per well, at voltages from 40 to 180. The amount of energy required varies from 0.5 kwhr to 10 kwhr per cu yd of soil drained.

Electro-osmosis requires expensive equipment and is relatively costly to operate; therefore it is used only when cheaper methods cannot produce sufficient drainage.

Desiccation Drainage of a soil by evaporation is an extremely slow process and is ineffective if the soil mass, by capillarity, can replace the moisture evaporated. Ventilation galleries have been used to dry out clay strata in hillsides when the clay is subject to swelling and loss of strength during wet seasons.

Drainage by Consolidation Soft, wet, cohesive soils are impossible to drain by gravity methods or even by vacuum or electro-osmosis, yet they may require a reduction in their water contents before they have sufficient strength to support heavy, concentrated loads without undue settlement or failure. Consolidation—the removal of water by a reduction of the volume of the voids through compression—is an effective process in spite of its inherent lack of speed.

Consolidation is produced by loading the soil with earth, crushed stone, iron ore, or any heavy material that can conform to the settlement irregularity. If the loading material is impervious, a blanket of free-draining sand is placed below the fill to allow the water that is squeezed from the soil to escape.

The process can be accelerated two ways. One is to provide an overload or surcharge that exceeds the ultimate load on the soil. Partial consolidation by the overload, which can be effective in a limited time, is equivalent to a greater degree of consolidation for the ultimate load, which would require a greater length of time to take place. The consolidation rate can also be accelerated by vertical drains, known as *drainage wicks,* or vertical sand piles[4:8,4:9] (Fig. 4:16). The sand pile is constructed by driving a pipe, 12 to 16 in. in diameter and with a removable bottom plate. The pipe is filled with sand and then withdrawn, leaving the sand in the hole. The drains are spaced 6 to 20 ft apart in both directions beneath the fill. Their upper ends connect with the sand-blanket drain at the top. Their purpose is to shorten the seepage path for the water being squeezed out of the soil and thereby increase the rate of consolidation. They are very effective in thick, homogeneous clay deposits where consolidation otherwise would be very slow. In deposits consisting of alternate strata of sand and clay, they are of little help because the seepage path is already short.

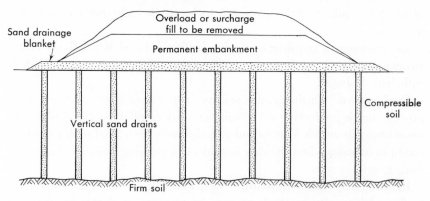

Fig. 4:16   Drainage by consolidation, accelerated by vertical sand drains and surcharge fill.

In very soft soils it is impossible to add enough weight at one time to provide the necessary drainage because the soil is too weak to support the load. In such cases the load is applied in stages. The second stage is deferred until the soil has been consolidated and strengthened enough to support the entire load.

4:6   Frost Action

Frost Action and Its Consequences   When the daily mean temperature remains below 32 F for a period longer than three or four days, the soil moisture at the ground surface freezes. The longer and the more intense the cold spell, the greater the depth to which the freezing extends.

The result of the freezing is a rise of the ground surface, known as *frost heave*, that sometimes is as great as 12 in. in the northern parts of the United States. If an excavation is made into frozen ground that has heaved, it will be seen that the soil has changed considerably. Its average water content has been greatly increased, and much of the water is concentrated into ice layers or lenses that lie parallel to the ground surface. The amount of heave is rarely uniform, and the force exerted by the expanding soil may lift roads, walls, and buildings.

Frost heave is particularly damaging to highways and airfield pavements, as they are generally built directly on the surface of the ground. Unequal heave can crack concrete pavement slabs or tip the individual slabs at angles. Heave beneath flexible pavements causes bumps or waves in the surface. Small structures with shallow foundations, such as small bridges, culverts, walls, sewer inlets, and light buildings, often suffer if their foundations are above soils subject to frost heave. Cold storage warehouses are lifted and torn apart by unequal heave brought about by improperly insulated floors.

Frost action is not limited to the process of heave. When the weather becomes warm again, the frozen soil begins to thaw from the top down, where the warmer air and sunshine are in contact. The uppermost portions of the soil become wet and soft as the ice layers melt. They remain wet until the excess water can drain downward through the deeper strata when the frost disappears.

Thawing beneath a highway or airfield pavement converts the soil into a liquid that supports the pavement. The weight of a truck or airplane under such conditions causes the liquid soil to spurt up through the expansion joints in concrete pavements (often called *pumping*) or to form holes known as *mud boils* in flexible (asphalt) pavements. Thawing beneath structural foundations may result in failure since the soft, water-filled soil has little ability to support heavy loads.

Frost action, therefore, is a combination of two processes: first, freezing of the soil and the formation of layers of ice that cause frost heave; and second, the thawing of the *ice lenses*, which provides an excess of free water in the soil and results in a lowering of the strength of the soil.

Mechanics of Frost Action[4:10]   When water goes from the liquid to solid form it expands about 10 per cent. In a saturated soil with a void ratio of 0.7, this means there would be a 4 per cent increase in the volume of the soil, or about a 1-in. heave in a soil frozen to a depth of 25 in. However, the observed heave in such a situation might be as much as 4 or 5 in. Furthermore, since the average water content and void ratio of the soil increase during the freezing process, it must be concluded that expansion of water in the voids is not the primary cause of heave. Examination of frozen soils indicates that the heave is about equal to the total thickness of all the ice layers formed during the process. Therefore it is concluded that the formation of ice layers (and the increase in average soil water content) is the basic cause of heave.

The temperature deep in the ground remains nearly constant throughout the year, while the temperature just below the ground surface fluctuates with the air temperature. After a period of cold weather in which the air temperature is below freezing, a thermal gradient is established in which the 32 F point is below the ground surface, as shown in Fig. 4:17. This point defines the *frost line*. Neither the frost line nor the thermal gradient is fixed; both vary with the duration and intensity of the cold.

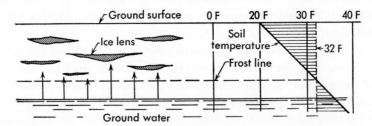

Fig. 4:17   Formation of ice lenses in zone of freezing.

The frost line is not found at a uniform depth, for it depends on the density, saturation, and composition of the soil.

Above the frost line the temperature is below the ordinary freezing point for water. However, in very small openings such as the voids of fine-grained soils, the freezing point may be depressed as low as 23 F. Thus, just above the frost line, water will freeze in the larger voids but remain liquid in the adjacent smaller ones. When water freezes in a larger void, the amount of liquid water at that point is decreased. The moisture deficiency and the lower temperature in the freezing zone increase the capillary tension and induce a flow toward the newly formed ice crystal. The adjacent small voids are still unfrozen and act as conduits to deliver the water to the ice. The ice crystal grows until an ice lens or layer forms. The capillary tension induced by the freezing and the low temperature sucks up water from the water table below or can even dehydrate and shrink adjacent compressible strata such as clays and micaceous silts when the water table is beyond reach. The result is a great increase in the amount of water in the frost zone, and *segregation* of the water into ice lenses.

In order for the water to be drawn into the freezing zone by capillary forces, the soil must be saturated or approaching saturation. Partially saturated soils freeze, but the ice is scattered in tiny crystals and the heave is small. For continued heave, the freezing zone must be within the height of capillary rise above the water table so that water can be sucked up from below. If the freezing zone is saturated but above the height of capillary rise (for example, when the upper strata have been saturated by rain or leaking pipes), the segregation and heave will be limited by the amount of water that can be sucked from the adjoining soil.

Second the soil must be fine-grained. Segregation seldom occurs in coarse soils where the pores are so large that water freezes in them at the same temperature as it freezes in cracks or fissures. The water simply freezes in the soil pores, and the heave, if any, is limited to a 10 per cent expansion of the voids. On the other hand, very fine-grained soils are so impervious that the water migrates to the ice lenses very slowly. The most rapid segregation takes place in soils whose permeability is great enough to permit easy movement of the water.

Third the temperature gradient in the soil must be favorable. When the rate of change in temperature with depth (temperature gradient) is very rapid, the zone of soil in which the pore water is unfrozen but below 32 F is narrow. The ice layers formed under such conditions tend to be thin, and the amount of heave small. When the temperature gradient is small, the zone in which the pore water is unfrozen but below 32 F is wide, and the ice lenses tend to be thick and the amount of heave great.

A rapidly varying gradient with alternating freezing and thawing can aggravate frost heave in sands but will have little effect on silts and clays.

Soils Susceptible to Frost Action The susceptibility of different soils to frost action has been studied by A. Casagrande and G. Beskow. They found that the coarse soils, sand and gravel containing no fines, are rarely subject to the formation of ice lenses and objectionable heave. On the other hand, fine sands and silts have the optimum combination of fine pores and relatively high permeability that results in maximum segregation and heave. Clays are usually considered to be frost susceptible because cracks and fissures may permit rapid movement of the water through them. According to Casagrande,[4:12] a uniform soil is susceptible to frost action if more than 10 per cent of its particles by weight are finer than 0.02 mm, and a well-graded soil is susceptible if more than 3 per cent of its grains are finer than 0.02 mm. Studies of frost action in Michigan, however, indicate that even sands may be susceptible to frost heave under some conditions. The potential frost action of the soil groups of the Unified Classification System are given in Table 4:2.

Table 4:2 POTENTIAL FROST ACTION OF UNIFIED SOIL CLASSIFICATION[4:13]

Soil Class	Potential Frost Action	Soil Class	Potential Frost Action
GW	None to very slight	ML	Medium to very high
GP	None to very slight	CL	Medium to high
GM	Slight to medium	OL	Medium to high
GC	Slight to medium	MH	Medium to high
SW	None to very slight	CH	Medium
SP	None to very slight	OH	Medium
SM	Slight to high	Pt	Slight
SC	Slight to high		

Depth of Frost Penetration   The depth below the ground surface to which a 32 F temperature extends is termed the *frost line*. Above the frost line, freezing occurs and ice lenses will form if the soil and water conditions are right. The depth of the frost line depends primarily on three factors: the air temperature, the length of time the air temperature is below 32 F, and the ability of the soil to conduct heat. The lower the air temperature and the longer it remains below 32 F, the greater the depth of the frost line; the higher the thermal conductivity of the soil, the greater the depth of frost penetration. The accompanying map (Fig. 4:18) shows the maximum depth of frost penetration in the United States. The map is only approximate: On mountain tops the depths will be much greater; in highly organic soils or coarse gravels above the water table, the depth will be smaller.

Preventing Frost Damage   Frost heave and frost damage may be prevented by correcting one or more of the factors responsible for the segregation of water and the formation of ice lenses: frost-susceptible soil, capillary saturation by rise of water from ground water table, and freezing temperatures in the soil.

One of the most effective methods of preventing frost heave is to remove the frost-susceptible soil throughout the depth of frost penetration and replace it with a soil that is not affected. In regions where large quantities of clean sands and gravels are readily available, soil replacement is an economical and permanent cure for frost heave.

Capillary saturation caused by the rise of water from the water table may be controlled by lowering the water table below the height of capillary rise or by obstructing the upward movement of the water. When the ground water table has a steep slope, or when it is perched on top of a saucer-shaped stratum of impervious soil, proper drainage may be very effective in preventing serious frost heave. In flat areas, and in areas in

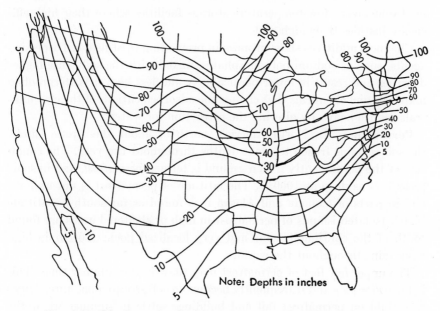

Fig. 4:18 Maximum depth of frost penetration in the United States.

which excessive rainfall or snow melting are quickly followed by freezing, even extensive drains may not prevent a rise in the ground water table and the subsequent capillary saturation. An impervious blanket, such as asphalt, plastic, or commercial bentonite, may prevent movement of water upward into the zone of frost penetration. Such blankets are seldom used, for they are expensive and they tend to puncture from the weight of the soil above or to deteriorate. Blankets of coarse-grained soils such as clean coarse sand, gravel, or crushed rock (with fines removed) placed above the water are effective water stops, for they break the capillary tension. They should be thicker than the height of capillary rise through

them and must be protected by filters so that the finer soils above or below
do not penetrate their voids. Such blankets must be well drained because
if they should fill with water, they would aggravate rather than prevent
frost heave.

Insulating blankets between the ground surface and the frost-susceptible soil reduce the penetration of the freezing line. Ordinarily these are
well-drained coarse sand and gravel. Often these are placed directly on
the ground surface and are employed beneath pavements or the floors of
cold-storage warehouses. Insulating blankets of foam glass and cork are
used under very low-temperature storage facilities where their high efficiency justifies their high cost.

Chemical additives show promise in preventing frost heave. Dispersing
agents, such as sodium polyphosphates, mixed with the soil cause higher
densities and result in lower permeability and less heave. Waterproofing
materials and chemicals that change the adsorbed cations of the clay minerals reduce heave by altering the attraction for water.

Permafrost   In North America, north of about the Arctic Circle,
the soil remains frozen to great depths throughout the year. The condition of the permanently frozen ground is termed *permafrost*, and in some
areas it is as deep as 1000 ft. The latitude of permafrost is not uniform
and in parts of Canada and Alaska it is found as far south as latitude
N. 62. Isolated islands of permafrost in high or sheltered areas are found
south of the continuous zone and very localized pockets occur in high
mountains throughout the world.

The upper few feet of permafrost may thaw in the summer time. This
is the *active zone* and it frequently becomes a soft, soupy quagmire. Highways laid on permafrost fail and buildings settle in summer when the
active zone softens. The heat of a building increases the depth of the
active zone and aggravates the situation. Permafrost is often covered with
an insulating blanket of moss and low, thickly matted vegetation called
tundra. This minimizes the depth of the active zone, and removal of this
natural insulation will greatly increase the active zone.

Foundations and subgrades must be placed below the active zone to
avoid movement, or the soil in the active zone must be replaced with a
non-frost-susceptible material like gravel or coarse crushed rock. Insulating blankets are sometimes used to minimize the thaw of the active zone.
In extreme cases cold-air conduits through the soil and cooling systems
are installed to offset the heat from buildings and boilers that would aggravate the thaw of the active zone.

REFERENCES

4:1 A. Casagrande, "Seepage Through Dams," *Journal New England Water Works Association*, July, 1937.

4:2 K. Terzaghi, *Theoretical Soil Mechanics*, John Wiley & Sons, Inc., New York, 1943, p. 258.

4:3 T. A. Middlebrooks, "Seepage Control for Large Earth Dams," *Third Congress of Large Dams*, Vol. 2, Stockholm, 1948.

4:4 N. F. Williams, Personal Communication with G. F. Sowers, 1950.

4:5 T. W. Smith and G. V. Stafford, "Horizontal Drains on California Highways," *Journal of the Soil Mechanics and Foundations Division, Proceedings, ASCE*, Vol. 83, SM3, July, 1957.

4:6 *The Wellpoint System in Principle and Practice*, Griffin Wellpoint Corporation, New York, 1950.

4:7 L. Casagrande, "Electro-Osmotic Stabilization of Soils," *Journal Boston Society of Civil Engineers*, Vol. 39, January, 1952, p. 51.

4:8 F. E. Richart, "A Review of the Theories for Sand Drains," *Journal of the Soil Mechanics and Foundations Division, Proceedings, ASCE*, Vol. 83, SM3, July, 1957.

4:9 *Vertical Sand Drains for Stabilization of Embankments*, Bulletin 115, Highway Research Board, Washington, 1955.

4:10 A. W. Johnson, "Frost Action in Roads and Airfields," *Special Report 1*, Highway Research Board, Washington, 1952.

4:11 G. Beskow, "Soil Freezing and Frost Heaving with Special Applications to Roads and Railroads," *Swedish Geotechnical Society 26th Yearbook*, Series C, No. 375, 1935 (translated by J. O. Osterberg, Northwestern University, 1957).

4:12 A. Casagrande, "Discussion on Frost Heave," *Proceedings Highway Research Board*, Washington, 1931, p. 168.

4:13 "The Unified Soil Classification System—Appendix B, Characteristics of Soil Groups Pertaining to Roads and Airfields," *Technical Memorandum 3–57*, Waterways Experiment Station, Vicksburg, March, 1953.

4:14 T. W. Lambe, "Modification of Frost Heaving Soils with Additives," *Bulletin 135*, Highway Research Board, Washington, 1956.

Suggestions for Further Study

1. References 4:1, 4:6, and 4:10 above.

2. D. W. Taylor, *Fundamentals of Soil Mechanics*, John Wiley & Sons, Inc., New York, 1949.

3. C. N. Zangar, "Theory and Problems of Water Percolation," *Engineering Monograph No. 8*, U.S. Bureau of Reclamation, Denver, 1953.

4. *The Moretrench Wellpoint System*, Moretrench Corporation, Rockaway, N.J., 1954.

5. *Stang Wellpoint System*, Catalog 50-2. Omaha (undated).

6. "Fundamental and Practical Concepts of Soil Freezing," *Bulletin 168*, Highway Research Board, Washington, 1957.
7. "Water and its Conduction in Soils," *Special Report 40*, Highway Research Board, Washington, 1959.
8. R. T. Martin, "Rhythmic Ice Banding in Soil," *Bulletin 218*, Highway Research Board, Washington, 1959.

PROBLEMS

4:1 a. Draw a flow net for seepage under a vertical sheet pile wall penetrating 25 ft into a uniform stratum of sand 50 ft thick; $k = 0.03$ cm per sec.

     b. If the water level on one side of the wall is 35 ft above the sand and on the other side of the wall is 5 ft above the sand, compute the quantity of seepage per foot width of wall.

4:2 Draw the flow net for seepage under a concrete dam that is 120 ft long and rests on a 35-ft thick uniform stratum of silty sand. Bottom of the dam is 5 ft below upper surface of silty sand. Compute the quantity of seepage if the head on the dam is 65 ft and the permeability of the soil is 0.0003 cm per sec.

4:3 Draw the flow net for an earth dam 80 ft high, 15-ft crest width with a slope of 2.5 (horizontal) to 1 (vertical) upstream and 2 to 1 downstream. Dam rests on a 25-ft thick stratum of soil with the same permeability. Headwater level is 70 ft above base of dam; tailwater is 10 ft above base of dam.

4:4 Compute the hydraulic gradient required to produce a "quick" condition at the surface of a level mass of sand through which water flows vertically upward. The void ratio is 0.63 and the specific gravity of solids is 2.66.

4:5 Compute the safety against boiling in problem 4:1 if the soil void ratio is 0.42 and the specific gravity of solids is 2.67.

4:6 Specify the grain size distribution of soils that would serve as satisfactory filters for the soils given in problem 1:14.

4:7 Sketch a wellpoint system for draining an excavation that is 55 ft wide at the bottom and extends 57 ft below the water table. Show stages of construction by separate diagrams.

4:8 a. Which of the soils listed in problem 3:3 would you consider for drainage with wellpoints?

     b. Which of the soils listed in problem 1:14 could be drained with wellpoints?

4:9 A long excavation is 20 ft deep and 12 ft wide at the bottom. The ground water table is normally at a depth of 10 ft below the ground surface. A single line of wellpoints extends 10 ft below the bottom of the excavation and is 16 ft from the center line of the excavation. The soil is fine sand, with $k = 0.01$ cm per sec, and it is underlaid at a depth of 35 ft by rock. The ground water table remains at its original level 200 ft from the excavation and is lowered 15 ft below its normal elevation along the line of the points.

    a. Draw the flow net for seepage into the wells, assuming the line of wells to be one continuous slot in the ground.

    b. Compute the quantity of water pumped per well if the wells are 6 ft apart.

    c. At what level should the header be placed?

4:10 Which of the soils in problem 3:3 would you expect to be susceptible to frost action. Is this confirmed by Table 4:2?

5 ... FOUNDATIONS

Foundation construction is one of the oldest of man's arts. The prehistoric lake dwellers of Europe built their homes on long wood poles driven securely into soft lake bottoms; the ancient Egyptians built their monuments on mats of stone resting on bed rock, and the Bible confirms this by stating that solid rock is more secure than shifting sand. The Babylonians found only deep alluvium in their flood plains between the Tigris and Euphrates, which settled under the weight of their cities. Buildings and walls were supported on mats of masonry, and adjacent parts of structures were provided with sliding connections so that they could settle different amounts without cracking apart. The artisans of the Middle Ages supported their masterpieces on inverted tables of stone, on rafts of timber, or on wood piling, following rules laid down by Roman builders before them. Until the twentieth century, however, the design of foundations was based entirely on past experience, ancient rules, and guesswork. Soil mechanics has given the foundation engineer a powerful tool with which he can analyze stresses and strains in the substructure, in the same way he does the superstructure, and formulate a rational design to fit the structure to the soil.

5:1 Essentials of a Good Foundation

The *foundation* is the supporting part of a structure. The term is usually restricted to the member that transmits the superstructure load to the earth, but in its complete sense it includes the soil and rock below. It is a transition or structural connection whose design depends on the characteristics of both the structure and the soil. A satisfactory foundation must meet three requirements:

150

(1) It must be placed at an adequate depth to prevent frost damage, heave, undermining by scour, or damage from future construction nearby.
(2) It must be safe against breaking into the ground.
(3) It must not settle enough to disfigure or damage the structure.

These requirements should be considered in the order named. The last two are capable of reasonably accurate determination through methods of soil mechanics, but the first involves consideration of many possibilities, some far beyond the realm of engineering. During the long period of time a soil must support a structure, it may be changed by many man-made and natural forces. These should be carefully evaluated in choosing the location for a structure and particularly in selecting the type of foundation and the minimum depth to which it must extend.

The surface zones of many soils change volume regularly with the seasons. In much of the United States, frost action swells the ground in winter, which means foundations should be placed below the maximum depth of frost penetration. This can be determined by local experience or estimated from Fig. 4:18.

Clay soils, particularly those with high plasticity, shrink large amounts on drying and expand when wet. In regions having pronounced wet and dry seasons, the soils close to the ground surface expand and contract. The outer walls move the most, while the inside, where the soil is protected from the sun and the rain, moves the least. In normally moist regions a prolonged dry spell can cause soil shrinkage and foundation settlement. Accelerated drying and settlement can be brought on by certain types of vegetation that extract moisture from the soil or by boilers and kilns that heat the soil abnormally. In very dry regions the opposite occurs. Added moisture from leaking pipes, irrigation, and even watering lawns can cause a desiccated clay to expand and lift a structure. In most cases the volume change becomes less with increasing depth, and if possible, foundations are placed below the volume-change zone.[5:1] Other methods of handling high volume change are given in Art. 5:8.

The scour of river bottoms, especially during periods of flood, has resulted in a number of bridge failures. This occurs in two ways: the normal scour of the river bed and the outsides of bends due to the increased velocity of flow during floods, and the accelerated scour caused by the obstruction offered by the bridge pier to the flow. The first is a characteristic of the stream, and the amount can be estimated by correlating the height of water surface rise during a flood to the increase in depth of the river bottom. In many streams with a sand or gravel bottom a foot rise of the surface is accompanied by a foot or more of scour.[5:2] The accelerated scour can be minimized by good hydraulic design including streamlining the piers and aligning them with the direction of flow.[5:3]

Ice is a serious problem with bridge piers and marine structures such as docks and wharves. Impact of floating ice, carried by river or tidal currents, can cause serious damage. The weight of ice and frozen spray can become great enough to overturn light structures.

All foundations should be designed with allowances for future excavation and construction. Bridge piers must be located to provide clear navigation channels and must be placed deep enough to allow for future dredging of the channel. Construction operations in congested city areas often affect building foundations. The undermining of foundations by deep excavation and subway tunneling can result in the settlement and failure of buildings that have stood safely for years. In such cases the contractors responsible for the damage have been liable, but it is usually cheaper in the long run if such trouble is anticipated when the foundations are designed. Many building codes make a contractor liable for damage to adjacent property only if his excavation is deeper than 10 ft.

Ground water is a factor in several ways. First, excavation below the ground water level is expensive and often hazardous because upward seepage loosens sands and tends to create a quick condition, and water standing over exposed clays may soften them. Second, when the ground water level is above the lowest floor, seepage into the structure and hydrostatic uplift become serious problems. Third, changes in the elevation of the water table have caused much trouble. In cities the water level drops because of drainage into sewers and deep excavations or because of pumping for water supply. This may increase building settlements by increasing soil stresses, or it may cause rotting of timbers formerly submerged well below the water level. On the other hand, if the water level rises through flooding, protracted rainfall, or broken water mains, soil strength is decreased and failures may occur. In some cases watertight structures such as empty concrete swimming pools and buried tanks have floated out of their normal locations because of the high water table that normally occurs in late winter and spring.

Underground cavities such as mines, caves, and sewers are hazards to foundations because they sometimes collapse from overload or structural deterioration. Piping or internal erosion of soil into leaky sewers or cavities likewise can cause trouble. If possible, foundations should be moved from these defects or corrective measures taken to make them harmless.

5:2 Stability—Bearing Capacity

The bearing capacity of a soil, often termed its *stability*, is the ability of the soil to carry a load without failure within the soil mass. It is analogous to the ability of a beam to carry a load without breaking. The load-carrying capacity of soil varies not only with its strength but also with the magnitude and distribution of the load. When a load Q is applied to a soil in gradually increasing amounts, the soil deforms, making a load-settlement curve similar to a stress–strain curve. When the critical or

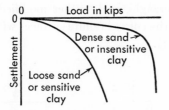

Fig. 5:1 Load settlement.

failure load, Q_0, is reached, the rate of deformation increases. The load-settlement curve goes through a point of maximum curvature, indicating failure within the soil mass. Different curves (Fig. 5:1) are obtained, depending on the character of the soil that is loaded. Dense sand and insensitive clay usually show a sharp sudden failure, whereas loose sand and sensitive clay show a more gradual transition associated with progressive failure.

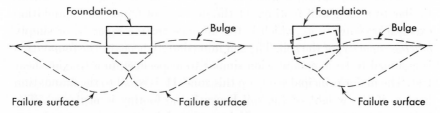

Fig. 5:2 Failure surfaces beneath foundations.

If the soil is observed during loading by means of a glass-sided model or by an excavation adjacent to a full-sized foundation, it will be seen that failure takes place in a number of stages. First the soil beneath the foundation deflects downward and bulges outward like a barrel; second there is local shear or cracking of the soil around the perimeter of the foundation; third a cone or wedge of soil forms beneath the footing which forces the soil downward and outward; and finally, in most soils a continuous surface of shear develops, as shown in Fig. 5:2. The foundation moves rapidly down and may tip, and a bulge of soil pushes up around the foundation. Such a *bearing-capacity failure* is not common, but it almost always results in a complete failure of the structure.

No exact mathematical analysis has been derived for analyzing such a failure. A number of approximate methods that have been developed are based on simplified representations of the complex failure surface and of the soil properties.

Bearing-Capacity Analysis   A simple and conservative analysis was developed by Bell, extended by Terzaghi, and further modified by the authors. The method approximates the curved failure surfaces with a pair of straight lines, as shown in Fig. 5:3.

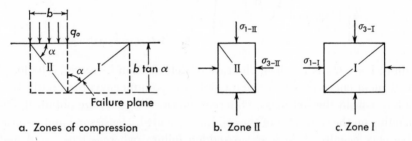

a. Zones of compression   b. Zone II   c. Zone I

Fig. 5:3   Assumed straight-line failure planes and prismatic zones of triaxial shear or compression beneath a uniform load q_0 of width b.

A foundation having a width of b and an infinite length is assumed, similar to a long wall footing. At the moment of failure the foundation exerts a pressure of q_0, which is the *ultimate bearing capacity*, or simply *bearing capacity*, of the soil. The soil immediately beneath the foundation is assumed to be in compression similar to a specimen in a triaxial shear test. The major principal stress on this zone, II, is equal to the foundation load q_0 if the weight of the soil beneath the footing is neglected. The minor principal stress on zone II is produced by the resistance of zone I to being compressed. Zone I is like a triaxial shear specimen lying on its side with the major principal stress horizontal. At the moment of foundation failure both zones shear simultaneously, and the minor principal stress on zone II, σ_{3-II}, equals the major principal stress on zone I, σ_{1-I}.

The minor principal stress on zone I is provided by the average vertical stress caused by the soil's own dead weight and any surcharge q'. The

surcharge (Fig. 5:4) is any permanent confining pressure above the foundation level such as the weight of a basement floor or the weight of soil
above the foundation level:

$$q' = \gamma D_f. \tag{5:1}$$

The height of the failure zone is $b \tan \alpha$, where α is the angle of the failure
zone, $\alpha = 45 + (\phi/2)$. The average minor principal stress due to soil
weight is therefore $(\gamma b/2) \tan \alpha$. The total minor principal stress is
therefore

$$\sigma_{3-\mathrm{I}} = q' + \frac{\gamma b}{2} \tan \alpha. \tag{5:2a}$$

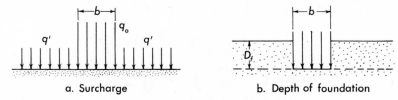

a. Surcharge   b. Depth of foundation

Fig. 5:4   Surcharge and depth of foundation.

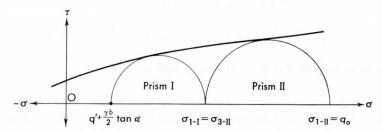

Fig. 5:5   Mohr's circle analysis of bearing capacity based on straight-line
failure planes and prismatic zones of triaxial shear.

If the minor principal stress is known, the major principal stress on zone I
can be found graphically by Mohr's circle (Fig. 5:5). Since this is equal to
the minor principal stress on zone II, a second Mohr circle will give the
major principal stress on zone II, the ultimate bearing capacity:

$$\sigma_{1-\mathrm{II}} = q_0. \tag{5:2b}$$

The graphical analysis can be used in any soil, regardless of the shape of
the Mohr envelope. If the Mohr envelope can be approximated by a
straight line of the form

$$s = c' + p \tan \phi', \tag{2:28}$$

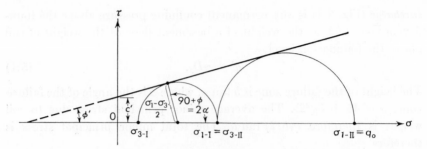

Fig. 5:6 Mohr's circle analysis based on a straight-line Mohr's envelope.

the ultimate bearing capacity can also be derived analytically from the trigonometry of the Mohr circle (Fig. 5:6):

$$\frac{\sigma_1 - \sigma_3}{2} = \left(\frac{c'}{\tan \phi'} + \frac{\sigma_1 + \sigma_3}{2}\right) \sin \phi',$$

$$\sigma_1 = \sigma_3 \left(\frac{1 + \sin \phi'}{1 - \sin \phi'}\right) + 2c' \left(\frac{\cos \phi'}{1 - \sin \phi'}\right),$$

$$\sigma_1 = \sigma_3 \tan^2 \alpha + 2c' \tan \alpha. \tag{5:2c}$$

$$\sigma_{1-I} = \left(q' + \frac{\gamma b}{2} \tan \alpha\right) \tan^2 \alpha + 2c' \tan \alpha,$$

$$q_0 = \sigma_{1-II} = \left[\left(q' + \frac{\gamma b}{2} \tan \alpha\right) \tan^2 \alpha + 2c' \tan \alpha\right] \tan^2 \alpha + 2c' \tan \alpha,$$

$$q_0 = \sigma_{1-II} = \frac{\gamma b}{2} \tan^5 \alpha + 2c' (\tan \alpha + \tan^3 \alpha) + q' \tan^4 \alpha. \tag{5:2d}$$

This is a general expression for the ultimate bearing capacity for any soil with a straight-line Mohr envelope. It can be used for a cohesionless soil by setting $c' = 0$ and for a saturated clay in undrained shear by setting $\phi' = 0$, $c = c'$ and $\tan \alpha = 1$.

General Bearing-Capacity Equation—Terzaghi–Meyerhof The equation for bearing capacity can be rewritten in a simple form:

$$q_0 = \frac{\gamma b}{2} N_\gamma + c' N_c + q' N_q. \tag{5:3}$$

The symbols N_γ, N_c, and N_q are *bearing-capacity factors* that are functions of the angle of internal friction. The term containing factor N_γ shows the influence of soil weight and foundation width, that of N_c shows the influence of the cohesion, and that of N_q shows the influence of the surcharge. The values of these factors for different values of ϕ (or ϕ') are given on Fig. 5:7.

This general expression was also derived by Terzaghi[5:4] from a more rigorous analysis of bearing capacity. It is based on approximating the surface of shear by a combination of straight lines and logarithmic spirals. The analysis was later improved by Meyerhof, but the results are expressed in the same form. Meyerhof's values for the bearing-capacity factors are given on Fig. 5:7.

Both the Terzaghi and the Meyerhof analyses assume the development of the full shear surface and complete shear failure. However, very loose sands and highly sensitive clays usually fail by progressive failure when

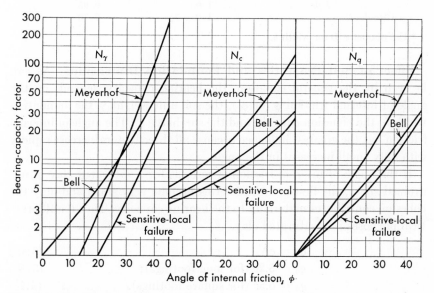

Fig. 5:7   Bearing-capacity factors for general bearing-capacity equation. (Adapted from Meyerhof.[5:5])

local cracking develops around the foundation or when the cone or wedge of soil under the foundation forms. Terzaghi suggested an empirical reduction to the bearing-capacity factors for this condition. The reduced Meyerhof factors, which apply to sands having a relative density of less than 20 or to clays with a sensitivity of more than 10, are also shown on Fig. 5:7. The factors of the simplified Bell analysis fall between the limiting values of the more accurate one.

Rectangular and Circular Foundations   Both the Bell–Terzaghi and the Terzaghi-Meyerhof analyses assume an infinitely long foundation. When the foundation has a limited length, shear develops on surfaces at right angles to those previously described, and the bearing-capacity factors N_c and N_γ are changed. Correction factors to be multiplied by the bearing-capacity factors are given in Table 5:1, where L is the foundation length and b the width.

Table 5:1   CORRECTION FACTORS FOR RECTANGULAR
AND CIRCULAR FOUNDATIONS

Shape of Foundation	Correction for N_c	Correction for N_γ
Square	1.25	0.85
Rectangular $L/b = 2$	1.12	0.90
$L/b = 5$	1.05	0.95
Circular*	1.2	0.70

* Use diameter D for width b.

Effect of Soil Properties and Foundation Dimensions   As can be seen by the general equation, the bearing capacity depends on the angle of internal friction ϕ (or ϕ'), the soil unit weight γ, the foundation width b, the cohesion c (or c'), and the surcharge q'. The angle of internal friction has the greatest influence because all three factors increase rapidly with only small increases in the angle.

If the angle of internal friction is zero, as for a saturated clay in undrained shear, the first and third terms become very small and only the cohesion contributes materially to the bearing capacity. Thus for all practical purposes in a saturated clay,

$$q_0 = cN_c; \tag{5:4a}$$
$$q_0 = 5.2c \text{ (for long footings);} \tag{5:4b}$$
$$q_0 = 6.5c \text{ (for square footings).} \tag{5:4c}$$

Both the first term and the third term in the equation depend on the unit weight of the soil. When the shear zone is above the water table (the bottom of the footing a height of about b above the water), the full soil unit weight is used in computations. When the water table is at the base of the foundation, the submerged unit weight, $\gamma' = \gamma - \gamma_w$, must be used in the first term. The effect is to reduce the bearing capacity by about one-half. If the water table is above the bottom of the footing, the surcharge weight is also affected.

The first term of the equation varies in direct proportion to the foundation width. This means that in cohesionless soils such as sands, the bearing capacity of small foundations is low and that of large foundations is high. Estimating the bearing capacity of sand by small scale tests can be misleading because the bearing capacity of a full-sized foundation will be much higher. In saturated clays in undrained shear, foundation width has little effect on bearing capacity.

The third term is proportional to the surcharge q'. For a saturated clay where ϕ is zero and $N_q = 1$, the contribution of surcharge to bearing capacity is small. In a soil with a high angle of internal friction, a small amount of surcharge produces a large amount of bearing capacity.

5:3 Stress and Settlement

When a load, such as the weight of a structure, is placed on the surface of a soil mass, the soil deflects, resulting in settlement of the structure. This is not a unique property of soils but one shared by all materials. In the same way that the deflection of a beam may be the limiting factor in structural design, the settlement of loads on soil is often the controlling factor in foundation design.

Settlement of the soil produced by loading comes from two sources: the change in void ratio of the soil, and the distortion or change in shape of the soil immediately beneath the load. The first is termed *compression settlement;* and the second, *distortion settlement* or *contact settlement.*

Both the compression and distortion settlements depend on the stresses produced in the soil by the foundation or other surface loads. By making simplifying assumptions about the physical properties of the soil, the stresses can be computed by the theories of elasticity. The settlements are then found from the stresses, using the physical properties of the soil determined by laboratory tests.

Stresses Due to Soil Weight   The initial vertical effective stress in a soil mass before a structure is built is approximately the weight of the soil minus the neutral stress. At a depth of z in a homogeneous soil,

$$\bar\sigma_0 = \gamma z - u. \tag{5:5}$$

If the soil consists of different strata, each with a different unit weight, the vertical stress at any level is equal to the sum of their loads minus the neutral stress.

Changes in the neutral stress can play an important part in the settlement of a structure. Lowering the ground water table at a site can increase the effective stress and produce settlement comparable to that produced by the weight of a building. In one case, draining a site prior to excavation lowered the water table beneath an adjoining building so much that the resulting settlement caused the building to split apart.

Example 5:1 Compute the effective stresses at a depth of 25 ft before and after the ground water table was lowered from 5 ft below the surface to 10 ft below the surface. The soil weighs 130 lb/cu ft below the water table and 110 lb/cu ft above.

Load	Before Lowering Water	After Lowering Water
Soil above water table	$5 \times 110 =$ 550 psf	$10 \times 110 =$ 1100 psf
Soil below water table	$20 \times 130 =$ 2600	$15 \times 130 =$ 1950
Neutral Stress	$-20 \times 62.4 =$ -1248	$-15 \times 62.4 =$ -936
	1902 psf	2114 psf

Lowering the water table 5 ft increased the stress 212 psf.

Stresses Due to Surface Loads When a load is applied to the

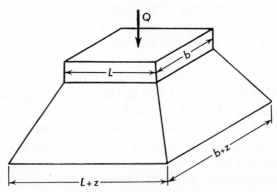

Fig. 5:8 Approximate method for computing the average increase in vertical stress at a depth of z beneath a rectangular foundation with dimensions $L \times b$. Foundation is assumed to be supported by a pyramid of soil whose sides slope at 2 (vertical) to 1 (horizontal).

surface of the soil mass, the vertical stress within the mass increases. If the soil were a series of independent columns, the load would be supported by the column immediately beneath it and the others would feel no change. The soil, however, is a coherent mass with the columns of soil interconnected elastically. Load at one point is transferred throughout the mass, spreading laterally with increasing depth.

As a very crude approximation, it can be assumed that load spreads through the soil as though it were supported by a flat-topped pyramid, as shown in Fig. 5:8. The sides of the pyramid are sloped 2 (vertical) to 1 (horizontal), which means that the base of the pyramid becomes 1 ft larger in length and width for each foot increase in depth. The average stress increase in the soil at any depth z beneath a foundation whose dimensions are L and b and which has a load of Q and a pressure of q is

$$\Delta\sigma_z = \frac{Q}{(L+z)(b+z)} = \frac{qLb}{(L+z)(b+z)}. \tag{5:6}$$

This approximation is useful in preliminary studies of settlement. It can be misleading because it fails to show the variation in stress at a uniform depth, and it does not indicate any stresses beyond the pyramid.

A more accurate representation of the stress distribution can be obtained from various theories of elasticity. These show that a load applied to the soil increases the vertical stress throughout the entire mass. The increase is greatest directly under the load, as shown in Fig. 5:9, but

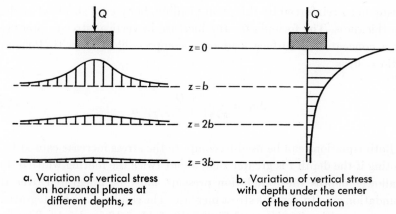

a. Variation of vertical stress on horizontal planes at different depths, z

b. Variation of vertical stress with depth under the center of the foundation

Fig. 5:9   Vertical stresses in a soil mass due to a load Q applied to the ground surface by a square foundation of width b.

extends infinitely far in all directions. As depth increases, the concentration of stress directly beneath the load decreases, but at any depth, if the increases in stress were to be integrated over the area to which they applied, the total force would equal the applied load Q. Near the surface the stress distribution depends on the size of the loaded area and on the contact pressure distribution, but at depths greater than about twice the width of the loaded area the stress distribution is practically independent of the way Q is applied.

Many formulas based on the theory of elasticity have been used to compute soil stresses. They are all similar and differ only in the assumptions made to represent the elastic conditions of the soil mass. One of the most widely used formulas is that published by Boussinesq, a French mathematician, in 1885 and adapted to soil engineering by Jurgenson.[5:6] He assumed a homogeneous, elastic, isotropic mass that extended infinitely in all directions below a level surface. A concentrated load of Q is applied to the surface of the mass, and the increase in vertical stress, $\Delta\sigma_z$, at a depth z and at a horizontal distance of r from the point of application of Q is calculated by the formula:

$$\Delta\sigma_z = \frac{3Q}{2\pi} \frac{z^3}{(r^2 + z^2)^{5/2}}. \qquad (5:7)$$

Westergaard in 1938 published a formula that more closely represents the elastic conditions of a stratified soil mass. He assumed a homogeneous, elastic mass reinforced by thin, non-yielding, horizontal sheets of negligible thickness. The formula for the increase in vertical stresses produced by a concentrated surface load on a compressible soil (with Poisson's ratio $= 0$) is

$$\Delta\sigma_z = \frac{Q}{\pi z^2[1 + 2(r/z)^2]^{3/2}} \qquad (5:8)$$

Both equations can be used to compute the stress increase caused by a footing if the depth z is greater than about twice the footing width b. For shallower depths the foundation pressure must be integrated over the foundation area to give the stress increase. The results of such integrations are presented in the charts of Figs. 5:10, 5:11, 5:12, and 5:13. The first two give contours of equal stress beneath foundations having widths of b and which exert a uniform pressure of q on the soil surface. The left side of each chart is for an infinitely long foundation and the right side for a square foundation. The depth and horizontal distances are expressed in terms of the foundation width b. The stress contours are expressed in fractions of the foundation pressure q. When the foundation is rectangular, the chart for a square foundation can be used with little error by assuming $b = \sqrt{A}$, where A is the foundation area.

Figures 5:12 and 5:13 are circular charts originally devised by Newmark.[5:8] The foundation is drawn on tracing paper to such a scale that the depth z, at which the stresses are to be computed, is equal (on the same scale) to the key line x-x on the chart. The paper is placed over the chart so that the point at which the stresses are to be computed is at the circle center. The number of squares covered by the foundation are counted.

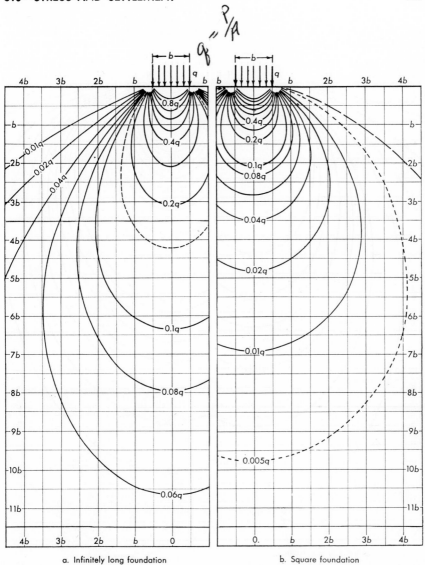

a. Infinitely long foundation   b. Square foundation

Fig. 5:10   Contours of equal vertical stress beneath a foundation in a semi-infinite
homogeneous isotropic elastic solid—the Boussinesq analysis. Stresses
given as functions of the uniform foundation pressure q; distances and
depths given as functions of the footing width b.

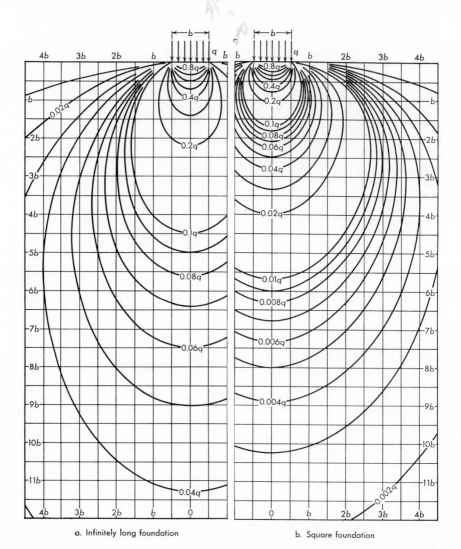

a. Infinitely long foundation   b. Square foundation

Fig. 5:11 Contours of equal vertical stresses beneath a foundation in a semi-infinite,
homogeneous, thinly stratified material—the Westergaard analysis.
Stresses given as functions of the uniform foundation pressure q; distances
and depths given as functions of the footing width b.

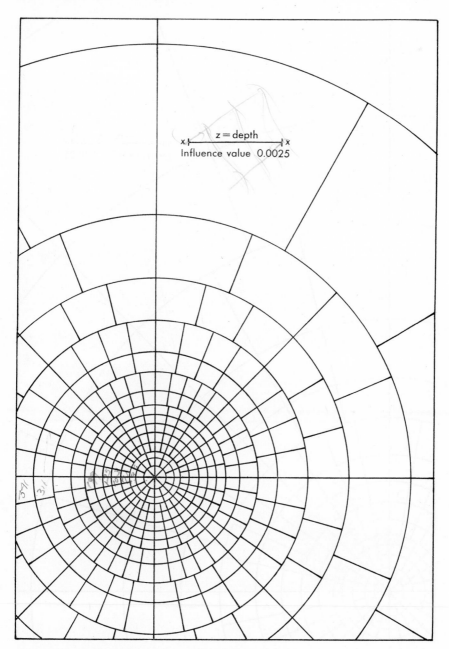

Fig. 5:12 Influence chart for computing vertical stresses beneath a uniformly loaded foundation on a semi-infinite homogeneous isotropic elastic soil— the Boussinesq analysis. (Adapted from N. Newmark; chart, courtesy of Soil Engineering Laboratory, Georgia Institute of Technology.)

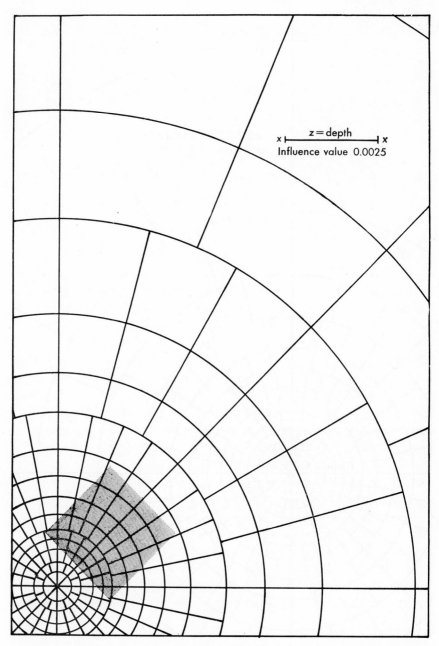

Fig. 5:13   Influence chart for computing vertical stresses beneath a uniformly loaded
foundation on a semi-infinite homogeneous thinly stratified soil—the
Westergaard analysis. (Adapted from N. Newmark; chart, courtesy of
Soil Engineering Laboratory, Georgia Institute of Technology.)

This number, multiplied by the foundation pressure and the chart influence value 0.0025, gives the stress increase at that depth.

Example 5:2   Compute the stress increase at a depth of 10 ft and at 8 ft from the center of a footing that is 10 ft square and which exerts a stress of 3000 psf on a stratified soil.

(a) Using Fig. 5:11, right side: The depth of the point, 10 ft, equals b. The horizontal distance, 8 ft, equals $0.8b$. From the chart, the contour is 0.09.

$$\Delta \sigma_z = 0.09 \times 3000 = 270 \text{ psf}$$

(b) Using Fig. 5:13: The footing (shaded area) covers 36 squares.

$$\Delta \sigma_z = 36 \times 0.0025 \times 3000 = 270 \text{ psf}$$

When several loads act simultaneously, such as the footings of a building, the total stress increase at a point is the sum of the stress increases produced by each load acting independently.

Computing Compression Settlement   The compression settlement for each soil stratum is computed by using the average initial stress, average stress increase, and the stress–void-ratio curve for the soil found by the laboratory consolidation test. The settlements for all the compressible strata are then added to obtain the total for that point.

The average initial effective stress in each stratum is the same as the initial stress at the middle of the stratum because the stress increases in direct proportion to the depth. The average increase in stress, however, is not the same as the stress at the stratum middle because the stress increase-depth relation is not linear. If the stratum is thin and relatively deep, it is sufficient to use the middle stress as the average. If the stratum is thicker than the footing width and if its depth is less than twice the footing width, it should be divided into thinner substrata and the average stresses computed for each.

The initial void ratio corresponding to the initial average effective stress and the change in void ratio caused by the average stress increase are found directly from the stress–void-ratio curve, as shown in Fig. 5:14. If it is certain that the stresses exceed any preconsolidation load, then the compression index can be used to compute the void-ratio change, as given by equation 2:10. The settlement is computed from the stratum (or substratum) thickness H by

$$\Delta H = \frac{H \, \Delta e}{1 + e_0}. \tag{2:11}$$

Compression settlement is often a slow process requiring years to develop fully, as shown in Fig. 5:14b. Estimates of the total settlement that will occur in any period can be made from the coefficient of consolidation of the soil by using equation 2:16. Since different strata are likely to have widely differing rates of consolidation, each stratum must be analyzed separately and the total settlement at any given time found from the sum of their individual settlements.

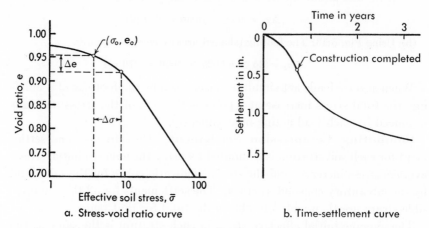

a. Stress-void ratio curve   b. Time-settlement curve

Fig. 5:14   Typical soil-stress void-ratio curve and time-settlement curve for a structure.

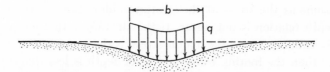

Fig. 5:15   Profile of distortion settlement of a uniformly loaded flexible foundation on a saturated clay

Distortion Settlement   Distortion settlement occurs because of a change in shape of the soil mass rather than because of a change in void ratio. The soil immediately under the foundation deflects downward and bulges laterally like a barrel, permitting the foundation above to settle.

Saturated clays and similar materials behave like a mass of gelatin or rubber when loaded because their modulus of elasticity is constant regardless of the confining stress. If a uniform pressure of q per square foot is applied over a cohesive soil, both the loaded area and the adjacent unloaded surface will deform in a sagging profile (Fig. 5:15). This is similar to the way in which a bed spring will deform or deflect downward if one sits in its center. The shape of the deformation curve can be computed by methods of the theory of elasticity. For a loaded square area of width b, the settlement ρ of a corner and of the center are given by the formulas:

$$\rho_{cor} = \frac{0.42qb}{E}; \tag{5:9a}$$

$$\rho_{cen} = \frac{0.84qb}{E}. \tag{5:9b}$$

The soil is assumed to have constant volume as the load is applied and to be homogeneous to a depth of at least twice the footing width. Distortion settlement of loaded rectangular areas may be found approximately by the above formulas, by assuming $b = \sqrt{A}$.

Distortion settlement of uniform loads on a noncohesive soil results in a deflection curve that is concave downward (Fig. 5:16). The soil near the edge of the loaded area is unconfined laterally and so is pushed aside by

| a. Narrow load | b. Wide load |

Fig. 5:16   Profile of distortion settlement of a uniformly loaded flexible foundation on a cohesionless soil.

the lateral pressure of the sand nearer the center of the area. The result is that the edges sag through lack of support. The sand at the center is confined by pressure from all sides; therefore it has a higher modulus of elasticity than the sand at the edges, which also means more settlement at the edge than at the center. So far no way has been devised for calculating the shape of the settlement curve. Experiments and observations indicate that the wider the loaded area, the flatter the curve at the center.

Uniform pressures are not common. They occur under large oil tanks where a relatively thin steel bottom rests directly on the soil or on a thin, concrete mat. Approximately uniform pressures occur over a large area when equally spaced columns carry their loads to a continuous, flexible foundation or to wide footings.

The most common way of applying a load to the soil surface is through a relatively rigid foundation of concrete.

The distortion settlement of rigid loads on saturated clays and similar soils whose modulus of elasticity is independent of confining pressure can be computed by the theory of elasticity. The following formula gives the distortion settlement ρ of square foundations of width b on a soil with a modulus of elasticity E. It can be used for other shapes by assuming $b = \sqrt{A}$, where A is the footing area:

$$\rho = \frac{0.6qb}{E}; \tag{5:10a}$$

$$\rho = \frac{0.6Q}{E\sqrt{A}}. \tag{5:10b}$$

This indicates that if the distortion settlement of an area with a load Q is to be reduced by one-half, the area must be increased four times. For equal contact settlement of loaded square areas under different total loads, the average pressure q must vary inversely as the total loads:

$$\frac{q_1}{q_2} = \frac{Q_2}{Q_1}. \tag{5:11}$$

Distortion settlement of rigid loads on non-cohesive soils cannot be estimated by theory. It depends largely on the relative density of the sand or gravel and is likely to be quite variable but small. Distortion settlement is essentially an elastic problem; usually it is of only minor magnitude and it takes place as rapidly as the load is applied.

Contact Pressure The pressure acting between the bottom of a foundation and the soil is the *contact pressure*. It is important in the design of the foundation structure because it determines shear and moment distribution. As shown in Figs. 5:15 and 5:16, the distortion settlement of a foundation that exerts a uniform pressure on the soil is not uniform. The foundation, therefore, must be flexible so that it can conform to the settlement and keep the pressure uniform. If the foundation is rigid, it cannot conform; it finds more support from the points that deflect the least, and it bridges over the areas that deflect the most. As a result there will be a redistribution of pressure, as shown in Fig. 5:17. The pressure will be greatest at the outside edges of a foundation on an elastic soil such as a saturated clay and greatest at the center of a foundation on a cohesionless soil. For very wide foundations on a cohesionless soil the pressure is uniform at the center but falls off at the edges where the confinement of the sand is less.

5:4 Settlement Observations

Whenever settlement exceeding $\frac{1}{2}$ in. is predicted for a structure, careful observations should be made to check the accuracy of the estimates.

So many assumptions are made in settlement studies that their accuracy is often poor, and the only way such studies can be improved is by correlating the actual, measured settlements with the predicted.

The first essential to accurate measurements is a stationary bench mark. This should be founded on bedrock if possible. In areas with deep soil such bench marks can be constructed by driving a 4-in. pipe into the soil, through all compressible strata. This pipe is cleaned out and the hole extended into the firm soil and rock strata below by boring with earth drills or a diamond drill (Chapter 10). A 2-in. pipe is placed inside the 4-in. outer casing and securely grouted into the firm stratum or rock. The inner pipe forms the bench mark and the outer pipe acts as a sleeve to insulate the inner pipe from the settling soil. The second essential is permanent reference points at different points on the structure. Readings of settlement should be taken once every few weeks during the con-

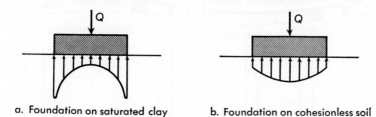

a. Foundation on saturated clay   b. Foundation on cohesionless soil

Fig. 5:17 Contact pressure on the base of rigid foundations.

struction period and once a year thereafter. Settlement can be read with a good engineer's level, or special water-level devices made for the purpose.

Settlement observations during construction often can give warning of trouble from other sources. Landslides, underground subsidences, and bearing-capacity failures usually begin with slow but gradually increasing settlement rates. Usually the trouble can be corrected before failure takes place if it is caught in time.

Excessive settlement usually leads to building cracks and in some cases structural failure. The engineer should recognize the causes of different types of cracking in order to correct them before structural failure results. Uniform settlement will produce no cracking except of water and sewer lines into the structure. Differential settlement can produce cracks, tipping of the structure, or both. The crack pattern depends on whether the center of the building or its edges settle more. The diagrams in Fig. 5:18 illustrate types of failure that may occur.

The concave settlement is the usual pattern for a uniformly loaded structure on a compressible soil. The zone of settlement is saucer shaped and extends well beyond the limits of the structure. Nearby buildings may be affected by the zone of settlement and develop new cracks. The convex pattern develops with wall-bearing structures or structures on loose sands.

Cracks often occur when footings are eccentrically loaded. This puts a bending moment into the base of the column or bearing wall and can cause failure. This is particularly true in outside bearing walls that are very close to the property line. The designer is tempted to make the footing wider inside the building than it is outside, and the result can be a crack, as shown in Fig. 5:18c and d.

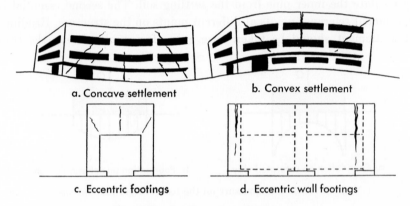

a. Concave settlement   b. Convex settlement

c. Eccentric footings   d. Eccentric wall footings

Fig. 5:18   Settlement crack patterns.

Tipping is serious in narrow, tall structures such as chimneys and bridge piers. It is likely to occur when the soil compressibility is not uniform. It can also develop when the major cause of the settlement is a heavy load at some distance from the tall structure, as shown in Fig. 5:19. The sagging settlement profile develops beneath the larger load and the tall but lighter structure tilts in that direction. Such settlement caused by the weight of an approach fill for a bridge resulted in the abutment tilting backward against the fill, as shown in Fig. 5:19b.

Not all cracks in structures are caused by settlement. Shrinkage of mortar or of concrete blocks and similar masonry units is a common cause of cracking. Plaster is likely to shrink differently from the wood or masonry base which supports it. Shrinkage cracks are usually vertical and horizontal and are of uniform width or become narrow at both ends. Thermal expansion and contraction are important causes of cracks in exterior walls.

Such cracks can be identified by their opening and closing with temperature changes. Vibration, shock, and earthquakes can cause cracking. Usually these have an x-pattern at the ends of walls and a $*$, or $+$, at the middle.

Gage marks on cracks can aid in studying their movement and in their identification. A straight pencil line is drawn across the crack at right angles to it and gage points are set a definite distance apart (such as 1 in.) on each side of the crack. Measurement of the gage distance at regular intervals will show how much and in which direction the crack is moving.

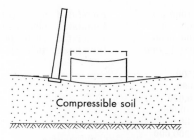

a. Tilt of smokestack caused by settlement profile of adjacent heavy building

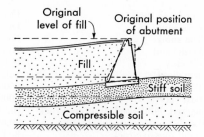

b. Backward tilt of bridge abutment from consolidation of compressible soil under fill weight

Fig. 5:19 Tilting of structures caused by adjacent heavy loads.

5:5 Allowable Pressure on Soil

After a foundation meets the requirements of location and minimum depth, two conditions remain that must be satisfied: First there must be adequate safety against a failure within the soil mass; and second the settlement of the foundation must not endanger the structure. It is obvious from the methods developed to analyze bearing capacity and settlement that these two conditions are completely independent of one another. For foundation design, however, it is desirable to know the maximum pressure that can be placed on soil without exceeding either of these two limits. This maximum is known as the *allowable soil pressure*, or *allowable soil loading* q_a.

Presumptive Bearing Pressure The oldest method of determining the allowable foundation pressure is to rely on past experience with similar soils in the region. Most engineers accumulate information on the success of their past designs, and these are used as a basis for future work. In many areas, such as the larger cities, the records of which design pressures were successful and which were not have been assembled and condensed in tabular form. These are called *presumptive bearing pressure* because it is presumed on the basis of past performance that the soil can support such a pressure without a bearing-capacity failure or excessive settlement. Most building codes include such tables, and they are often a helpful guide to local practice.

Table 5:2 gives presumptive bearing pressures based on the author's experiences for simple structures up to four stories.

Table 5:2   TYPICAL PRESUMPTIVE BEARING PRESSURES

Very loose sand	Dry 0–1000 psf	Inundated	0–600 psf
Loose sand	Dry 1000–3000	Inundated	600–2000
Firm sand	Dry 3000–6000	Inundated	2000–4000
Dense sand	Dry 6000–12,000	Inundated	4000–8000
Soft clay	0–1500		
Firm clay	1500–2500		
Stiff clay	2500–5000		
Hard clay	5000–10,000		
Layered, laminated, fractured rock	10,000–30,000		
Massive rock, occasional seams	30,000–80,000		
Sound massive rock	80,000–200,000		

(See Art. 3:6 for meaning of descriptive terms.)

Unfortunately the use of presumptive bearing pressures often leads to trouble. Most of the tables are based on experiences going back to the nineteenth century and on entirely different types of structures than are built today. The soil characteristics are defined only by a description, and often the most important properties are not mentioned. Sometimes the building code table is a copy of that from some other city and does not reflect local practice at all. Finally, the table does not reflect the influence of the size and weight of the structure. As a result the use of the table value does not always mean a safe, economical foundation. The engineer has just as much responsibility in determining the allowable foundation pressure for his structure as he has in determining the size of a beam or thickness of a floor slab, and to rely only on experience can be disastrous.

Load Test   The *load test* or *test plate* method of determining allowable soil pressure (Fig. 5:20) was developed because of the failures of the design tables. Essentially the load test is a model test of a foundation. A small plate, usually 1 ft square, is placed on the undisturbed soil and is loaded in increments. The results of the test are presented in a load-settlement curve of the test plate. Properly conducted and correctly interpreted, the load test is a valuable *aid* to rational design, but as usually conducted, it is a waste of time and money and often leads to a dangerous sense of false security.

A pit is dug to the level at which it is desired to determine the allowable soil pressure. The pit width should be at least five times the width of the test plate. The minimum size of the test plate is 1 ft square but larger sizes are desirable. A load is placed on the plate, as shown in Fig. 5:20, by means of a loading platform weighted with pig iron or lead or by jacking with calibrated hydraulic jacks against a beam held down by earth anchors or weights.[5:10] Loads should be applied in increments of one-fourth the estimated allowable soil pressure and increased until two times the estimated allowable soil pressure is reached for sands and gravels and until 2.5 times the estimated pressure is reached for clays. Settlement under each increment should be read to 0.001 in. and must be referred to a bench mark beyond the limits of the possible settlement profile. Each

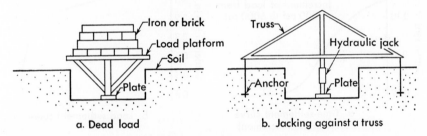

a. Dead load   b. Jacking against a truss

Fig. 5:20 Methods for making plate load tests.

increment should be maintained constant until the rate of settlement is less than 0.002 in. per hr, before adding another increment. The final increment should be maintained at least 4 hr before ending the test. A time-settlement curve (Fig. 5:21a) should be plotted on semilogarithmic coordinates for each increment of load. The semilog plot will show a break into a straight, nearly flat line, point A. This point should be selected as the "ultimate settlement" under each load increment. The loads and their corresponding ultimate settlements should be plotted to form a load-settlement curve (Fig. 5:21b). A definite break or the intersection of tangents to this curve represents the ultimate bearing capacity of a foundation the same *size*, *depth*, and *location* as the test plate.

The load test is useless unless its results are interpreted in terms of a full-size foundation. Interpretation must be based largely on theory because so few field observations have been reliable enough to correlate foundation performance with load test results. Since bearing capacity of footings on a clay soil is independent of the width of the loaded area, the critical pressure determined by the load test is the same for all footing sizes:

$$q_0 \text{ (foundation)} = q_0 \text{ (load test)}. \tag{5:12a}$$

In sands and gravels the bearing capacity increases in direct proportion to the width of the loaded area, and so the following correction should be made:

$$q_0 \text{ (foundation)} = q_0 \text{ (load test)} \times \left(\frac{\text{width foundation}}{\text{width test plate}}\right). \tag{5:12b}$$

If the soil is not homogeneous to a depth of at least the width of the pro-

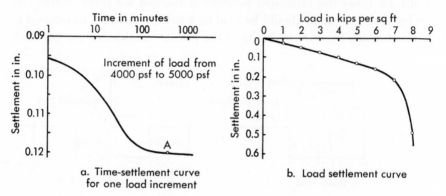

a. Time-settlement curve
for one load increment

b. Load settlement curve

Fig. 5:21 Plate load-test results.

posed foundation, the load test results are meaningless as far as bearing capacity is concerned.

The load test can be used to determine distortion settlement in a homogeneous soil, provided the soil is uniform to a depth of twice the footing width. For saturated clays, the distortion settlement at a given pressure per square foot varies directly with the width of the loaded area, or

$$\rho \text{ (foundation)} = \rho \text{ (test plate)} \times \left(\frac{b \text{ foundation}}{b \text{ plate}}\right). \tag{5:13a}$$

In sands no such simple relation exists, but from Terzaghi and Peck's work[5:11] the following expression is derived:

$$\rho \text{ (foundation)} = \rho \text{ (test plate)} \times \left[\frac{b_f(b_p + 1)}{b_p(b_f + 1)}\right]^2. \tag{5:13b}$$

In this the widths of both the foundation and the plate are in feet.

The distortion settlement of foundations that are 5 or more feet wide on sand is approximately three times the settlement of a 1 ft × 1 ft test plate with the same soil pressure or approximately two times the settlement of a 2 ft × 2 ft test plate. In partially saturated, cohesive soils the distortion settlement is probably somewhere in between that for sands and for saturated clays.

The load test cannot predict compression settlement. Compression requires time, particularly in the more critical soils such as clays, and the few hours or days allotted to the load test can allow only a negligible part of the total volume change to take place. Furthermore, if the compressible soil extends to any depth, the stresses throughout the stratum resulting from the loaded test plate will be very small. The same pressure applied by a wide foundation will produce much greater stresses in the deep stratum and correspondingly greater settlement.

Example 5:3   Compute stresses in soil stratum 1 ft thick, 10 ft below the ground surface, due to (a) load test, 1 ft × 1 ft, pressure 3000 psf; and (b) foundation, 8 ft × 8 ft, pressure also 3000 psf. Use approximate method for computing stress.

(1) Load plate:

$$\Delta\sigma = \frac{3000 \times 1 \times 1}{(10 + 1)(10 + 1)} = 24.8 \text{ psf.}$$

(2) Foundation:

$$\Delta\sigma = \frac{3000 \times 8 \times 8}{(10 + 8)(10 + 8)} = 590 \text{ psf.}$$

Rules for conducting load tests contained in various building codes usually prescribe the method of interpreting the tests. Too often strict observance of the rules leads to failure because the rules are usually based only on limited experience or guesswork. A load test cannot be the entire answer to the question of allowable soil pressure, for it answers only part (bearing capacity and distortion settlement) of the two basic conditions and that part only if a rational interpretation is made of the results.

5:6   Rational Procedure for Allowable Pressure and Design

A rational determination of allowable foundation pressure is similar to the design of other parts of the structure. First a trial pressure is assumed based on experience. Second the trial pressure is checked by a bearing-capacity analysis to determine the safety against soil failure. Third, if it is safe, an analysis is made of the settlement produced, to see if it is excessive. Fourth the trial pressure is revised to increase the safety, reduce the settlement, or improve the economy, depending on the analytical results.

In order to do this, the engineer must have accurate data on the soil below and the structure above the foundation. The soil data include the depth and thickness of the soil and rock strata, the level of ground water, and the physical properties of each soil, including its strength and compressibility. If the soil deposit is uniform, the analyses are based on the average properties of each material; if it is variable, the analyses are based on the worst combination of soil properties as determined from the tests.

The data required on the structure are the general features of the structure and its loads. The general features include the use or purpose, the elevations of the lowest floors and particularly basements and pits, the type of structural framing and its sensitivity to deflection, and the possibility of future additions. The load data required are the depth and extent of general excavation and filling and the dead loads and live loads on columns, including the amount of live load that is likely to be continuous. If the lowest floor is supported directly on the ground, its average sustained load is needed.

The *safety factor* of a foundation, SF, is the ratio of the ultimate bearing capacity q_0 to the actual foundation pressure q. The *safe bearing capacity* q_s is the ultimate bearing capacity divided by the minimum permissible safety factor SFM:

$$SF = \frac{q_0}{q}, \tag{5:14a}$$

$$q_s = \frac{q_0}{SFM}. \tag{5:14b}$$

The allowable foundation pressure q_a cannot exceed the safe bearing capacity, but it often is less.

Safety Factor   The safety factor required for design depends on how accurately the soil conditions and the structural loads are known and what hazards are involved in a bearing-capacity failure. Any future changes in the site, such as a rising water table or excavation adjacent to a footing that will reduce the surcharge, must be taken into account by the ultimate bearing-capacity equation or else included in the safety factor. For temporary construction work where a failure would be inconvenient but not disastrous, a safety factor of 1.5 is required. For most cases of structural design where there is reasonably accurate data on the soil and loadings, a safety factor of 2.5 is employed with dead load plus full live load. If a large part of the live load is not likely to develop, a minimum safety factor of 2 is permissible. When the conditions are questionable, a safety factor of 4 is sometimes warranted.

Permissible Settlement The settlement is computed by using the assumed foundation design pressure (not the ultimate bearing capacity). For foundations on soils that settle slowly, such as saturated clays, only the dead load plus any sustained live load is used in the analysis; but for partially saturated clays, silts, and organic soils, which usually settle rapidly, the dead plus total live load is used. In some cases it is necessary to compute the settlement of every column or part of a structure. In many cases it is sufficient to know the settlement of the more critical parts such as footings for delicate machinery, smoke stacks, and the heaviest columns.

The amount of settlement a structure can tolerate depends on its size and construction, and whether it is uniform or non-uniform. If all parts of the structure settle the same amount, the structure will not be damaged. Only access, drainage, and utility connections will be affected, and these can tolerate movements of several inches. Differential settlement causing tilting is important for floors, crane rails, machinery, and tall narrow structures such as stacks, and the limits are established by their operation. Differential settlement causing curvature affects the structure itself and is limited by the flexibility of its construction. Table 5:3 gives the maximum settlements that can be permitted. It is based on both theory and observations of structures that have suffered damage.[5:13,5:14]

Table 5:3 MAXIMUM ALLOWABLE SETTLEMENT

Type of Movement	Limiting Factor	Maximum Settlement
Total settlement	Drainage and access	6 in. to 24 in.
	Probability of differential settlement	
	Masonry walls	1 to 2 in.
	Framed buildings	2 to 4 in.
Tilting	Towers, stacks	$0.004b*$
	Rolling of trucks, stacking of goods	$0.01B*$
	Crane rails	$0.003B*$
Curvature	Brick walls in buildings	$0.0005B$ to $0.002B*$
	Reinforced concrete building frame	$0.003B*$
	Steel building frame, continuous	$0.002B*$
	Steel building frame, simple	$0.005B*$

NOTE: b is base width; B is column spacing.
* Differential settlement in distance b or B.

The allowable foundation pressure for each footing must satisfy both the requirements of safety and settlement. For convenience in its determination for each foundation, the results of the bearing capacity and settlement analyses should be expressed graphically, as shown in Fig. 5:22. The safe bearing pressure represents the upper limit without regard to settlement. Curves of equal settlement for different column loads or foundation sizes are also shown. A number of such charts are prepared, each for a different set of soil conditions, different shape of foundation, or for varying ground water and depth of excavation. From these the designer can select the allowable pressure that will keep the total settlement and differential settlement within limits.

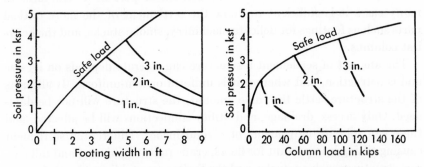

Fig. 5:22 Footing design charts showing safe bearing as the upper limit and curves for equal settlements of 1, 2, and 3 in.

Redesign Alternatives[5:12] When the analyses show that the assumed foundation pressure is not safe or that the settlement will be excessive, or when they indicate that the safety is so high and settlement so low that the foundation is uneconomical, a redesign is necessary. Ordinarily this is limited to the foundation, but it is often fruitful to extend the redesign to the structure and even to the soil.

The simplest procedure is to change the foundation. By reducing the design pressure, the safety factor against failure is increased. Reducing the pressure is not always effective in reducing settlement, however. If the compressible strata are at a shallow depth below the foundation, the settlement will be reduced almost in proportion to the pressure; but if the compressible layer is far below the foundation, a reduction in pressure may not reduce the settlement materially.

Example 5:4 What is the effect of reducing the foundation pressure from 6000 psf to 3000 psf on the stresses at a depth of 10 ft beneath a column supporting a load of 120,000 lb? A square footing at 6000 psf will be 4.5 ft wide, and at 3000 psf, 6.3 ft wide. From Fig. 5:11 the stress at 10 ft below the 6000-psf footing will be $6000 \times 0.06 = 360$ psf, and beneath the 3000-psf footing it will be $3000 \times 0.12 = 360$ psf. No change.

The limit in size is reached when the foundations touch and form a continuous footing. Such a continuous foundation can bridge over small soft areas, but it cannot reduce the dished-in settlement profile produced by thick compressible strata.

Increasing the foundation depth will increase the bearing capacity in homogeneous soils by increasing the surcharge, particularly if the soils have a high angle of internal friction. If the soil is stratified and becomes stronger with increasing depth, then depth will improve the bearing capacity; but if the soil deposit has a hard crust underlain by softer soil, an increase in depth will reduce the bearing. In most cases, increasing the depth will reduce settlement. However, if the compressible strata are deep, increasing the depth will bring the foundation closer to the source of trouble and will aggravate the settlement. Very deep foundations that transfer the load below the weak or compressible strata are considered in Chapter 6.

Sometimes great benefits can be had by changes in the structure. The column loads can be reduced by reducing the spacing. This helps if the bearing capacity is limited, but it will usually not reduce settlement appreciably because the total structural load is not changed materially. Substituting lightweight construction for conventional forms will reduce the total weight and benefit both the safety against failure and settlement. If the site is sufficiently large, the structure may be spread over a larger area and the concentration of load reduced, which will also benefit safety and settlement. If extensive fill is planned to support the ground floor, its weight is a major factor in settlement. For example, 5 ft of fill weigh as much as four stories of building. Eliminating such fill will reduce settlement materially. Changing the structure by making it so rigid that it will resist distortion is occasionally possible, as shown in Fig. 5:23. The floors and walls can be combined structurally to develop a box girder stiff enough to prevent differential settlement. Introducing trusses into the building frame can do the same thing in steel structures. For very small buildings a continuous mat can be made rigid if its thickness is about one-tenth its span, but the weight of the mat itself becomes a major load on the soil.

Making the structure flexible so that it can conform to the settlement is a simple method of preventing damage from differential movement. Simple structural framing, small wall panels that are not rigidly connected to the floors and columns, masonry walls with low-strength mortar, and ground floors that are reinforced, jointed, and keyed like a pavement will permit the maximum movement with minimum damage. Flexible construction is best adapted to wide, low buildings where the structural framing would ordinarily be light.

Reducing the net load on the soil by excavation (Fig. 5:23b) is a very old method for minimizing settlement. If the weight of the soil excavated equals the structural weight, there will be no increase in the stresses in the soil below and therefore little settlement. Such a design is often called

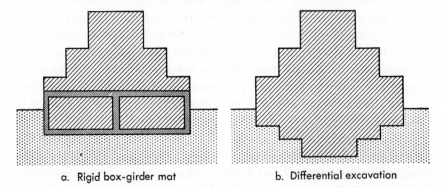

a. Rigid box-girder mat   b. Differential excavation

Fig. 5:23 Reducing differential settlement by changes in the structural framing or excavation.

"floating the structure," since the structure appears to be buoyed up by the weight of the soil displaced. The soil, however, is a solid that expands when the load is relieved by excavation and which recompresses when reloaded; therefore there will be some settlement even with a good balance. A perfect balance is impossible because of the variable live load in the structure and the variations in the unit weight of the soil excavated. A changing water table also can upset the balance. This method requires a very careful evaluation of the soil and loading conditions in order to be successful.[5:12]

Changing the soil to increase the safety or reduce the settlement includes drainage, densification, altering the soil by an additive, and changing to another site. Drainage improves the soil by reducing the neutral stress. In a cohesionless soil the bearing capacity is often doubled by lowering the water table below the foundation shear zone, but it must be permanent before it can be counted on in design. Reducing the neutral stress in a compressible soil will cause it to consolidate and become stronger and, of course, to settle. If the consolidation can be completed before the structure is built, the bearing capacity will be increased and the settlement reduced. Loss of drainage after construction is complete is not critical in the compressible soil and can be helpful because, as the neutral stress increases, the effective stress decreases.

Preconsolidating a compressible soil by a surcharge load is very effective in increasing strength and reducing settlement. In effect this is another form of drainage, by consolidation, and was discussed in Chapter 4. Stage loading makes it possible to improve the soil by the weight of the structure itself. For example, the soil at a riverside site was too weak to support with safety the full load of a grain elevator. The load was limited to half the capacity for the first year to maintain safety. The soil consolidated and became stronger and could then support the full load.

Densification of loose sands by shock and vibration is effective in increasing bearing capacity and reducing settlement. Altering the soil by injecting cementing agents, changing the chemistry of clays, and fusing it with heat are collectively termed *soil stabilization*. All these methods are discussed in Chapter 8.

Sometimes it is better to move to a different site. It is physically possible to design a satisfactory foundation for any site if enough money can be spent. However, the cost of foundations added to the cost of the property can make cheap real estate very expensive. A complete study of all the economic factors involved is required to determine if special foundations are worth their cost.

5:7 Footings and Mats

Footing Foundations A footing is an enlargement of a column or wall in order to reduce the pressure on the soil to the maximum allowable. Beneath a wall the footing may be continuous, forming a long, rectangular, loaded area, called a *wall footing*. Beneath a column the footing may be any shape, but economy in construction favors the square. Rectangular shapes are often used if clearances prevent squares, or two or more square footings may be joined to form a single, rectangular footing under several columns. Occasionally hexagonal footings are used, especially under smoke stacks or heavy machines, but the economy in materials of such shapes is usually overbalanced by the additional labor required for their construction.

Structurally the footing is a wide beam, acted on by a distributed load (the soil pressure) and supported by a concentrated force (the column). Modern practice calls for reinforced concrete, which is designed by the usual methods. The soil pressure is usually assumed to be acting uniformly over the footing. This is a conservative assumption for footings on sand but may be somewhat unsafe for footings on saturated clays. The soil pressure under a rigid load on clay is high at the outer edges of the loaded area and decreases to about half the average at the center. The pressure under a concrete footing will not have such extreme variation, owing to upward deflection of the footing edges, but it will not be uniform. Therefore it is well to be conservative in the structural design of footings on clay.

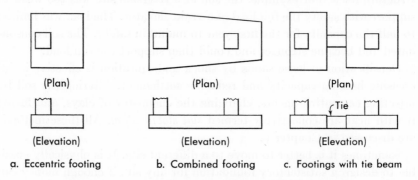

(Plan)	(Plan)	(Plan)
(Elevation)	(Elevation)	(Elevation)
a. Eccentric footing	b. Combined footing	c. Footings with tie beam

Fig. 5:24 Footing designs to avoid eccentric moments.

To avoid eccentricity, the centroid of the footing should coincide with the centroid of the load coming on it. Ordinarily this is no problem, but along the exterior walls where the property line limits the extent of the footing or where elevator pits, machinery, and utilities obstruct the space, a concentrically loaded footing is impossible. If the eccentricity is small, it is sometimes possible to design the footing and column to absorb the unbalanced moment (Fig. 5:24a). A better method is to combine two adjacent footings into one large footing, as shown in Fig. 5:24b. The footing should be proportioned so that its center of gravity is at the same point as the center of gravity of the two column loads. If the column spacing is large, two adjacent footings can be connected by a small tie beam that absorbs the eccentric moment (Fig. 5:24c).

Strap Foundations A *strap foundation* is a continuous footing that supports three or more columns in a straight line. It consists of a number of spread footings that have been connected together. Straps are employed for two reasons: to provide structural continuity and to achieve construction economy. When single footings are large and closely spaced in one direction, they can be combined to form a continuous shallow beam. This can bridge over small (less than half the column spacing) weak areas and achieve some economy through structural continuity. The strap foundation is often cheaper to build because the foundation excavation is a continuous trench rather than a series of isolated pits. The strap is designed like a continuous beam with a uniform load on one side and with concentrated supports on the other.

Mat Foundations A *mat* or *raft* is a combined footing supporting more than three columns not in the same line. The mat provides the greatest total foundation area for a given space and the minimum foundation pressure, and therefore the maximum safety against soil failure. If the compressible strata are located at a shallow depth, the mat will minimize the settlement. However, if the compressible strata are deep, it will have little effect and in some cases, because of its weight, can increase the settlement slightly.

A mat has other advantages. Like the strap it can bridge over small isolated soft areas in the foundation. It provides economy in design and construction by developing structural continuity and by permitting a uniform excavation depth. Cost comparisons between mats and large footings show that when the total area of the spread footings is more than from one-half to two-thirds the building area, a mat will be cheaper. Mats are employed when hydrostatic uplift must be resisted because the weight of the building is used to overcome the upward pressure.

The contact pressure of soil on the mat depends on the stiffness of the structure-foundation system and the settlement of the soil. If the structure-foundation system is flexible, the pressure will be relatively uniform. If the structure-foundation system is very rigid, the pressure distributions will be similar to those given in Fig. 5:17 and can be determined by a trial-and-error process. A pressure distribution is assumed. The settlement of the soil and the deflection of the structure resulting from this pressure are computed. If the soil settlement curve has the same shape as the structural deflection curve, the assumed pressure distribution is correct. If not, the assumed pressure is revised until the two curves are the same.

The structural design of a mat is similar to that of an inverted floor. Flat slab designs are used for small mats and have the advantage of unobstructed surface. If additional thickness is required at the columns, it is provided by lowering the bottom of the mat. Beam and slab designs are used for larger mats. To minimize thickness, the beams are wide and shallow. The space between the beams is filled with lightweight concrete to provide a flat floor surface, or a solid mat is used with the beams defined only by their reinforcing steel. Mats can be combined with the basement walls to form an inverted T-beam foundation or with the walls and upper floors to form a box girder (Fig. 5:23). Such a rigid foundation-structure system can be designed to resist differential settlement.

5:8 Special Problems in Shallow Foundation Design

Hydrostatic Uplift Structures below the ground water level are acted on by uplift pressures. If the structure is weak, the pressure can break it and cause a blow-in of a basement floor or collapse of a basement wall. If the structure is strong but light, it may be forced upward or *floated* out of its original position. Uplift is taken care of by drainage or by resisting the upward force. Continuous drainage blankets as described in Chapter 4 are very effective but must be designed to function indefinitely without clogging. If possible the water should be disposed of by gravity because pumps sometimes fail.

The entire weight of the structure can resist uplift if a mat foundation is employed. In addition it is sometimes possible to increase the mat thickness to provide more weight. However, it must be kept in mind that each foot of extra thickness of mat concrete resists about $1\frac{1}{2}$ ft of head because the uplift is also increased by 1 ft. Anchors, grouted into bed rock or driven into hard soil, can provide uplift resistance. The anchor resistance is limited to the buoyant or effective weight of the soil or rock engaged and to the connection between the anchor and the earth, whichever is the smaller. Pull-out tests are essential to determine the latter. Temporary flooding of the structure can prevent a blowout failure at the expense of water damage to the basement contents. Relief holes are sometimes installed to allow the area to fill with water in case of a drainage failure.

Severe Volume Change Soils having high volume change were discussed in Art. 2:8, and under depth in Art. 5:1. In most cases the best way to avoid trouble from high volume change is to place the foundation below the level of severe movement. Movement of the upper soil strata along the column extending upward from the footing can break the column and lift the structure. This can be prevented by placing a layer of weak, isolating material around the column. Mineral wool, vermiculite, and even sawdust have been used for this purpose. When the building is supported by deep footings, any grade beams must be separated from the soil so that they will not be damaged by soil expansion. The space between the beams and the soil should be filled with vermiculite or mineral wool to keep out soil.

In arid regions where swelling is the most serious problem, it is sometimes possible to utilize a bearing pressure that exceeds the swell pressure. This is not always successful because the stress increase produced by the foundation decreases rapidly with increasing depth, while the swell pressure may not.

Small structures can be placed on relatively stiff mats that rise and fall with the volume change but which do not deflect enough to cause trouble. Flexible foundations and structures that can deform without damage can be used if the volume change is not very irregular.

In arid regions special attention must be paid to drains, leaking pipes, and other sources of water that could cause heave. Piping under floor slabs can be placed in concrete troughs so that leakage can be kept out of the soil and so that soil movements will not cause the pipes to leak.

Loess Loess soils are ordinarily hard and incompressible from the partial cementing of clay and calcium carbonate. If they become wet, they soften and are very compressible. Surface water must be drained away from foundations on loess and piping must be routed so that leaks will not cause damage.

Cold-Storage Structures Frost action beneath cold-storage warehouses is a serious problem even in warm regions. If the temperatures are not very low, replacement of the frost-susceptible soil with a clean coarse sand or gravel is sometimes sufficient. This also provides some insulation. Insulation with cork or foam glass from 4 to 8 in. thick is effective if the soil is warm. Isolation, by placing the cold area on piers so that air can circulate below is sometimes used for small structures. When the cold is severe, it may be necessary to warm the soil by hot-air ducts or hot-water coils. Methods for analyzing the heat balance in such cases have been published.[5:15]

Boilers and Furnaces Foundations for boilers, furnaces, and hot industrial processes can heat the soil and cause it to lose moisture and settle. The preventive measures are similar to those for cold-storage warehouses: soil replacement, insulation, and isolation.

Foundations on Rock The analysis of foundations on homogeneous rock is the same as for foundations on soil. Most rock formations, however, contain numerous defects that limit their capacity severely. These defects include seams of weak or compressible materials, joints, sloping planes of weakness such as bedding planes or weathered dikes, deep pits or crevices in the surface, and cavities or caverns. A rational analysis of the effect of these defects is seldom possible. The engineer must study the conditions and develop a design on the basis of judgment.

Foundations Subject to Vibrations Foundations are subject to vibrations from a number of sources, natural and artificial. Wind on tall narrow structures, high-velocity water currents, and wave action on marine structures produce both transient and continuous vibrations under some conditions. Machinery is the most important cause of vibration. Reciprocating engines, compressors, pumps, and oscillating machines are important sources of continuous, low frequency vibrations and are usually the most serious causes of trouble. Electric motors, rotary pumps, and

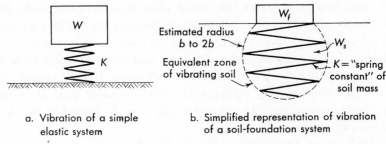

a. Vibration of a simple
elastic system

b. Simplified representation of vibration
of a soil-foundation system

Fig. 5:25 Soil-foundation vibration.

turbines produce continuous high-frequency vibrations. Shock and transient vibrations often are caused by stamping machines, forges, pile drivers, moving vehicles, and blasting. Vibration consists of complex repeating motions and can include both rotation and translation in all three directions. Continuous vibrations usually have a constant frequency determined by the source and complicated by harmonics generated by its supports, while transient vibrations from shocks may have a variable frequency, depending on both the source and its supporting system.

If an impulse of short duration is applied to a body, it will vibrate at its *natural frequency*, which depends on its mass and elastic properties. For a perfectly elastic body (Fig. 5:25a) whose weight is W and whose resistance to deflection in force per unit of deflection (pounds per foot or grams per centimeter) is K, the natural frequency f_n is given by[5:16]

$$f_n = \frac{1}{2\pi} \sqrt{\frac{Kg}{W}}. \tag{5:15}$$

This means that the natural frequency increases as the square root of the rigidity and decreases with the square root of the weight of the body. When energy is lost in the process, the vibration is said to be *damped*, and the natural frequency is somewhat less.

When the vibration applied to a structural member or the soil is different from its natural frequency, the amplitude of the vibration is limited by the energy received. If the vibration should occur at the natural frequency, the vibration amplitude in that body increases tremendously. This is *resonance* and is the most serious condition because of the magnified severity of the vibration.

The natural frequency of a structural column or beam can be estimated from its weight and rigidity, using equation 5:15. The natural frequency of a foundation-soil system as shown in Fig. 5:25b is much more complex. The resistance per unit of deflection K can be estimated from the distortion settlement ρ. This depends on both the modulus of elasticity of the soil and the size of the foundation. The weight of the vibrating body, W, is the sum of the weight of the foundation, W_f, and the portion of the soil mass below the foundation which is vibrating, W_s. Therefore the natural frequency of the soil is not a property of the soil alone but also depends on the weight and size of the foundation and the load it carries.

The intensity of the vibration is also a factor because the modulus of elasticity of some soils changes with confining pressure and with the strain. Tests of soil masses with vibrators having masses of from 2000 to 6000 lb and with square bases from 2 ft to 3 ft wide indicate natural frequencies of from 700 vibrations per minute for peat to 1800 vibrations per minute for very dense sand. For heavier and wider foundations the natural frequency would be less. These natural frequencies, unfortunately, are comparable to the vibrations or multiples of the vibrations generated by many reciprocating machines such as pumps and compressors. They are much lower than the frequencies generated by turbines and high-speed motors, however.

Soil vibrations have a number of important effects. First the vibration can be transmitted to other foundations and to other structures at some distance from the vibration source. These transmitted vibrations can be annoying and even damaging. If some foundation-soil system should be in resonance, severe damage could result. Second the vibration can cause a reduction in the void ratio of cohesionless soils and result in severe settlement. Ordinarily the settlement will be small if the relative density is greater than 70 per cent, but if the vibration is severe, as in the case of resonance, settlements can occur until the relative density is nearly 100 per cent. Third, vibration in loose, saturated cohesionless soils can bring about a quick condition, loss of strength, and failure. Soils with cohesion are resistant to vibration settlement and are not affected appreciably.

Corrective measures include reducing the vibration of the source, changing the soil-foundation system to prevent resonance, and stabilizing the soil to prevent vibration damage. Vibration can be reduced by installing isolating systems such as spring mounts on the source or by cushioning them on vibration-absorbing materials. It also can be minimized by changing the type of machine, such as substituting rotary for reciprocating compressors. The frequency of resonance is changed by altering one or more of the factors in equation 5:15. Increasing the size and weight of the foundation will reduce the resonant frequency of the system. Increasing the modulus of elasticity of the soil by densification or stabilization (Chapter 8) will increase it. Changing the speed of the source can be helpful, of course, if it is possible mechanically. In general the natural frequency should be less than half or more than one and one-half the vibration frequency. Stabilizing the soil by injecting a cementing agent or by densification can prevent settlement or loss of strength. This is discussed in Chapter 8.

REFERENCES

5:1 "Theoretical and Practical Treatment of Expansive Clays," *Quarterly Colorado School of Mines*, Vol. 54, No. 4, Oct., 1959.

5:2 E. W. Lane and W. M. Borland, "River Bed Scour During Floods," *Transactions*, ASCE, Vol. 119, 1954, p. 1072.

5:3 E. M. Laursen and A. Toch, "Scour Around Bridge Piers and Abutments," *Bulletin 4, Iowa Highway Research Board*, Ames, 1956.

5:4 K. Terzaghi, *Theoretical Soil Mechanics*, John Wiley & Sons, Inc., New York, 1943.

5:5 G. G. Meyerhof, "The Influence of Roughness of Base and Ground Water on the Ultimate Bearing Capacity of Foundations," *Geotechnique*, Vol. 5, No. 3, September, 1955, p. 227.

5:6 L. Jurgenson, "The Application of Theories of Elasticity and Plasticity to Foundation Problems," *Journal, Boston Society of Civil Engineers*, July, 1954.

5:7 H. M. Westergaard, "A Problem of Elasticity Suggested by a Problem of Soil Mechanics: Soft Material Reinforced by Numerous Strong Horizontal Sheets," *Contributions to Mechanics of Solids*, The Macmillan Company, New York, 1938.

5:8   N. M. Newmark, "Influence Charts for Computation of Stresses in Elastic Soils," *Bulletin 38, University of Illinois Engineering Experiment Station*, Urbana, 1942.

5:9   K. Terzaghi, "Settlement of Structures in Europe and Methods of Observation," *Transactions, American Society of Civil Engineers*, 1938, p. 1432.

5:10 G. F. Sowers, "New Equipment and Methods Streamline Load Tests," *Engineering News Record*, February 16, 1950.

5:11 K. Terzaghi and R. B. Peck, *Soil Mechanics in Engineering Practice*, John Wiley & Sons, Inc., New York, 1948.

5:12 A. Casagrande and R. E. Fadum, "Applications of Soil Mechanics in Designing Building Foundations," *Transactions, American Society of Civil Engineers*, 1944, p. 383.

5:13 A. W. Skempton and D. H. McDonald, "The Allowable Settlement of Buildings, *Proceedings, Inst. of Civil Engineers*, Vol. 5, No. 3, London, December, 1956, p. 727.

5:14 D. E. Polshin and R. A. Tokar, "Maximum Allowable Differential Settlement of Structures," *Proceedings, Fourth International Conference on Soil Mechanics and Foundation Engineering*, Vol. 1, London, 1957, p. 402.

5:15 W. Ward and E. C. Sewell, "Protection of the Ground From Thermal Effects of Industrial Plant," *Geotechnique*, Vol. 2, No. 1, June, 1950, p. 64.

5:16 G. P. Tschebotarioff, *Soil Mechanics, Foundations, and Earth Structures*, McGraw-Hill Book Co., Inc., New York, 1951.

Suggestions for Further Study

1. G. A. Leonards, *et al.*, *Foundation Engineering*, McGraw-Hill Book Co., Inc., New York, 1961.

2. G. F. Sowers, "Shallow Foundations," *ibid.*

3. C. W. Dunham, *Foundations of Structures*, McGraw-Hill Book Co., Inc., New York, 1950.

4. P. Anderson, *Substructure Analysis and Design*, 2d ed., Ronald Press Co., New York, 1959.

5. E. E. Seelye, *Foundations, Design and Practice*, John Wiley & Sons, Inc., New York, 1956.

6. References 5:11 and 5:12.

7. *Proceedings of the International Conference of Soil Mechanics and Foundation Engineering*, held in Cambridge, Massachusetts, 1936; Rotterdam, 1948; Zurich, 1953; London, 1957; and Paris, 1961.

PROBLEMS

5:1   A long footing is 3 ft wide. Its base is 2.5 ft below the ground surface. Find the safe bearing capacity if the soil is a saturated clay having a unit weight of 110 lb per cu ft and a strength c, of 3000 psf. The safety factor is 3. Use Mohr's circle and compare with bearing capacity computed by the general formula, using both the Bell–Terzaghi and Meyerhof factors.

5:2 A square footing is 8 ft wide with its base 4 ft below the ground surface. The soil is saturated clay having a unit weight of 120 lb per cu ft and a cohesion of 4000 psf. Find the safe bearing capacity by the Meyerhof factors if a minimum safety factor of 2.5 is required.

5:3 A long footing 5 ft wide is 3 ft below the surface of a sand weighing 130 lb per cu ft saturated and 110 lb per cu ft dry, and having an angle of internal friction of 37°. Compute the safe bearing capacity for a safety factor of 2.5, using (1) the graphical method; (2) the general equation with the Bell–Terzaghi factors; and (3) the Meyerhof factors. For each case find the capacity (a) the water table 10 ft below the footing; (b) the water table at the base of the footing; and (c) the water table at the ground surface.

5:4 A column carries 200,000 lb. The soil is a dry sand weighing 115 lb per cu ft and having an angle of internal friction of 40°. A minimum safety factor of 2.5 is required, and the Meyerhof factors are to be used in computation.
    a. Find the size of square footing required if it is placed at the ground surface.
    b. Find the size of square footing required if it is placed 3 ft below the ground surface.
    c. Find the size of footing required for (b) if the water table rises to the ground surface, increasing the soil weight to 132 lb per cu ft.

5:5 A steam turbine whose base is 20 ft × 12 ft weights 2400 kips. It is to be placed on a clay soil with $c = 3000$ psf. Find size of foundation required if the minimum safety factor is 3. The foundation is to be 2 ft below the ground surface.

5:6 A column carries 340 kips. It is to rest on a square footing on sand with $\phi = 38°$ and $\gamma = 120$ lb per cu ft. The safety factor is 2.5.
    a. Find size of square footing if it is at ground surface.
    b. Find size of square footing if it is 4 ft below the ground surface.
    c. Would it be cheaper to lower the footing as in (b) if the column is 18 in. square and the footing is 2 ft thick than to place it at the ground surface? Concrete costs $40.00 per cu yd in place, and excavation costs $0.95 per cu yd.

5:7 A column carries 475,000 lb to a square footing that rests 3 ft below the surface of a partially saturated clay. If $\phi' = 15°$, $c' = 1000$ psf, and $\gamma = 113$ lb per cu ft, find the footing size required for a safety factor of 2.5.

5:8 A smoke stack foundation 35 ft × 35 ft exerts a pressure of 5000 psf at the surface of a sand that weighs 108 lb per cu ft dry and 125 lb per cu ft saturated. Below the sand at a depth of 30 ft is a clay seam that is 6 ft thick, weighing 105 lb per cu ft saturated.
    a. Construct a diagram showing the variation of vertical stress increase under the center of the foundation as a function of depth.
    b. Construct a similar diagram showing the initial effective stress in the soil as a function of depth. The water table is at a depth of 10 ft.
    c. Construct a diagram showing the increase in stress at the center of the clay stratum (a depth of 33 ft) as a function of the horizontal distance from the footing centerline. What is the average stress increase directly beneath the foundation?

5:9 The clay of problem 5:8 is normally consolidated and has a compression index of 0.63 and a void ratio of 1.42.

    a. Find the settlement caused by the initial load and the average stress increase in the stratum.

    b. Below the clay is more sand. If the coefficient of consolidation is 0.02 sq ft per day, compute the time required for (1) 25 per cent, (2) 50 per cent, and (3) 75 per cent consolidation.

5:10 Find the additional increase in stress and increased settlement of problem 5:9 caused by permanently lowering the water table to a depth of 20 ft. This occurs after the settlement due to the foundation load is completed.

5:11 An elevated water tank weighing 250 tons rests on four square footings 20 ft apart (center to center). The allowable soil pressure is 5000 psf. The soil consists of 25 ft of gravel underlain by 8 ft of clay underlain by more gravel. The water table is below the clay. Both clay and gravel weigh 110 lb per cu ft. The void ratio of the clay is 0.80 and the compression index 0.32.

    a. Compute the average effective stress in the clay before and after construction. Use the Westergaard chart.

    b. Compute the tank settlement.

    c. Compute the tank settlement if the footing area is doubled. How much was the settlement reduced? (Express as a percentage of the original settlement.)

5:12 A monument has a base 40 ft × 60 ft. It weighs 3000 kips. It rests on a stratum of sand 40 ft thick underlain by a stratum of soft clay 5 ft thick. The clay rests on bedrock. The water table is at the ground surface and the γ of the sand is 130 lb per cu ft saturated and the γ of the clay is 110 lb per cu ft.

    a. Compute the average effective stress in the clay before and after construction. Use the Westergaard chart.

    b. Compute the settlement of the monument if, for the clay, $e_0 = 1.13$ and $C_c = 0.31$.

    c. Compute the time required for 80 per cent of the ultimate settlement to take place if $k = 7 \times 10^{-9}$ cm per sec.

    d. Recompute stress and settlement, using approximate method.

5:13 A turbine foundation mat 20 ft × 40 ft carries a load of 1600 psf. The soil consists of 25 ft of clay overlying dense sand. The water table is at the ground surface. The clay has the following characteristics: $c = 2000$ psf, $\gamma = 110$ lb per cu ft, $E = 750,000$ psf, $c_v = 0.0015$ sq ft per day. The stress–void-ratio curve is given in problem 2:9.

    a. Is the foundation safe if a minimum factor of safety of 2.5 is necessary?

    b. What is the contact settlement?

    c. What is the average stress increase in the upper 5-ft substratum of clay, the next 10 ft, and the bottom 10 ft of clay?

    d. What is the total compression settlement?

    e. How much settlement will take place in one year if a thin layer of sand is placed between the clay and the concrete mat?

5:14 Prepare a report describing the failure or excessive settlement of a structure due to faulty foundations. Include the following items:

a. Soil conditions.

b. Foundation.

c. Description of failure.

d. Cause of failure.

e. Corrective measures if any.

5:15 A building 100 ft × 80 ft of reinforced concrete weighs 700 psf of gross area. Columns are to be spaced 20 ft apart. The soil is deep, dry sand weighing 120 lb per cu ft. The following results were obtained with a load test made at the soil surface, using a 1 ft square plate.

Load (lb)	Settlement (in.)
1000	0.05
2000	0.10
3000	0.15
4000	0.20
5000	0.30
6000	0.60

The footings are to be placed 3 ft below the ground surface. The minimum safety factor is 2.5.

a. Plot load test and get failure q_c.

b. Compute ϕ.

c. Find minimum square-footing sizes.

d. Find footing settlements for (c). (Assume that the settlements at higher pressures can be found by extending the straight-line portion of the load settlement curve and that formula 5:13b applies.)

e. If settlement is excessive what should be done?

6... DEEP FOUNDATIONS

When the soil strata immediately beneath the structure are so weak or compressible that they are not capable of supporting the load, it is necessary to lower the foundations until more suitable soils are reached. Two general forms of *deep foundations* have been developed for this purpose: piles and piers. Piles are relatively small-diameter shafts (less than 24 in. ordinarily) that are forced into the ground. Piers are larger, are usually constructed by excavation, and permit visual inspection of the soil or rock on which they rest. A sharp distinction between piles and piers is impossible because some foundations combine features of both.

6:1 Development and Use of Piles

Piles are older than history. The Neolithic inhabitants of Switzerland 12,000 years ago drove wooden poles in the soft bottoms of shallow lakes and on them erected their homes, high above marauding animals and warring neighbors. Similar structures are in use today in jungle areas of Southeast Asia and South America. Venice was built on wood piling in the marshy delta of the Po River to protect early Italians from the invaders from Eastern Europe and at the same time enable them to be close to the sea and their source of livelihood. Today, pile foundations serve the same purpose: to make it possible to build homes and maintain industry and commerce in areas where the soil conditions are unfavorable.

Uses of Piles Piles are used in many ways, as shown in Fig. 6:1. *Bearing piles* that support foundation loads are the most common form. They do this either by transferring the load of the structure through soft strata into stronger, incompressible soils or rock below, or by spreading the load through soft strata that are not capable of supporting the concentrated loading of shallow footings. Bearing piles are used when there is danger of the upper soil strata being scoured away by current or wave action, or when wharves and bridges are built in water.

Tension piles are used to resist upward forces. These are used in structures subject to uplift, such as buildings with basements below the ground water level, aprons of dams, or buried tanks. They are also used to resist overturning of walls and dams and for anchors of guy wires, bulkheads, and towers.

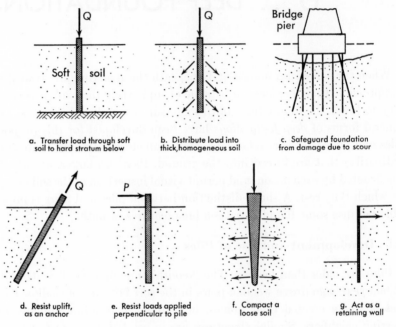

a. Transfer load through soft soil to hard stratum below   b. Distribute load into thick, homogeneous soil   c. Safeguard foundation from damage due to scour

d. Resist uplift, as an anchor   e. Resist loads applied perpendicular to pile   f. Compact a loose soil   g. Act as a retaining wall

Fig. 6:1 Uses of piles.

Laterally loaded piles support loads applied perpendicular to the axis of the pile, and are used in foundations subject to horizontal forces such as retaining walls, bridges, dams, and wharves, and as fenders and dolphins for harbor construction. If the lateral loads are great, they can be resisted more effectively by *batter piles* driven at an angle. Frequently a combination of vertical and batter piles is used, as in Fig. 6:1c. Piles are sometimes employed to compact soils or to serve as vertical drains through strata of low permeability. Closely spaced piles and wide thin *sheet piles* that interlock together are used as retaining walls, temporary dams, or seepage cutoffs.

6:2   Pile Driving

The operation of forcing a pile into the ground is *pile driving*. The oldest method and the one most widely used today is by means of a hammer. Oriental constructors have used a stone block as a hammer for centuries. It is lifted by ropes held taut by laborers arranged in a star pattern around the pile head. The rhythmic pulling and stretching of the ropes throws the stone up in the air and guides the downward blow on the pile head. The Romans used a stone block hoisted by an A-frame derrick with slave or horse power, and guided in its fall by vertical poles.

Pile Driving Equipment   While the simple A-frame, pile-driving rig of the Romans is still in use today (with mechanical power), the more

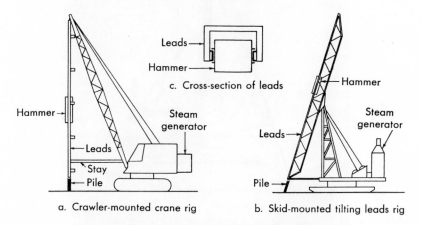

Fig. 6:2   Essential parts of pile-driving rigs.

common machine is essentially a crawler-mounted crane (Figs. 6:2 and 6:3). Attached to the boom are the *leads:* two parallel steel channels fastened together by U-shaped spacers and stiffened by trussing. These serve as guides for the *hammer*, which is fitted with lugs so as to slide between them. The leads are braced against the crane with a *stay*, which usually is adjustable to permit driving of batter piles. A steam generator or air compressor is required for steam hammers.

The pile is placed between the sides of the leads under the hammer. Lateral support is sometimes provided by sliding guides placed in the leads at the mid-point or quarter-points of the pile.

Some large pile-driving rigs are mounted on I-beam bases that are supported by steel beams and timber cribbing. They are moved by skidding them along the beams or on rollers. Barge-mounted rigs are available for marine construction and compact rail-mounted rigs for work on tracks. Sometimes small *swinging leads* suspended from cables are used when there is insufficient room for a crane.

Fig. 6:3   Pile-driving rig mounted on crawler treads with leads that can be tilted for driving batter piles. (Courtesy of Raymond International Inc.)

The most important feature of the driving rig, from the engineer's point of view, is its ability to guide the pile accurately. It must be rugged and rigid enough to keep the pile and hammer in alignment and plumb in spite of wind, underground obstructions, and the movement of the pile hammer.

Pile Hammers   The simplest hammer is the *drop hammer*, a block of cast steel commonly weighing from 500 to 2000 lb. It is raised 5 to 10 ft above the pile by a winch and then released and allowed to drop. The drop hammer is simple but very slow and is used only on small jobs where the contractor must improvise his equipment or where the cost of bringing in heavy driving equipment is not justified.

The *single-acting* steam hammer employs a heavy cast-steel block known as the *ram*, a piston, and a cylinder (Fig. 6:4a). Steam or compressed air is introduced into the cylinder to lift the ram 2 or 3 ft and then is released to allow the ram to fall on the head of the pile. These hammers are simple and rugged, and they deliver a low-velocity blow whose energy is relatively constant in spite of wear, adjustment, or small variations in steam pressure. Their characteristics are given in Table 6:1.

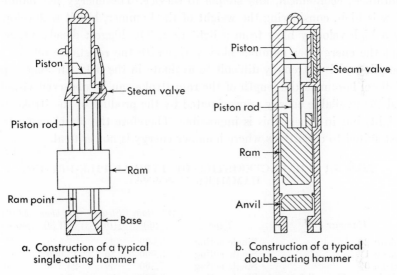

a. Construction of a typical single-acting hammer

b. Construction of a typical double-acting hammer

Fig. 6:4 Construction of steam pile hammers.

The *double-acting* or *differential-acting* hammer (Fig. 6:4b) employs steam or air pressure to lift the ram and then accelerate it downward. The blows are more rapid, from 95 to 240 blows per minute, thus reducing the time required to drive the pile and even making the driving easier in loose sands. They can lose some of their effectiveness with wear or poor valve adjustment. The amount of energy delivered in each blow varies greatly with the steam or air pressure and careful inspection is necessary to ensure that it is constant and the amount specified. If the number of hammer blows per minute is approximately the rated value, as given in Table 6:1, the steam pressure is probably correct.

Steam hammers can operate on both steam and compressed air. Steam operation is more efficient, particularly with circulating steam generators.

If the hammer is to be operated underwater, as can be done with enclosed double-acting types, air is required.

Diesel pile hammers are available in a limited range of sizes. They consist of a solid-bottom cylinder and an enclosed piston ram. The ram is raised upward mechanically and then allowed to fall. Fuel is injected into the cylinder while the hammer drops and is ignited by the heat of the air compressed by the ram. The impact and the explosion forces the cylinder down against the pile and the ram up, to repeat the cycle automatically. The important advantages of the diesel hammers are that they are self-contained, economical, and simple to service. The energy per hammer blow is high, considering the weight of the hammer, but it is developed by a high-velocity blow from a light ram. The biggest disadvantage is that the energy per hammer blow varies with the resistance offered by the pile and is extremely difficult to evaluate in the field. In some types of diesel hammers the length of the ram stroke can be observed visually and the available energy approximated by the product of the stroke and weight, but in others this is impossible. Therefore the diesel hammer is best suited to conditions where hammer energy is not critical.

Table 6:1 CHARACTERISTICS OF TYPICAL PILE-DRIVING HAMMERS[6:1,6:2,6:3,6:4,6:5]

Hammer	Type	Wt. Ram (lb)	Stroke (in.)	Energy per blow (ft lb)	Strokes per min
Vulcan 2	Single acting	3,000	29	7,620	70
Vulcan 1	Single acting	5,000	36	15,000	60
Vulcan 0	Single acting	7,500	39	24,375	50
McKiernan–Terry S-3	Single acting	3,000	36	9,000	65
McKiernan–Terry S-5	Single acting	5,000	39	16,250	60
McKiernan–Terry 9B3	Double acting	1,600	—	8,700	145
McKiernan–Terry 11B3	Double acting	5,000	—	19,150	95
Vulcan 50C	Double acting	5,000	—	15,100	120
Vulcan 80C	Double acting	8,000	—	24,450	111
Vulcan 140C	Double acting	14,000	—	36,000	103
McKiernan–Terry DE30	Diesel	3,000	72*	18,000*	52
			84†	24,000†	48
Link Belt 520	Diesel	5,000	—	30,000†	80

* Average.
† Maximum.

The choice of the proper size of hammer to use depends largely on the weight of the pile to be driven. The energy, in foot-pounds, of the falling ram of the single-acting hammer is the product of the ram weight and the drop in feet. A light ram, such as a drop-hammer, falling many feet, or the light double-acting hammer, will develop the same foot-pounds of energy at the instant of contact with the pile head as the heavy ram of a single-acting steam hammer falling 2.5 to 3 ft. The effects of the two blows, however, are quite different, owing to the widely different velocities of the falling rams at the instant of striking. Consider the driving of a railroad spike, using first a tack hammer and striking a hard, fast blow. Then use a heavy iron sledge hammer that drops a few inches so as to develop the same amount of energy. The slow, heavy blow drives the spike, whereas the tack hammer bounces. The same difference in effect can be observed in the driving of piles. Experience has shown that the weight of the driving ram should be from one-half to two times that of the pile.

Most pile hammers require the use of *driving heads*, *helmets*, or caps that distribute the force of the hammer blow over the butt of the pile. The head is made of cast steel and contains a renewable wood, fiber or

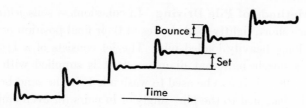

Fig. 6:5 Graph of movement of the head of the pile during driving.

plastic cushion block on which the hammer strikes. Heads for driving reinforced concrete piles may also provide for a wood or rope cushion between the driving head and the pile.

Behavior of the Pile During Driving Pile driving is a fascinating operation that never fails to attract crowds of onlookers. Clouds of steam and the repeated hammering are arresting, but they often obscure what merits much attention from the engineer—the behavior of the pile during driving. In very soft soils the first few blows of the hammer may drive the pile several feet; in fact, the pile may "run" into the ground under the static weight of the hammer. In harder soils, however, each blow of the hammer is accompanied by definite distortion of the pile and consequent losses of energy. If a piece of chalk is held against a pile and is moved with a steady horizontal motion while the driving is progressing, a graph will be traced on the pile that represents the vertical movement of the pile with time. A typical example of such a graph is shown in Fig. 6:5. The blow of the hammer produces an initial downward movement of the pile, but this is followed by a partial rebound or *bounce* that represents the temporary elastic compression of the pile and the soil surrounding it. The initial movement minus the bounce is called the *set* and is the net movement of the pile into the soil under one hammer blow. The average set for several hammer blows can be found from the driving resistance, which is the number of blows necessary to drive the pile a specified distance, usually 1 in., 6 in., or 1 ft.

When the pile is very long and the driving hard, the pile behavior is more complex. At the instant of impact the top part of the pile moves downward. The section of pile immediately below is compressed elastically and the tip of the pile momentarily remains fixed. The zone of compression travels swiftly down the pile, reaching the tip a fraction of a second after the initial impact. As a result of this compression wave the entire pile does not move downward at any one instant but instead moves in shorter segments.

Other Methods of Pile Driving   In cohesionless soils *jetting* can be used to place short, lightly loaded piles in their final position or as an aid to driving long, heavily loaded piles. The jet consists of a 1½- to 2-in. pipe, with a nozzle half that diameter, that is supplied with water at from 150 to 300 psi. It can be used to wash a hole in the sand before driving or can be fastened to the pile, singly or in pairs (or even embedded in concrete piles), so that driving and jetting can proceed simultaneously. Since jetting loosens the soil, it is usually stopped before the pile reaches its final position, and the last few feet of penetration secured only by hammering. If too much water is used, the jetting can loosen previously driven piles. It is of greatest benefit in dense sands and of little help in clays.

Where stiff clays or soft rock must be penetrated at high levels in order to reach the bearing stratum, time and expense can be saved by *preboring*. In dry soils this is done with an auger, and the pile is dropped into the open hole. If the soil is continuously stiff, a concrete pile can be cast in the open hole, forming a *bored pile* (discussed later in the chapter). If the soil contains soft seams, the hole can be made with a rotary well drill and kept open by a slurry of soil and water. The pile is driven through the slurry to bearing in firm strata below.

Spudding is the driving of a heavy steel W⌐ section into the soil to punch through obstructions or to break up hard seams that could damage or even prevent penetration of small piles. The spud is withdrawn before the pile is driven.

Jacking is employed to drive piles when the vibration of hammering is not permissible or when the head room is too small to permit use of a pile hammer. It is used principally in underpinning where the piles are jacked in short sections, using the existing structure as a reaction.

Vibrators have proved effective in driving piles in silty and sandy soils.[6:6] The vibrators consist of pairs of counterrotating weights oriented to provide an up-and-down motion. Speeds of from 735 to 2500 rpm have been used with vibrators weighing from 26,000 to 3,000 lb, respectively. The 26,000-lb vibrator, driven by a 200-hp electric motor, develops a dynamic force of nearly 200,000 lb. Sonic and supersonic vibrations also show much promise in driving piles and might eventually replace hammering in some applications.

6:3 Supporting Power of Piles

The ability of a pile foundation to support loads without failure or excessive settlement depends on a number of factors: the pile cap, the pile shaft, the transfer of the pile load to the soil, and the soil and underlying rock strata which ultimately support the load. The pile-cap analysis and design is essentially a structural problem and is covered adequately in textbooks on reinforced concrete design. It is rarely a critical problem or a source of trouble. The analysis and design of the pile shaft involves both the pile and the soil. Ordinarily the shaft capacity is dictated by construction needs and is far more than is needed for the ultimate load, but it can be critical with heavily loaded slender piles or when construction difficulties are encountered. The transfer of the pile load to the soil is termed the *pile-bearing capacity*. It is a frequent source of trouble in pile foundations. The ability of the underlying strata to carry the load depends on the combined effect of all the piles acting together. Although the capacity of the underlying strata seldom receives attention, it is a frequent source of trouble in pile foundations.

Pile Shaft The pile shaft is a structural column that is fixed at the point and usually restrained at the top. The elastic stability of piles, their resistance against buckling, has been investigated both theoretically and by load tests.[6:7,6:8] The buckling of a pile depends on its straightness, length, moment of inertia, and modulus of elasticity, and the elastic resistance of the soil that surrounds it. Both theory and experience demonstrate that the lateral support of the soil is so effective that buckling will occur only in extremely slender piles in very soft clays or in piles that extend through open air or water. Therefore the ordinary pile in sand or soft clay can be designed as though it were fully braced or were a short column. This is substantiated by load tests of 100 ft long piles in soft clay at a Midwest site. H-piles failed above the ground surface at the yield point of their steel, and concrete piles failed by crushing at the compressive strength of their concrete (Fig. 6:16).

The most important consideration in limiting the capacity of the shaft is faulty construction, particularly of connections between two sections of pile. This can lead to deflection of the lower part of the pile and the development of a dog-leg and to a reduction of the pile cross-section and a loss of strength as a short column. A study of dog-legged piles shows that their capacity is not materially reduced, provided the surrounding soil is firm.[6:9]

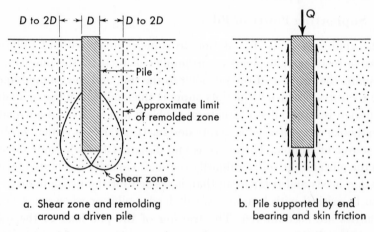

a. Shear zone and remolding
around a driven pile

b. Pile supported by end
bearing and skin friction

Fig. 6:6   Effect of a pile on the soil and the forces in the soil that support the pile.

The reduction in column strength can be prevented by careful control of the construction procedures.

Effect of Pile on Soil   In analyzing the forces that support a pile, it is necessary to consider the effects of the pile on the soil. The point of the pile is like a small footing that punches into the soil and creates successive bearing-capacity failures during driving. A zone of soil shear is created at the pile tip (Fig. 6:6a) which extends from the tip to the sides of the pile. A zone of soil remolding is created around the pile from the tip to the ground surface, the width of which is from one to two pile diameters and in which the degree of remolding probably varies with the distance from the pile surface. If the pile is placed by jetting or drilling, the zone of remolding is much smaller and probably does not exceed a few inches. The effect of the remolding is a loss of strength in sensitive clays, expansion and a reduction of the angle of internal friction in dense cohesionless soils, and densification and an increase in the angle of internal friction of loose cohesionless soils.[6:10]

The displacement of driven piles has two effects. First there is heave of the ground in saturated clays and dense cohesionless soils. The heave sometimes pushes previously driven piles laterally as much as 1 or 2 ft or raises the ground surface an amount equivalent to the volume of soil displaced. Second, high lateral pressures are set up in the soil. The limited data available indicate that the total lateral pressure in saturated clay can be as much as twice the total vertical overburden pressure;[6:11] and in sands, the effective lateral pressure can be from one-half to four times the vertical effective stress.[6:12] In saturated clays even higher pressures have been indirectly indicated by the collapse of cofferdams and thin-walled open pipe or steel shell piles and the shoving of structures near piles being driven. In saturated clays the pressure increase is largely neutral stress. This is dissipated into the surrounding soil with time, causing the lateral pressure to drop towards its original value, somewhat less than the overburden pressure. The reduction in neutral stress in the clay is accompanied by a regain in strength, which in some cases eventually exceeds the original strength of the undisturbed soil.

Static Analysis of Pile Capacity   The pile transfers its load to the soil in two ways, as shown by Fig. 6:6b: first by bearing capacity at the point, often termed *end bearing;* and second by shear or friction along its sides, usually known as *skin friction* (although true friction does not develop in many soils). Piles that are driven through soft strata to a hard soil or rock are sometimes called *end-bearing* piles even though some of their support comes from skin friction; piles in a homogeneous sand or clay are sometimes called *friction* piles even though a substantial part of their support is from end bearing.

The ultimate end bearing of a deep foundation is computed in the same way as the ultimate bearing capacity of a shallow foundation, by the general bearing capacity equation

$$q_0 = \frac{\gamma b}{2} N_\gamma + q'N_q + cN_c. \qquad (5:3)$$

NOTE: Substitute $0.9D$ for b in the case of round piles.

If the soil above the pile point (for a distance of at least ten diameters) is the same as that below, a shear zone shaped like an inverted heart (Fig. 6:6a) will develop. The bearing-capacity factors for this condition (Fig. 6:7) have been adapted from the work of Meyerhof[6:10,6:13] and are considerably greater than those for shallow foundations because of the greater extent of the shear zone. In many cases it is questionable that the ultimate bearing capacity fully develops beneath a pile because of local soil failure, and therefore the factors may be too high. On the other hand

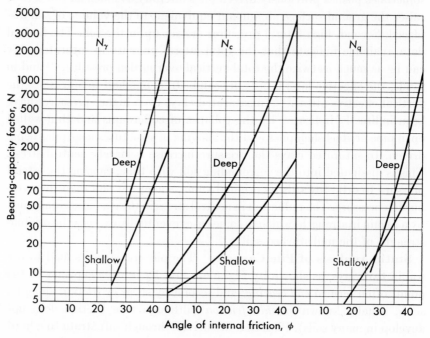

Fig. 6:7   Bearing-capacity factors for shallow and deep cylindrical or square foundations. (Adapted from Meyerhof[6:10, 6:13].).

in some soils the factors are too low because the pile driving increases the density and therefore the angle of internal friction. For piles in saturated clays the value of $N_c = 9$ has been verified by a limited number of field tests, but for other conditions the factors must be used with caution.

If the soil above the point is weaker than that below, the bearing-capacity factors for shallow foundations apply. These values, corrected for square (or round) foundations, are also given on Fig. 6:7.

The skin friction that acts along the pile shaft is equal either to the sum of the friction and adhesion of the soil on the pile or to the shear strength of the soil immediately adjacent to the pile, whichever of the two is the smaller. If f is the skin friction, then

$$f = \begin{cases} c' + \bar{p} \tan \phi', & (2{:}24\text{b}) \\ a + \bar{p} \tan \delta, & (6{:}1) \end{cases}$$

where a is the adhesion in pounds per square foot and δ is the angle of friction of soil on the pile surface.

The values of a and $\tan \delta$ can be determined by direct shear tests in which the bottom half of the shear box is replaced by the same material as the pile surface. Typical values for a range from $0.8c$ to $1.0c$, depending on the surface roughness. There are some indications that the adhesion does not increase greatly beyond 1000 psf no matter how high the shear strength becomes. The cause is probably the formation of a minute gap between the pile and the soil caused by the slap or transverse vibration of the pile during driving.[6:14] Typical values for $\tan \delta$ based on limited test data are given in Table 6:2.

Table 6:2 COEFFICIENT OF FRICTION FOR COHESIONLESS SOILS ON PILES AND SIMILAR STRUCTURES

Material	Coefficient of Friction, $\tan \delta$
Wood	0.4
Rough concrete, cast against soil	0.8
Smooth concrete, cast against forms	0.3
Smooth steel	0.2–0.4

The effective lateral pressure for computing both the friction and the soil shear strength depends on the pile displacement, as was previously discussed. The ratio of the effective lateral stress to the effective vertical pressure is K_s. Typical values based on fragmentary data are given in Table 6:3.

Table 6:3 COEFFICIENT OF EFFECTIVE LATERAL PRESSURE OF COHESIONLESS SOILS ON PILES

Condition	K_s
Bored or jetted pile	0.5
Pile jetted, then driven a few feet	1
Pile driven in loose soil	1
Pile driven in dense soil	2–4

Immediately after driving, the soil strength (and adhesion) are in the remolded condition. After a clay soil has had an opportunity to reconsolidate and, in some cases, to harden thixotropically, the adhesion and the strength immediately adjacent to the pile increase and can even exceed the original soil strength. Piles pulled out of clay frequently are covered with a skin of soil several inches thick that adheres tightly to their surface.

The total pile capacity is generally the sum of the end bearing and the product of the skin friction and the surface area of the pile. This is not always so, however. First the end bearing and the skin friction along different sections of the shaft may not be mobilized simultaneously. Consider a pile whose shaft is in a weak, non-rigid soil but whose point rests on a rigid stratum. A relatively small downward movement of the pile would be sufficient to produce bearing-capacity failure, but the same movement would not be great enough to produce skin-friction failure. Therefore only part of the skin friction would be mobilized at the instant of failure. The deflection of the pile shaft under load (which is greatest at the ground surface but less at the point), the different rigidities of different strata in contact with the pile, and the compression of soil beneath the pile point also contribute to the unequal mobilization of end bearing and skin friction. As a result the actual pile capacity can be materially less than the computed value. The difference is aggravated in ultrasensitive soils where failure brings about a loss of strength. For these reasons the skin frictions of weaker strata are generally neglected in analysis.

A second cause of difference between the computed and the actual capacity of piles arises from negative skin friction.[6:15] The stresses introduced into the soils by the pile and by any surface loads such as fill not supported by piles will cause the soils to consolidate. If there is a highly compressible stratum at some level above the pile point, its consolidation will cause the soils above to move downward with respect to the pile. Instead of supporting the pile, these strata, by their downward movement. now add load. This negative skin friction has been great enough to cause failure of pile foundations in a few cases and must be considered in design.

Example 6:1 Compute the ultimate bearing capacity of a 14 in. square reinforced concrete pile 65 ft long driven into a thick stratum of homogeneous, insensitive clay. The shear strength of the clay is given by $s = c = 1250$ psf, and the unit weight of the clay is 113 lb per cu ft. The adhesion is 0.9 times the cohesion. The water table is at the ground surface.

(1) End bearing (Fig. 6:7):

$$q_0 = 9 \times 1250 + 65 \, (113 - 62.4),$$
$$q_0 = 11{,}250 + 3{,}280 = 14{,}530 \text{ psf},$$
$$Q_0 = 14{,}530 \times \frac{14 \times 14}{144} = 19{,}800 \text{ lb}.$$

(2) Skin friction S:

$$S = 1250 \times \frac{14}{12} \times 4 \times 65 \times 0.9 = 341,000 \text{ lb.}$$

(3) Total ultimate capacity:

$$Q_0 = 19,800 + 341,000 = 360,800 \text{ lb.}$$

Dynamic Analysis of Pile Capacity—Pile Formulas Since the driving of a pile produces successive pile-bearing failures, it should be possible theoretically to develop some relationship between pile capacity and the resistance offered to driving with a hammer. Such *dynamic analyses* of pile capacity, often termed *pile formulas*, have been employed for over a century. While in some cases they have been able to predict pile capacity accurately, in others they have not, and their indiscriminate use has led to both overdesign and failures.

The pile loading and "failure" produced by driving with a hammer occurs in a small fraction of a second, whereas in the structure the load is applied over a period ranging from hours to years. A fixed relation between the dynamic and long-term capacity can exist only in a soil whose shear strength is independent of the rate of loading. This is approximately true in a dry cohesionless soil, and in wet cohesionless soils that are of intermediate density or so coarse grained that shear does not develop appreciable neutral stresses. In clays and in both very loose or dense fine-grained saturated cohesionless soils, the strength depends on the rate of shear; in such soils a dynamic analysis can have no validity.

All the dynamic analyses are based on the transfer of the kinetic energy of the falling pile hammer to the pile and the soil. This accomplishes useful work by forcing the pile into the soil against its dynamic resistance. Energy is wasted in the mechanical friction of the hammer, in the transfer of energy from the hammer to the pile by impact, and in temporary compression of the pile, pile cap (if any), and of the soil. The basic relationship, therefore, will be

$$(R_0 \times s) + \text{losses} = W_r \times h \times (\text{efficiency}) \qquad (6:2)$$

where R_0 is the resistance of the pile to driving; s, the distance it moves into the ground from one hammer blow (the set); W_r, the weight of the pile hammer; and h, the height that the hammer drops. The relation is solved for R_0 which is then assumed to be equal to the capacity of the pile under sustained loading, Q_0.

The major uncertainty in this approach and the basic difference between all the pile formulas is the way in which the energy losses and the mechanical efficiency of the process is computed. The most complete is that of Hiley as described by Chellis.[6:16] The mechanical efficiency of the hammer is expressed by e, a coefficient that ranges from 0.75 for drop hammers operated by a drum winch, or for most steam pile hammers that are not new, to 0.9 for new double-acting hammers. The energy available from the hammer after impact can be approximated by the method of impulse and momentum. This considers the coefficient of restitution, n, which ranges from 0.6 for steel on steel to 0.25 for a hammer striking on the head of a wood pile or a wood cushion block in a pile helmet or cap. In addition it involves the weight of the hammer, W_r, and the pile weight W_p. The available energy after impact is the hammer energy multiplied by

$$\frac{W_r + n^2 W_p}{W_r + W_p}.$$

This shows that as the weight of the pile increases with respect to that of the hammer, the relative inertia increases and there is less energy available for useful work. For long piles this is not strictly valid because the pile moves in a wave rather than as a rigid body. In such cases the pile weight for the upper 30 to 50 ft can be used as a rough approximation of the moving mass.

The energy lost by elastic compression of the pile, any helmet, and the soil can be approximated by assuming a linear increase in the stress acting from 0 to R_0 while the compression develops. The energy loss will therefore be

$$\frac{R_0 c_1}{2} + \frac{R_0 c_2}{2} + \frac{R_0 c_3}{2},$$

where c_1, c_2, and c_3 are respectively the temporary elastic compression of the helmet, pile, and soil. The value of $c_2 + c_3$ is the bounce of the pile with each hammer blow (Fig. 6:5) and is easily measured as described before. The value of c_1 must be estimated from the value of R_0 and the shape and material of the helmet. The resulting energy balance and dynamic formula are,

$$\overbrace{R_0 s + R_0 \left(\frac{c_1}{2} + \frac{c_2}{2} + \frac{c_3}{2}\right)}^{\text{Work done on pile}} = \overbrace{W_r h e \left(\frac{W_r + n^2 W_p}{W_r + W_p}\right)}^{\text{Energy available to pile}}; \qquad (6\!:\!3a)$$

$$Q_0 = R_0 = \frac{W_r h e}{s + \frac{1}{2}(c_1 + c_2 + c_3)} \left(\frac{W_r + n^2 W_p}{W_r + W_p} \right). \tag{6:3b}$$

NOTE: The formula is dimensionally homogeneous and both h and s must be in the same units.

For double-acting hammers the rated energy E in the same length units as s is substituted for $W_r h$.

Detailed tables of the constants for use in the Hiley formula have been published.[6:16] Although the values of e, n, and (for long piles) W_p must be estimated, which requires considerable experience, the method is reasonably accurate for piles driven in cohesionless soils. A safety factor of from 2 to 2.5 is ordinarily employed to obtain the safe load.

The formula can be simplified by substituting arbitrary constants for the different factors in the equation. The *Engineering News* formula was derived from observations of the driving of wood piles in sand with a free-falling drop hammer. The value of $c_1 + c_2 + c_3$ is assumed to be 2 in., and both the hammer efficiency and impact factor are assumed to be 1. The result is

$$R_0 = \frac{W_r h}{s + 1}. \tag{6:4a}$$

A safety factor of 6 was introduced to make up for any inaccuracies arising from the use of the arbitrary constants. Since the height of fall of drop hammers is usually measured in feet and s is measured in inches, a factor of 12 was added to make it possible to use the mixed units. This reduced to the familiar form of the equation:

$$R_s = \frac{1}{6} R_0 = \frac{W_r(h' \times 12)}{6(s + 1)},$$

$$R_s = \frac{2 W_r h'}{s + 1}. \tag{6:4b}$$

In this expression, h' is the hammer drop in feet and s is in inches. R_s is the safe pile load, including the built-in safety factor. The formula was later modified for steam hammers by substituting 0.2 in. for the temporary compression to give

$$R_s = \frac{2 W_r h'}{s + 0.1}. \tag{6:4c}$$

Numerous pile-load tests show that the real safety factor of the *Engineering News* formula averages 2 instead of its apparent 6, and that the safety factor can be as low as $\frac{2}{3}$ and as high as 20. For wood piles driven with free-falling drop hammers and for lightly loaded short piles driven with a steam hammer, the *Engineering News* formulas are a crude indication of pile capacity. For other conditions they can be very misleading.

Load Testing   The most reliable method of determining pile capacity for most sites is a load test. Pile load tests are made to determine the ultimate failure load of a pile or group of piles or to determine if the pile or pile group is capable of supporting a load without excessive or continuous settlement.

The bearing capacity of all piles except those driven to rock does not reach the ultimate until after a period of rest. Load tests are not a good indication of performance unless made after this period of adjustment. For

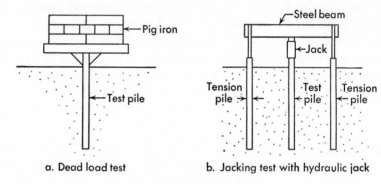

a. Dead load test   b. Jacking test with hydraulic jack

Fig. 6:8   Pile load testing.

piles in permeable soils this period is two or three days, but for piles partly or wholly surrounded by silt or clay it can be more than a month.

Pile load tests can be made by constructing a loading platform or box on top of the pile or group of piles (Fig. 6:8a) on which the load is applied, using sand, pig iron, concrete blocks, or water. A safer and more easily controlled test uses a large, accurately calibrated hydraulic jack to apply the load (Fig. 6:8b). The resistance above the jack can be secured with a loaded platform or by a beam held down by piles in tension. An added advantage of the jacking method is that the load on the pile can be varied rapidly and cheaply. Settlements are measured by a precision level or preferably by micrometer dial gages mounted on an independent support.

The loads are applied in increments of one-fifth or one-fourth the design load until failure or two times the design load is reached; the load is then reduced to zero by increments. Each load is maintained constant and the settlement is measured at regular intervals until the rate of movement is less than 0.0005 in. per hr. A load final-settlement curve is plotted similar to that for the plate load test.

Many different criteria for working load have been proposed, but the best is the same as for any other foundation: the load having an adequate safety factor (1.5 to 2 when a test is made) or the load giving the greatest permissible total settlement (as described in Chapter 5), whichever is the smaller.

Settlement of a Single Pile Settlement of a single isolated pile comes from the elastic shortening of the pile shaft and to some extent from the distortion of the soil around the pile. These can be determined best from a load test. Settlement can be computed from the static analysis of pile capacity by computing the elastic shortening of each section of the pile shaft from that portion of the total load remaining in that section.

The major settlement of all piles except those that are end bearing on rock comes from the consolidation of the underlying soil by stresses developed by the pile group. This is considered in Art. 6:4.

Tension Piles Tension piles can be analyzed by the static method (with no end bearing) or by tension load tests. The resistance of tension piles with enlarged bases can be determined only by load tests.

Horizontal Thrust Resistance Piles are not capable of supporting heavy loads applied perpendicular to the pile axis. The resistance can be computed by assuming that passive earth pressure acts against the pile or against the group of piles. If the pile butts are embedded deeply in masonry, the piles will act as cantilever beams. Load tests are the best method of determining the resistance to horizontal loads but are often cumbersome and expensive. In general, laterally loaded piles are capable of supporting loads of $\frac{1}{20}$ their vertical load without excessive deflection in homogeneous soils.

6:4 Pile Groups

Since piles are ordinarily closely spaced beneath footings or foundations, the action of the entire pile group must be considered. This is particularly important when purely "friction" piles are used and when the hard stratum on which the points of end-bearing piles rest is underlain by more compressible soils.

Group Bearing Capacity The group bearing capacity is computed by assuming that the piles form a giant foundation whose base is at the level of the pile points and whose length and width are the length and width of the group (Fig. 6:9a)[6:17]. The group capacity is the sum of the bearing capacity developed by the base of the "foundation" and the shear developed along the vertical sides of the group "foundation."

The bearing is computed by using the general bearing-capacity equation (5:3). The factors for deep foundations are used when the pile length

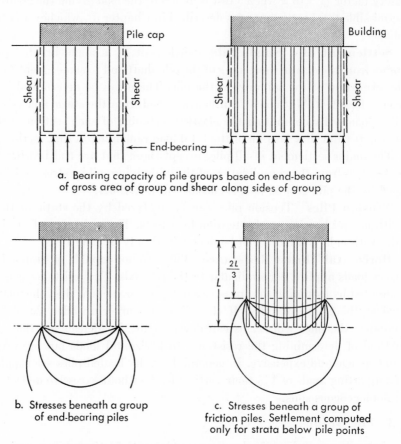

a. Bearing capacity of pile groups based on end-bearing of gross area of group and shear along sides of group

b. Stresses beneath a group of end-bearing piles

c. Stresses beneath a group of friction piles. Settlement computed only for strata below pile points

Fig. 6:9 Approximate method for analyzing bearing capacity and settlement of pile groups by assuming a group to act as a single foundation unit.

is at least ten times the group width and when the soil is homogeneous; in all other cases the factors for shallow foundation are used. The shear around the group perimeter is the soil strength, determined without any increase in lateral pressure from pile displacement, multiplied by the surface area of the group. While model tests show that the actual group capacity is always slightly less than the computed values, the difference is well within a safety factor of 2.

Pile Spacing   The piles should be spaced far enough apart so that the computed bearing capacity of the group, acting as a unit, is at least as great as the sum of the capacities of the individual piles. For long friction piles in clay this occurs at spacings of from two to three pile diameters, with the smaller spacing for square groups of four and with the spacing increasing slowly with the number of piles. In cohesionless soils it is impossible to drive the piles so close together that the group capacity will be less than the sum; therefore the spacing is based on construction convenience, usually 2.5 diam.

Group Settlement   The settlement of a group of piles results from consolidation of the soil strata beneath the pile points. Such settlement will exceed that of an isolated pile that carries the same load as each pile in the group unless the piles are end bearing on rock or on a thick stratum of incompressible soil. The group settlement may be analyzed by again considering the group to represent a giant foundation. When the piles are end bearing, the base of the imaginary footing is assumed to be at the level of the pile tips, as shown in Fig. 6:9b, and the stresses are computed on that basis. When the piles are supported by friction, the stresses beneath the footing are computed by assuming that the entire group load is introduced in the soil at a depth of from one-half to two-thirds the pile length. The load is distributed at this level over the gross area of the group. Settlements of the soil strata beneath the pile points are computed from these stresses. Such computations are approximate at best and are likely to give settlements that are higher than the observed values. They can indicate when trouble from settlement is likely to occur.

Example 6:2   Compute the soil stresses due to piles at a point 10 ft below the tips of a group of friction piles 60 ft long. The outer or gross dimensions of the group are 6 ft × 6 ft and the group load is 500 kips.
(1) The group load of 500 kips is assumed to act at a depth of $\frac{2}{3} \times 60 = 40$ ft. The area over which it acts is 6 ft × 6 ft = 36 sq ft.
(2) The depth at which the stresses are to be found is 10 + 20 = 30 ft below the point the 500-kip load is applied. This is $\frac{30}{6} = 5$ times the group width or $5b$.
(3) From Fig. 5:11 the stress at a depth of $5b$ directly beneath a loaded area is $0.014\ q$.
(4) The stress due to the piles is

$$\Delta\sigma = 0.014 \times \frac{500}{36} = 0.194 \text{ kips per sq ft.}$$

Batter Piles in Groups Batter piles combined with vertical piles are the most effective device for resisting horizontal thrusts. Anchors for wharves and bulkheads that combine a vertical pile in tension and a batter pile in compression, as shown in Fig. 6:10, have proved to be compact and economical. Batter piles combined with vertical piles have been utilized to support retaining walls and similar structures that develop horizontal loads. A rational analysis of batter-pile loading is impossible because the problem is statically indeterminate to a high degree. One approximate method assumes the piles to be hinged at their points and at their butts. A more elaborate method that recognizes the relative rigidity of the piles, the soil, and the structure has been proposed by Hrennikoff.[6:18]

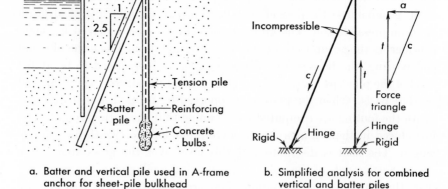

a. Batter and vertical pile used in A-frame anchor for sheet-pile bulkhead

b. Simplified analysis for combined vertical and batter piles

Fig. 6:10 Batter and vertical piles.

6:5 Types of Piles and Their Construction

Pile Shapes Constructors through the ages have tried and used with varying degrees of success many shapes and types of piling. Each shape has probably been successful under certain conditions. However, the use of a certain type or shape of pile that has proved successful in one job may not meet with success in a different situation. In the United States the establishment of large and well-equipped pile-driving organizations has led to the general use of a few types and shapes of piles.

Four basic shapes are commonly used: first, uniform cross-section throughout the length; second, enlarged base; third, tapered; and fourth, sheet. These are shown in Fig. 6:11.

The uniform-section pile comes in a variety of forms: cylindrical, square, octagonal, fluted, and H-section. The uniform section provides uniform column strength from the point to the butt, and "skin friction" is well distributed over the entire shaft. It is well adapted to splicing and cutting, since each section of the pile is identical.

In order to increase the end bearing and the friction on the lower portion of the pile, different forms of enlarged points have been used. In one form a large, precast point is attached to a cylindrical pile, while in another form a bubble of concrete is forced into the soil at the pile point. Piles of this shape have proved very effective in developing end bearing on firm, cohesive soils and even in loose sands. They are of little value as friction

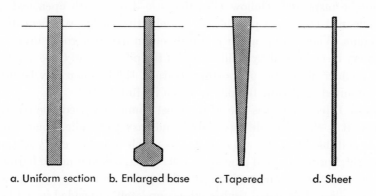

a. Uniform section b. Enlarged base c. Tapered d. Sheet

Fig. 6:11 Basic pile shapes.

piles and have little advantage over uniform-section piles when used as end bearing on rock.

The tapered shape originated with wood piles that conform to the natural shape of the tree. However, the taper has been imitated in concrete and steel in order to permit easier construction. Tapered piles are useful in compacting loose sands because of their wedge action but in other cases may be less effective than uniform-section piles. Both the point bearing and the skin friction on the lower portions of the tapered pile are low, since both the point area and the surface area of the pile are small. The result is that end-bearing, tapered piles require greater lengths than uniform-section piles in order to support a given load. Tapered piles that depend on friction for support may transmit a large portion of their load to the upper, weaker soil strata and produce objectionable settlement.

Sheet piles are relatively flat and wide in cross-section so that when they are driven side by side they form a wall. Many different forms of wood, concrete, and steel sheet piles have been developed for special purposes such as cofferdams, wharves, retaining walls, and cutoffs. Some have arch-shaped and Z-shaped cross-sections to provide rigidity, and most all types are made to interlock with adjacent sheet piles to form a soiltight wall.

Piles that are hollow have a distinct advantage over those that are not, for it is possible to inspect the entire length of the piles after driving. Piles may deviate from the vertical, develop sharp bending or "dog-legs," or may be damaged from overdriving. Hollow piles may be inspected by dropping a burning flare into them or by reflecting the sun's rays into them with a mirror, but other forms must be assumed satisfactory without any check. Therefore higher safety factors should be used with piles that cannot be inspected. Hollow piles that are driven with open ends and then cleaned out make possible an examination of the soil beneath the pile point. When an open-end pile rests on an irregular rock surface, the rock may be smoothed by drilling; and if the pile is found to be hung on a large boulder above the supporting stratum, the boulder may be drilled or dynamited to permit the pile to reach its full depth.

Wood Piles Wood is one of the most commonly used pile materials because it is cheap, readily available, and easy to handle. Some kind of timber suitable for piling will be found available in nearly every section of the world. Spruce, fir, and pine up to 100 ft long; oak and mixed hardwood piles up to 50 ft; southern pine up to 75 ft; and palmetto are commonly used for piling. Untreated timber piles completely imbedded in soil below the water level will remain sound and durable indefinitely. When the campanile of St. Mark's in Venice fell in 1902, it was found that the 1000-year-old piles were in such a good state of preservation that they were left in place and used to support the new tower. Sound timber piles that have been water soaked for many years should not be allowed to dry before redriving, since in drying the wood fiber becomes "short" and brittle.

Above the water table untreated timber is subject to decay and damage from termites and other insects. In salt water timber is susceptible to marine borer attack.[6:19] Many types of marine borers are found but most are related to the lobster and crab or to the clam and oyster families. The crab-like limnora destroy the wood from the outside in, leaving the pile as a slender spindle of wood (Fig. 6:12a). The clam-like toredo destroy the wood from the inside out; they enter the pile through a small opening, destroy the inside of the pile, and leave it a hollow shell. Timber piles can be made to last longer through treatment with zinc chloride, copper sulfate, or numerous patented chemicals. Creosote impregnation has proved to be one of the most efficient and long lasting means of protecting timber piles.[6:20] From 12 to 25 lb of creosote per cubic foot of timber are forced into the wood by vacuum- and pressure-treatment processes.

Timber piles tend to suffer badly from overdriving. The tops of the piles become "broomed," and the shafts are very likely to split or break, as shown in Fig. 6:12b, when stiff resistance to driving is encountered. On one lock construction job on the Mississippi River it was necessary to drive several thousand wood piles through an undisclosed stratum of cemented sand. Subsequent excavation disclosed that many of the piles

(Courtesy of R. D. Chellis)

a. *Marine borer attack.*   b. *Damage from over-driving.*
Fig. 6:12   Wood pile hazards.

had splintered and broken. It was later found necessary to spud a steel beam through the cemented stratum before driving the timber piles.

Timber piles are ordinarily capable of supporting safely from 10 to 20 tons per pile, although loads as high as 30 tons may be used in some cases. The very low cost for materials and for driving often makes timber the cheapest pile foundation per ton supported.

Precast Concrete Piles[6:21]   Precast concrete piles are uniform-section circular, square, or octagonal shafts with sufficient reinforcing to enable them to withstand handling stresses. The smaller sizes are 8 to 12 in. wide and are usually solid. Larger sizes are solid or are hollow so as to reduce their weight. Prestressing makes it possible to secure adequate strength with relatively thin concrete walls; diameters up to 54 in. with walls 4 in. thick, similar to concrete pipe, have been used where great stiffness and high bearing capacity are required.

Precast piles are used principally in marine construction and bridges where durability under extreme exposure is important and where the pile extends above the earth as an unsupported column. In the latter case the reinforcing is increased as dictated by the column requirements. Typical lengths of the small, solid piles are 50 to 60 ft, and of the longer hollow piles, up to 200 ft. Typical loads for the small piles are 30 to 50 tons, and for the larger piles, over 200 tons.

Two factors limit the use of precast piles. First they are relatively heavy

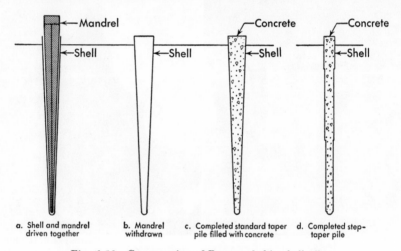

Fig. 6:13 Construction of Raymond thin-shell piles.

compared with other piles of comparable size. Second it is difficult to cut them off if they prove to be too long and even more difficult to splice them to increase their length.

Cast-in-Place Concrete Piles Concrete piles that are cast in the ground are the most widely used types of piles for 30 to 60 ton loads. These can be divided into two groups: *cased piles* in which a thin metal casing is driven into the ground to serve as a form, and *uncased* piles where the concrete is placed directly against the soil. Many types of each have been developed, and the engineer will find it enlightening to study the catalogs of pile contractors to see the different methods of construction.

The *Raymond Standard* pile (Fig. 6:13a-c) is one of the earliest cased types. A thin metal shell with an 8-in. diam tip and with a taper of 0.4 in.

in diameter for each foot of length is driven into the ground on a close-fitting steel core or mandrel. After the mandrel is withdrawn, the tapered hole, supported by the shell, is filled with concrete. This pile is employed for lengths up to 37 ft and for loads of 30 to 40 tons.

The *Raymond–Step-Taper* pile (Fig. 6:13d) consists of a series of cylindrical, corrugated sheet-metal sections, each 8 ft long and 1 in. in diameter larger than the one below and screwed together to form a continuous tube. The minimum tip diameter is 8⅝ in. but larger tips up to 13⅜ in. can be used by starting the pile with the larger cylindrical sections. The pile is driven by a loosely fitting mandrel that drives against the tip and the shoulders or *plow rings* of each larger section. Lengths up to 96 ft and loads of from 40 to 75 tons, depending on the tip diameter, are used.

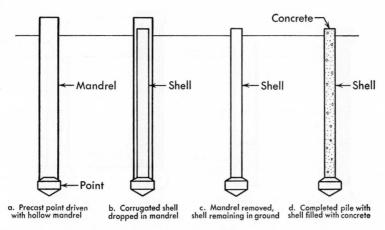

a. Precast point driven with hollow mandrel   b. Corrugated shell dropped in mandrel   c. Mandrel removed, shell remaining in ground   d. Completed pile with shell filled with concrete

Fig. 6:14   Construction of Western Button-Bottom pile.

The Western *button bottom* pile (Fig. 6:14) combines a precast point 17 in. in diameter with a cast-in-place shaft 11 in. in diameter. The point is driven into the ground on the end of a 12¾-in. diam pipe. The corrugated shell is dropped into the mandrel and locked on the point, after which the mandrel is withdrawn and the shell concreted. This enlarged base pile is particularly well adapted to developing end bearing on strata of limited capacity. Lengths of 100 ft and capacities up to 75 tons are ordinarily used.

The *Cobi pile* and the *Hercules pile* employ a cylindrical corrugated sheet-metal shell, similar to drainage pipe, from 8 to 21 in. inside diameter. The shell is closed at the lower end with a flat or cone-shaped boot. It is driven with a cylindrical steel core that expands to grip the inside of the pipe and its corrugations tightly. The Cobi-type core expands by air pressure in a rubber tube, whereas the Hercules type expands by mechanical wedging. Lengths up to 100 ft are possible.

The *Union Monotube* consists of a thin-walled, fluted steel tube that is driven into the soil without a mandrel or core. The fluting makes the thin steel shell capable of withstanding the driving stresses without buckling. Monotubes as long as 125 ft, carrying loads of 30 to 50 tons, are used. They are particularly suited to small jobs because they require no special driving equipment such as the mandrel.

The thin shell piles have a number of features in common. It is easy to cut them off if too long or to increase their length during driving by welding on more shell. They can be inspected after driving to check their

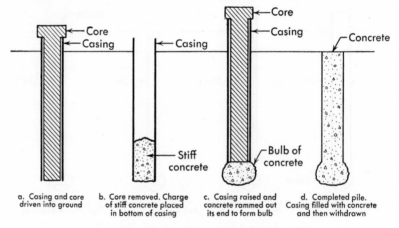

Fig. 6:15 Construction of uncased bulb pile.

straightness. The shell keeps water and soil away from the wet concrete and develops a shaft of uniform quality. The thin shells sometimes are damaged by obstructions that tear them or smooth out their corrugations and reduce their strength, or they may collapse because of the extremely high lateral pressures that develop in stiff clays and dense sands.

The uncased concrete pile formed by a temporary casing, is shown in Fig. 6:15a. A steel pipe or *casing* is first driven into the ground. Soil is kept out of the lower end by a precast concrete plug or a metal pan that is supported by a core. After driving the core is removed and the pile filled with concrete. The core is lowered into the concrete and the casing is pulled out while the core forces the concrete against the soil and prevents it from moving upward with the casing. The *bulb pile* is formed similarly except that the casing is initially only partly filled with concrete. The casing is then raised and the core forced downward by hammering, which forces the concrete out in a bulb (Fig. 6:15b and c). After forming the bulb, the casing is filled with concrete and then pulled out, leaving the bulb or *pedestal pile*. The uncased piles ordinarily are not reinforced. The bulb piles, however, make excellent tension piles but in such applications require reinforcing.

Uncased piles formed in a casing are suitable for loose sands and firm clays where the lateral pressures developed will not squeeze the unprotected fresh concrete. Lengths of 60 ft and loads of from 30 to 75 tons are the usual limits for such piles. Uncased piles require heavy driving rigs and special apparatus for pulling the casing and are economical where the size of the job justifies the initial expense of equipment.

The *Franki* uncased concrete pile is formed by ramming a charge of dry concrete in the bottom of a 20-in. steel casing so that the concrete grips the walls of the pipe and forms a plug. A 7000-lb ram falling 10 to 20 ft inside the casing forces the plug into the ground, dragging the casing downward by friction. At the bearing level, the casing is anchored to the driving rig, and the concrete plug is driven out its bottom to form a bulb over 3 ft in diameter. The casing is then raised while successive charges of concrete are rammed in place to form a rough shaft above the pedestal. Lengths up to 100 ft with capacities of from 100 to 1000 tons are typical. With reinforcement they make excellent tension piles.

The *Intrusion mixed-in-place* pile is formed by drilling a hole in the soil with a paddle-shaped drill that cuts and breaks the soil but does not remove it from the hole. At the same time a portland cement–water mixture is pumped through the drill rod to the blades where it is mixed with the pulverized soil to form a soil cement. The cement grout spreads out through loose soils, creating an irregular-diameter shaft that has intimate contact with the soil. The method is best in loose sandy soils, and it is particularly advantageous where vibration and shock of pile driving could be hazardous. Lengths up to 60 ft and diameters of from 12 to 24 in. are used with capacities of about 30 tons.

Bored piles consisting of augered holes filled with concrete can be used where the soils are firm enough to stand without support. Diameters from 6 in. up and lengths of more than 50 ft are commonly constructed. (Diameters larger than 22 in. are considered as piers and will be discussed later.)

When the soil at the bottom of the bored hole tends to cave in because it is weak or because of high ground water, it is sometimes possible to prevent collapse by injecting cement grout under pressure through the auger stem while the auger is being withdrawn and thus in effect concrete the hole from the bottom up.

Structural Steel Piles Structural steel shapes, particularly the H-pile and W sections, are widely used for bearing piles, usually when high end bearing is required on soil or rock. The cross-sectional area is small compared with the strength and makes driving much easier through

Fig. 6:16 Failure of long H-piles above ground at yield point stress in steel. Piles were driven through 100 ft of soft clay to end bearing on rock.

obstructions such as hard, cemented seams, old timbers, and even thin layers of partially weathered rock. The sections can be obtained in pieces and can be easily cut off or spliced. The sections ordinarily driven are 8BP36 to 14BP117, with working loads of from 40 to 150 tons. Wide-flange sections as deep as 36 in. have been driven, and built-up piles from channels and railroad rails are occasionally used. The lengths are limited only by driving; 14-in. H-sections over 300 ft long have been installed.

H-piles driven onto rock have demonstrated their capability of supporting loads up to the yield point of the steel. Figure 6:16 shows the local buckling of a 100 ft long H-pile driven through soft clay and then load-tested to 400 tons, approximately the yield point. Apparently the pile bites into the rock and establishes full bearing in spite of irregularities in the surface. In very hard rock, the point end is sometimes reinforced by gusset plates on the web to prevent local buckling. The H-pile penetrates soil with minimum displacement and development of heave and lateral pressure.

The structural sections have three disadvantages. First they are relatively flexible and easily deflected by boulders. In fact a few H-piles have been deflected so far that their points skidded along the bearing stratum instead of biting in. Second the soil packs between the flanges so that the friction area is equal to the rectangle which encompasses the pile rather than to the total area of the pile surface. Third, corrosion reduces the effective cross-section. In most soil a corrosion allowance of 0.05 to 0.1 in. is realistic because a heavy film of rust protects the pile from further attack. In strongly acid soils such as fill and organic matter, and in sea water, corrosion is more serious. Cathodic protection or jacketing with concrete is necessary to prevent deterioration.

Steel Pipe Piles   Steel pipes filled with concrete make excellent piles. In most cases they are driven with the tip closed by a flat plate or a conical point. The flat plates are cheapest and tend to form a conical point of soil ahead of them during driving. An X-shape of plate welded to the tip helps the pile to break through gravel and cemented layers and to bite into bed rock. Open-ended pipes are used where minimum displacement is essential. The plug of soil that pushes up into the pipe must be removed at intervals to prevent its packing and causing the pile to drive as though it had a closed end.

Both the closed-end and the open-ended pipes are filled with concrete after driving (after cleaning the open pipe, of course). This increases the shaft load capacity because both the strength of the steel and of the concrete contribute to the column strength.

Pipes from 10.75 in. OD $\times$ 0.188-in. wall to 36 in. OD $\times$ 0.50-in. wall have been driven with capacities of from 50 to more than 200 tons. Lengths are limited by the driving equipment; pipe piles over 200 ft long have been installed.

Pipes are light, easy to handle and to drive, and can be cut off and spliced readily. They are stiffer than H-piles and not so likely to deflect when they strike an obstruction. They have the distinct advantage that they can be inspected internally after driving and before concreting.

In driving steel piles, the hammer must strike squarely over the centroid of the section. An off-center or wobbling hammer will "accordion" pipes and batter structural sections, which destroys the effectiveness of the blow. The carbon content of the pile is important, for if it is too high, the pile will split; if too low, the steel will yield. On one job where 100 miles of 10.75-diam by 0.25-in. steel pipe were driven through clays in lengths up to 160 ft, it was found that cold-formed steel with 0.22 per cent carbon and 0.6 per cent manganese drove best.

Composite Piles   Composite piles are a combination of a steel or timber lower section with a cast-in-place concrete upper section. In this way it is possible to combine the economy of a wood pile below the ground water level with the durability of concrete above water, or to combine the low cost of cast-in-place concrete with the great length or relatively greater driving strength of pipes or H-sections.

The design and construction of the splice between the two sections is the key to a successful composite pile. The head of the lower section must be protected against damage; a tight joint must be maintained to exclude water and soil from the shell; good alignment between the sections must be maintained to prevent dog-legging; and the splice must be as strong as the weakest member it connects.

Two methods are used. In one the lower section is driven its full length. The metal shell, on its driving core, is attached to the lower section, and the whole assembly is driven to the final penetration. The core is then withdrawn and the shell concreted. A second method (Fig. 6:17) consists in driving a steel casing first. The core is withdrawn and the lower section is placed in the casing like a projectile in a gun. The lower section is then driven out the casing by the core. The thin steel shell for the cast-in-place section is lowered into the casing and locked on the lower section, after which the casing is withdrawn and the pile concreted.

Composite wood-concrete piles 140 ft long and steel pipe–concrete piles 180 ft long have been used with loads of up to 30 and 60 tons, respectively.

Sand Piles   Holes rammed into soil and filled with sand or crushed slag for the purpose of compacting and draining a soil are known as *sand* or *wick* piles. They have little structural strength other than that of the compacted sand. They are constructed in the same way as uncased cast-in-place concrete piles but a free draining material is used instead of concrete.

6:6   Design of Pile Foundations

The design of a pile foundation is similar to the design of any other part of a structure. It consists of assuming a design, then checking the proposed design for safety and revising it until it is satisfactory. Several such designs are then compared, and the final one is selected on the basis of cost and time required for construction.

Piles in a foundation may be valueless in some locations, and under some conditions their use actually may be very harmful. For example, a layer of reasonably firm soil over a deep bed of soft soil might act as a

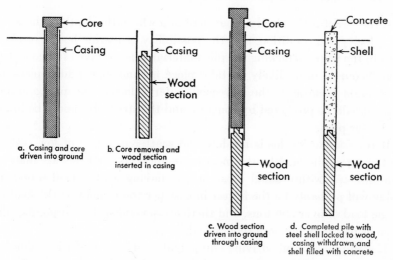

Fig. 6:17   Construction of projectile-type wood-concrete composite pile.

natural mat to distribute the load of a shallow-footing foundation. The driving of piles into the firm layer might break it up or remold it. The result would be a concentration of load in the soft soil strata, with excessive settlement likely to take place.

Selection of Pile Length   The selection of the approximate pile length is made from a study of the soil profile and the strength and compressibility of each soil stratum. Such studies may be made by using the methods of pile group analysis discussed in Art. 6:4. End-bearing piles must reach a stratum that is capable of supporting the entire foundation without undue settlement or failure, and friction piles must be long enough to distribute the stresses through the soil mass so as to minimize settlement and obtain adequate safety of the entire group of piles.

Selection of Possible Pile Types   The pile type and the material from which it can be made must be carefully chosen to fit:

(1) The superimposed load.
(2) The amount of time available for the completion of the job.
(3) The characteristics of the soil strata through which it penetrates as well as that of the strata to which the load must be transferred.
(4) The ground water conditions.
(5) The size of the job.
(6) The availability of equipment and getting it onto the site.
(7) The availability of material for the piles.
(8) The building code requirements.

If the structure is a bridge abutment or a wharf, the depth of the water, its velocity, ice condition, and the possibility of marine borers or chemicals in the water attacking the pile material must be given full consideration. Scour is quite likely to take place around new bridge piers and abutments because of the increased water velocity; the piling in such cases should be protected by concrete and the structure should be braced by batter piles.

If the foundation loads are low and scattered, a pile of low cost per foot and per pile may be the most economical. If the loads are high and concentrated within small areas, a pile having a high load-supporting value will probably be the lowest in cost per ton of load. If the load is a single load of over 300 tons, and there are several such load points, some type of pier may be more economical.

The shipping of pile-driving equipment is always expensive. The contractor who has his equipment within truck-hauling distance of a job has a marked advantage over the contractor who must load and unload his equipment from railroad cars. A few piles required on a job do not justify the cost of moving heavy, large pile-driving equipment. Light, easily handled piles, which may be driven by equipment that will be used for erecting the superstructure may provide the most economical job. When the job includes several hundred piles 40 ft and longer, the large pile-driving rigs are more economical, since more piles can be driven per working shift and a greater variety of pile types is available.

If a pile foundation job is located in the heavy timber portions of the country, the delivered price of wood piles is low. Therefore the total cost of using many piles at 15 tons each is less than that of using concrete piles at 30 tons each.

Since concrete is generally a part of every construction job, it is available in all parts of the country for piling. Steel may be cheaper in industrial areas but may be more expensive when the job is a long distance from the mill.

The characteristics of handling and shipping the piles may influence the choice of type. The ability to "nest" pile shells one within another makes a more compact load, especially for shipment by water. Light weight with high resistance to rough handling is a decided advantage with steel pipe piles, fluted pile shells, and the corrugated shells used as a part of many cast-in-place piles. Wood piles are also light and easy to handle. Long H-beams and precast concrete piles must be handled in slings to prevent bending or breaking.

The requirements of building codes are becoming more uniform throughout the country. Codes generally specify certain maximum loads allowed per pile and more generally are providing for load tests to determine the allowable maximum loads.

Pile Design Loads The design of the pile shaft is governed by stresses produced by driving. During driving the actual or working load on the shaft equals the failure load between the pile and the soil, R_0. The driving stresses can be estimated from equation 6:3b, regardless of the type of soil because only the dynamic resistance is concerned. The shaft should have a safety factor of at least 1.3 with respect to R_0, which means that the safety factor with respect to the design load, Q_0 is larger than for other short columns. The safe load on the pile is governed by the soil-to-pile connection and the group capacity. These are analyzed as described in Art. 6:3 and 6:4, and the appropriate safety factor applied depending on the reliability of the analyses and the structural loading data.

Spacing The final pile spacing is based on the analysis of pile group action. The piles are placed so that the capacity of the pile group acting as a unit is equal to the sum of the capacities of the individual piles.

Inspection and Records No important pile-driving job should be carried out without competent engineering inspection and the keeping of complete records of the driving of every pile. The field reports should record the following:

(1) Time, weather, and working conditions.
(2) Type and size of hammer, weight of driving ram, weight of driving cap.
(3) Actual length of the hammer stroke.
(4) The number of blows struck per minute by the hammer.
(5) Steam or air pressure at the hammer or boiler. The length of pipe and hose between the boiler and hammer should be noted.

(6) Length driven.
(7) Number of blows of continuous driving required to drive the last foot or few inches. The count should not begin until the pile is in motion if there has been a suspension of driving.
(8) Rebound or bounce of the pile. This may be observed by enscribing a graph on the surface of the pile with a fixed bar or crayon.
(9) Suspension of driving if prior to the final penetration.
(10) The condition of the inside of *every* pile shell *immediately* before filling with concrete. (An electric light or flashlight on a line, sunlight reflected by mirrors, a burning ball of oil soaked rags, or other light source may be used.)
(11) Heaving of the adjacent ground.
(12) Shrinkage of the adjacent ground.
(13) Heaving of the piles after driving or heaving of the soft concrete inside the pile shell.

6:7   Pile Cap

The load of a wall or column must be transferred to the pile by means of a footing or pile cap. In designing the cap, consideration must be given to the fact that the pile butts may be from 2 to 4 in. out of their required position. In some cases the piles may be pulled or jacked into position, depending on the rigidity of the pile and the soil, but it is cheaper if the pile cap is designed with allowances for some misalignment. In dock structures the pile must resist horizontal forces and often must resist rotation. In such cases the pile must be anchored to the cap by adequate embedment and in some cases with reinforcing steel. The structural design of the cap is similar to the design of a footing foundation. Care must be taken to see that the footing is rigid enough to transfer the load to the outermost piles in the group.

6:8   Pier Foundations

The pier foundation is a relatively large, deep foundation. Its function is to transfer a foundation load through soft soil to hard soil or rock or to transfer a load through soils that may be scoured away by river or tidal currents. The chief differences between piles and piers are size (piles larger than 24 in. in diameter are sometimes called *piers*) and the method of construction. Piles are ordinarily forced into the ground without previous excavation whereas piers usually require soil excavation ahead of or during their construction.

Piers are divided into two classes, *open shafts* and *caissons*, depending on the method of construction. Open shafts are merely deep excavations that are provided with bracing or lining as the work progresses. A caisson is a box or chamber that excludes water and soil from the excavation. It is usually constructed above ground and then sunk to the required level by excavation from within. The word caisson is often applied to any pier but, strictly speaking, it refers only to those that employ the box or chamber that is lowered as excavation proceeds.

The materials employed and the type of structure are dependent upon the load, ground water conditions, depth of load-supporting strata, building code requirements, and the availability of materials and equipment. If the pier is to be in water, the velocity of the water, its maximum depth under scouring conditions, and the effect of ice and debris must be provided for in the design.

Bearing Capacity and Settlement   A pier is actually an oversized footing foundations that is supported by end bearing and by shear or friction along its sides. The end bearing is computed by the general bearing-capacity equation (5.3), using the appropriate bearing-capacity factors in Fig. 6:7. The skin friction on the pier is either friction plus adhesion or shear strength, whichever is the smaller. In computing friction and shear, no allowance is made for any increase in lateral pressure from displacement because the piers are constructed by excavation. Ordinarily piers depend primarily on end bearing on relatively rigid strata. Even though the soil strength indicates that potentially there is some skin friction, it is not mobilized by the time the pier fails in end bearing. Therefore skin friction is frequently neglected in design.

The settlement of piers is often the governing factor in their design. Settlement can be estimated by the methods described in Chapter 5, by assuming the end of the pier to be a footing. The stresses in the soil below such a "footing" are considerably less than those computed by the Boussinesq or Westergaard methods because those analyses are based on loads at the ground surface. Based on the Mindlin[6;22] analyses the stresses beneath a narrow deep end-bearing pier can be as little as half those computed by surface load methods.

Open Shafts   The simplest form of the open shaft is an open excavation similar to a dug well (Fig. 6:18a and b). Shallow wells in firm soil can be dug by hand. Large power augers are capable of drilling open excavations as large as 84 in. in diameter and more than 60 ft deep. Special underreaming drills can be used to enlarge or *bell out* the bottom of the shaft to nearly double the shaft diameter. After it is drilled, the shaft is filled with concrete to form the pier.

When the pier must extend below the ground water level, or when the soil is not strong enough to stand without support, some form of bracing is required. The simplest is a metal cylinder that is lowered into the shaft immediately after drilling to hold it open until the concrete can be placed. The cylinder is lifted out as the concrete is poured, because the pressure of the wet concrete is ordinarily capable of supporting the soil and keeping out water. In very soft or wet soils it is sometimes necessary to drill and install lining cylinders successively in short sections, 8 to 16 ft long. The cylinders telescope, forming a tapering shaft known as the *Gow caisson* (Fig. 6:18c). Piers as deep as 100 ft with belled bottoms have been installed by this method, using both hand and auger excavation.

If the pier rests on rock, a man is lowered into the hole to clean the

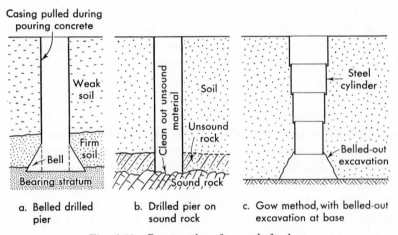

Fig. 6:18   Construction of open shaft piers.

surface so that there is no soil between the rock and the concrete. This is hazardous because of gas and danger of blow ins. If the rock is seamy or the surface is badly weathered, it is sometimes necessary to remove the unsound materials by air hammers or even blasting. A level bottom is unnecessary. If the surface is steep, the pier should be keyed to it by a socket into the rock or by steel dowels placed in drilled holes.

The *Chicago well* is an open shaft lined with vertical wood sheeting held in place by steel hoops inside the shaft. It is dug by hand and the sheeting installed in 4- to 6-ft lengths. Shafts as deep as 200 ft and 12 ft in diameter have been placed by this method.

The wet excavation method is sometimes used in soils that are too soft to permit open excavation without support. A large rotary well drill bores a hole that is the diameter of the finished pier. The hole is kept full of a mixture of clay, water, and heavy minerals that has the same unit weight as the soil and which provides an internal pressure that keeps the hole open. After drilling, a cylindrical steel shell is lowered into the excavation, and then the mud is replaced by clean water. Concrete is tremied through the water to form the pier. Such methods do not permit thorough cleaning of the excavation or an inspection of the stratum on which the pier rests.

Caissons   Three forms of caisson are used in the United States; the caisson pile, the open caisson, and the pneumatic caisson. The caisson

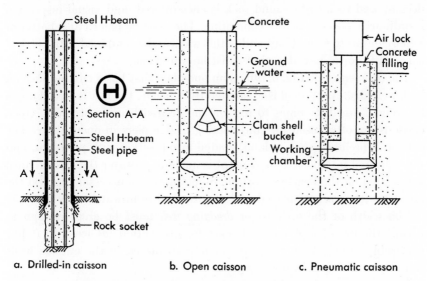

Fig. 6:19   Construction of different types of caissons.

pile is a large diameter pipe (24 to 60 in. in diameter) which is driven with open ends by a very large pile-driving rig. The soil within the pipe is excavated, after which the pipe may be entered for inspection or for cleaning the surface on which the caisson rests. It is then filled with concrete to form the pier.

In the process known as the *drilled-in-caisson* (Fig. 6:19a) the pipe is fitted with a tool-steel cutting edge that can be driven into rock. The soil inside can be removed with a small-size bucket, by blowing out with a jet of compressed air, by driving a coring tube into the soil and then pulling the tube, or by adding water and churning the soil into a slurry, after which it can be bailed out. After cleaning, a large well drill bit is placed inside the pipe and used to drill a socket in the rock. The pipe is then driven until the cutting edge develops a watertight seal against the rock. The drilling continues until a socket from 2 to 10 ft deep is formed in the solid rock. The caissons may be unwatered and the rock sockets inspected before concreting. In order to increase their column capacity, they may be provided with a steel H-beam core. Drilled-in-caissons have been built with diameters from 24 to 30 in., as long as 250 ft, and with capacities as high as 2000 tons each. They have the advantages that any type of soil may be penetrated and obstructions such as boulders can be drilled out, they can be extended through partially decomposed rock until sound rock is encountered, and visual inspection is ordinarily possible before concreting. They can be placed at a batter of 1 (horizontal) to 6 (vertical) and in this way can be combined with vertical caissons to form A-frames that resist lateral loads.

The open caisson (Fig. 6:19b) is an open box that has a cutting shoe on its lower edge. As the soil is excavated from inside, the box is forced down by weights until it comes to rest on the desired bearing stratum. Open caissons are often used for constructing bridge piers in open water. The caisson is prefabricated on land, floated into position with pontoons, and then lowered into place. No attempt is made to unwater the caisson until it is seated on the bearing stratum. Sometimes it is necessary to seal the bottom with concrete placed under water before unwatering is possible.

The width of the opening or *dredging well* must be great enough to permit the use of a clamshell bucket for excavation (at least 10 ft but preferably more). Water jets are sometimes placed in the outside walls to reduce friction during sinking.

Large caissons for bridge piers are made up of a number of small caissons, or *cells*, each with an independent dredging well but all opening into a common bottom chamber. The depth to which open caissons may be extended is limited by skin friction which overcomes the effects of weighting. Boulders and other obstructions that catch under the cutting edge may limit the depth, since it is difficult to remove them.[6:23]

Pneumatic Caissons. Compressed air or pneumatic caissons must be used when an acceptable bearing strata cannot be reached by open caisson methods because of water conditions. The high cost is justified only where the loads to be supported are very high.

The pneumatic caisson (Fig. 6:19c) is like an inverted tumbler lowered into water. It is a box with an open bottom and an airtight roof or cover that is filled with compressed air to keep the water and mud from coming into the box. The lower section is a working chamber in which the excavating is carried on and the pier is constructed. Above the working chamber is the air lock, which permits the workmen and materials to enter and leave without loss of air pressure in the working chamber.

The pneumatic caisson process provides a better means for controlling the sinking of the caisson and makes possible the removal of boulders, logs, and debris from under the cutting shoe. Also the foundation bed upon the rock or bearing strata can be better prepared and inspected.

The workmen have to work under air pressure sufficient to balance the pressure of the surrounding mud and water. This working pressure limits the depth to which peneumatic caissons may be used and greatly slows down the progress of sinking the caisson. There are numerous hazards in the use of the pneumatic caisson and only experienced engineers and contractors should undertake their design and use.

6:9 Underpinning

Underpinning is the construction of new foundations under existing structures. The underpinning of structures is a highly specialized type of foundation engineering involving construction methods adapted to very limited working space and the handling of soils already under load. The work is done by only a few highly skilled contractors whose many years of experience qualify them for such exacting and critical work.[6:24]

Underpinning is necessary when the foundations of a structure prove incapable of supporting the structure with adequate safety or without undue settlement. Underpinning also is required when changing conditions, such as the construction of a nearby building with a deep basement or the excavation for a subway, make existing foundations inadequate.

Two procedures are commonly used: first, installing new foundations in small pits excavated beneath the existing foundations; and second, installing new foundations adjacent to the old and transferring the load between new and old with steel beams.

The pit method (Fig. 6:20a) requires excavating a small hole beneath part of the existing foundation. A new, deep footing is poured in this hole, or pipe piles are forced into the soil by jacking against the existing foundation. The pipes, in sections about 2 ft long, are jacked into the soil and then excavated by small buckets, a steam jet, or augers. The new foundation is placed section by section so that the old foundation is never without some support.

The second method (Fig. 6:20b) involves driving piles or constructing a new foundation as close as possible to the old. This is necessary when the old foundation is so small or weak that a pit beneath it is impossible. It is often cheaper than the pit method, for more room in which to work is available. The load is transferred from the old to the new foundation by horizontal *needle beams* which are placed beneath the old footing or through it.

The transfer of the load from the old to the new foundation is accompanied by some settlement. This may be eliminated by jacking the new foundation against the old until the new carries the load. The settlement is prevented by extending the jack as the new foundation deflects under load. After the new foundation has stopped settling, the jack is replaced

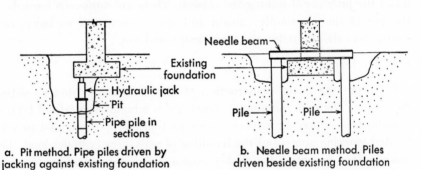

a. Pit method. Pipe piles driven by jacking against existing foundation

b. Needle beam method. Piles driven beside existing foundation

Fig. 6:20 Methods for underpinning an existing foundation with piles. Where the new bearing stratum is close to the surface deep footings or piers are substituted for the piles.

by steel wedges which are then encased in concrete. This is known as the *Pretest method* of underpinning and was originally developed by *Lazarus White*.[6:24]

REFERENCES

6:1 "Warrington Vulcan Single-Acting Steam Pile Hammer," Bulletin 68D, Vulcan Iron Works, Chicago.

6:2 "Super Vulcan Differential-Acting Pile Hammer," Bulletin 70D, Vulcan Iron Works, Chicago.

6:3 "McKiernan–Terry Double-Acting Pile Hammers and Extractors," Bulletin 68, McKiernan–Terry Corp., Dover, N.J.

6:4 "McKiernan–Terry Diesel Pile Hammers," Bulletin 674, McKiernan–Terry Corp.. Dover, N.J.

6:5 "Diesel Pile Hammers," Catalog 2582B, Link Belt Corp., Cedar Rapids, Iowa, 1959.

6:6 D. D. Barkan, "Foundation Engineering and Drilling by the Vibration Method," *Proceedings, Fourth International Conference on Soil Mechanics and Foundation Engineering*, Vol. 2, London, 1957, p. 3.

6:7 A. E. Cummings, "The Stability of Foundation Piles Against Buckling Under Axial Loads," *Proceedings, Highway Research Board*, Vol. 18, 1938, p. 112.

6:8 L. Bjerrum, "Norwegian Experiences with Steel Piles to Rock," *Geotechnique*, Vol. 7, No. 2, June, 1957, p. 73.

6:9 J. D. Parsons and S. D. Wilson, "Safe Loads on Dog-Leg Piles," *Transactions, ASCE*, Vol. 121, 1956, p. 695.

6:10 G. G. Meyerhof, "Compaction of Sands and Bearing Capacity of Piles," *Journal of Soil Mechanics and Foundations Division, Proceedings, ASCE*, Vol. 85, SM 6, December, 1959.

6:11 L. C. Reese and H. B. Seed, "Pressure Distribution Along Friction Piles," *Proceedings, ASTM*, 1955.

6:12 H. O. Ireland, "Pulling Tests on Piles in Sand," *Proceedings, Fourth International Conference on Soil Mechanics and Foundation Engineering*, Vol. II, London, 1957, p. 43.

6:13 G. G. Meyerhof: "The Ultimate Bearing Capacity of Foundations," *Geotechnique*, Vol. 2, No. 4, December, 1951, p. 301.

6:14 M. J. Tomlinson, "The Adhesion of Piles Driven in Clay Soils," *Proceedings, Fourth International Conference on Soil Mechanics and Foundation Engineering*, Vol. 2, London, 1957, p. 66.

6:15 W. W. Moore, "Experiences with Predetermining Pile Lengths," *Transactions, ASCE*, Vol. 114, 1949, p. 351.

6:16 R. D. Chellis, *Pile Foundations*, McGraw-Hill Book Co., Inc., 1951.

6:17 G. F. Sowers, L. Wilson, B. Martin, and M. Fausold, "Model Tests of Friction Pile Groups in Homogeneous Clay," *Proceedings, Fifth International Conference on Soil Mechanics and Foundation Engineering*, Paris, 1961.

6:18 A. Hrennikoff, "Analysis of Pile Foundations with Batter Piles," *Transactions, ASCE*, 1950, p. 351.

6:19 R. D. Chellis, "Finding and Fighting Marine Borers," *Engineering News Record*, March 4, March 18, April 1, April 15, 1948.

6:20 "Pressure Treated Timber Foundation Piles," American Wood Preservers Institute, Chicago, 1955.

6:21 *Concrete Piles*, Portland Cement Association, Chicago, 1949.

6:22 R. D. Mindlin, "Force at a Point in the Interior of a Semi-Infinite Elastic Solid," *Physics*, Vol. 7, 1936, p. 195.

6:23 C. W. Dunham, *Foundations of Structures*, McGraw-Hill Book Co., Inc., New York, 1950, p. 470.

6:24 E. A. Prentis and L. White, *Underpinning*, 2d ed., Columbia University Press, New York, 1950.

Suggestions for Additional Study

1. References 6:16, 6:23, 6:24.
2. F. D. C. Henry, *The Design and Construction of Engineering Foundations*, McGraw-Hill Book Co., Inc., New York, 1956.
3. E. E. Seelye, *Foundations Design and Practice*, John Wiley & Sons, Inc., New York, 1956.
4. J. H. Thornley, *Foundation Design and Practice*, Columbia University Press, New York, 1959.
5. J. Leonards, *et al.*, *Foundation Engineering*, McGraw-Hill Book Co., Inc., New York, 1961.
6. *Sweets Catalog File—Engineering*.
7. Catalogs of pile-driving contractors and manufacturers of piling and pile-driving equipment who advertise in *Civil Engineering*, *Engineering News Record*, and similar magazines are valuable sources of information on pile foundations.

PROBLEMS

6:1   Prepare a table showing the point diameters, point areas, and surface areas of the lower 10 ft of different sizes of concrete, steel, and wood piles. Consult the catalogs of different pile-driving contractors and manufacturers of wood and steel piling.

6:2   A wood pile with an 8-in. diam tip and a 14-in. diam butt 35 ft long is driven into a dry loose sand weighing 107 lb per cu ft; angle of internal friction of 32°. Compute its bearing capacity.

6:3   A 10BP57 steel pile 40 ft long is driven into saturated clay weighing 110 lb per cu ft and having an undisturbed c of 2000 psf and a remolded c of 1000 psf. Compute its skin friction, assuming (1) the skin friction is developed over the entire pile surface and (2) the skin friction is developed along the surface of a rectangle that encloses the pile. Depending on which governs, compute the end bearing for either the gross area of the enclosing rectangle or the net area of the pile. (Use the undisturbed c for end bearing and the remolded c for skin friction.)

6:4   A 14-in. OD pipe pile 150 ft long with a flat end is driven into a deep deposit of clay having the following characteristics:

Depth (ft)	c (psf)	Weight (lb/cu ft)
0–40	1600	120
40–110	500	105
110–140	900	110
140–180	3400	130

Water table is at ground surface.

a. Compute the capacity in kips.

b. If 25 of these piles are to be driven in a group, determine the minimum spacing to ensure that the group capacity will not be less than the sum of the capacities of the individual piles.

6:5 A steam hammer weighing 3000 lb and falling 29 in. is used to drive a precast concrete pile 12 in. square and 40 ft long. The total bounce is 0.3 in. per blow, and the driving resistance is 4 blows per inch. The coefficient of restitution is estimated to be 0.25 and the value of c_1 is 0.2 in.

    a. Compute the safe capacity by the Hiley formula, using a safety factor of 2.

    b. Compute the safe capacity by the *Engineering News* formula.

    c. How do they differ and why?

6:6 A steam hammer weighing 1000 lb that falls 3 ft is used to drive wood piling. Compute the dynamic resistance according to the *Engineering News* formula if the pile penetrates $\frac{1}{2}$ in. under each of the last few hammer blows.

6:7 Compute the safe bearing capacity of a steel $10\frac{3}{4}$ OD $\times \frac{1}{4}$ in. wall pipe pile 45 ft long driven into sand by a steam hammer with a 5000-lb ram and 36-in. stroke. The "bounce" is measured and found to be 0.3 in., and the net penetration or "set" is 0.4 in. per blow. The hammer efficiency is 75 per cent and the coefficient of restitution of the pile hammer on the pile cap is estimated to be 0.20; c_1 is 0.1 in.

    a. Compute the safe load, using the Hiley formula and including a safety factor of 2.

    b. Compute the safe load, using the *Engineering News* formula.

    c. Which shows the greater safe load and why?

6:8 A pile load test produces the following data. The pile is 10 in. $\times$ 10 in., 57-lb H-section.

Load (tons)	Settlement (in.)	Load (tons)	Settlement (in.)
20	$\frac{1}{8}$	80	$\frac{9}{16}$
40	$\frac{1}{4}$	100	$\frac{13}{16}$
60	$\frac{3}{8}$	120	$1\frac{1}{2}$

    a. Find the safe pile load, using a safety factor of 2.

    b. How much of the above settlement can be attributed to elastic shortening of the pile if the pile is assumed to be end bearing? Assumed length of pile is 30 ft.

6:9 A machine weighing 2500 kips is to be supported on piles. The wood piles at 20 tons must be 40 ft long, and steel pipe piles loaded to 50 tons must be 50 ft long. Which will be cheaper? The wood piles will cost $2.25 per ft driven; the pipe piles, $5.00 per ft.

6:10 An anchor consists of a vertical tension pile and a pile driven on a batter of 1 (horizontal) to 3 (vertical). Both piles are 70 ft long. If the horizontal load is 20 kips, compute the load in each pile. Assume the piles hinged at both ends.

6:11 Prepare a report describing a pile or caisson construction job. Include the
following items:
- (1) Soil profile.
- (2) Reason for selection of piles or caissons.
- (3) Equipment.
- (4) Description of features of piles and their construction.
- (5) Tests, if any.

7 ... PROBLEMS in EARTH PRESSURE

Engineering structures such as retaining walls, trench and excavation bracing, bulkheads, and cofferdams have a common function—to provide lateral support for a mass of soil. The pressure exerted by the soil on these structures is known as *earth pressure* and must be determined before a satisfactory design can be made.

Some of the earliest theories of soil mechanics dealt with earth pressure on retaining walls. Unfortunately the engineers using these theories have not always realized the significance of the assumptions made in their development. The result has been many failures and a discrediting of soil mechanics by engineers who have had to deal with soils in construction work—an attitude that persists today.

The design of retaining structures is complicated by the fact that the earth pressure is not a fixed property which depends on the character of the soil alone. Instead, it is also a function of the structure that supports the soil and particularly of the deflection or movement of the structure.

7:1 Theory of Earth Pressure

The general theory of earth pressure can be developed from the stresses in an extremely large, level mass of soil. The total vertical stress in a mass of soil at a depth of z is equal to the weight of the soil above. When ground water is present, the vertical stress can be separated into two components: neutral stress and effective stress, as previously described.

$$\sigma_v = \gamma z, \tag{7:1a}$$
$$\bar{\sigma}_v = \gamma z - u. \tag{7:1b}$$

241

Earth Pressure at Rest   The stress conditions of an element of soil at depth z are shown in Fig. 7:1a.   The element can deform vertically under load, but it cannot expand laterally because it is confined by the same soil under the same loading conditions. This is equivalent to the soil being placed against an immovable frictionless wall that maintains the same lateral dimension in the soil regardless of the vertical load. The soil is in a state of *elastic equilibrium*, and the stresses in the lateral direction can be computed from the stress-strain relationships of the soil. The relation between lateral and vertical strain is described by Poisson's ratio

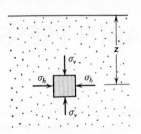
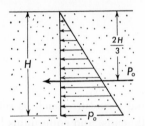

a. Horizontal and vertical stresses   b. Pressure distribution and resultant
in a soil mass at depth Z   force, P_o, on vertical surface
                                                              of height, H

Fig. 7:1   Earth pressure at rest.

(Art. 2:17), and for the condition of zero lateral strain the principal stresses are related by

$$\frac{\sigma_3}{\sigma_1} = \frac{\nu}{1 - \nu}. \tag{2:30a}$$

The lateral pressure exerted in the at-rest state is given the symbol p_0 and can be computed from the vertical stress σ_v in a dry soil by

$$\sigma_h = \sigma_v \frac{\nu}{1 - \nu} = p_0,$$

$$p_0 = \gamma z \left(\frac{\nu}{1 - \nu}\right) = K_0 \gamma z \qquad \text{(dry soil).} \tag{7:2a}$$

Below the water table the pressure is found from its effective and neutral components:

$$\bar{p}_0 = (\gamma z - u)K_0 \qquad \text{(wet soil, effective),} \tag{7:2b}$$

$$p_0 = (\gamma z - u)K_0 + u \qquad \text{(wet soil, total).} \tag{7:2c}$$

K_0 is the *coefficient of earth pressure at rest* and is found from Poisson's ratio. The value of K_0 for saturated clays in undrained loading or quick loading is sometimes also expressed in total stresses that include the neutral stress, and for which equation 7:2a should be used.

Table 7:1 VALUES OF K_0

Soil	K_0, effective, Drained	K_0, total, Undrained
Soft clay	0.6	1.0
Hard clay	0.5	0.8
Loose sand, gravel	0.6	
Dense sand, gravel	0.4	

The total pressure at any depth is the sum of the effective and the neutral stresses (except where the undrained total K_0 is used with saturated clays).

The resultant force per unit of width of the wall, P_0, acting on a wall of height H, can be found by integrating equation 7:2a or from the pressure

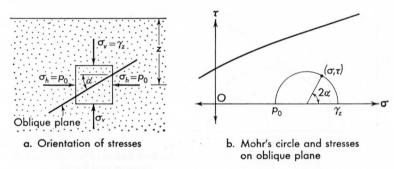

a. Orientation of stresses

b. Mohr's circle and stresses on oblique plane

Fig. 7:2 Mohr's circle for earth pressure at rest.

diagram (Fig. 7:1b). For a dry soil (or a saturated clay in undrained loading), the diagram is triangular and the resultant force is

$$P_0 = \frac{K_0\gamma H^2}{2},$$

(7:3a)

and the location of the resultant is at a depth of

$$z = \frac{2H}{3}.$$

(7:3b)

With ground water the effective and neutral pressure diagrams must be computed separately and the magnitude and location of the resultant found by the methods of mechanics.

The stress conditions in the soil mass are far from failure, as can be seen in Fig. 7:2. Stresses in an oblique direction can be computed by Mohr's circle.

Active Earth Pressure If the unyielding frictionless vertical wall of the at-rest condition is allowed to move away from the soil, each element of soil adjacent to the wall can expand laterally. The vertical stress remains constant, but the lateral stress or earth pressure is reduced in the same way the stress in a compressed spring becomes less as the spring is allowed to expand. Initially the stress reduction is elastic and proportional to the deformation; but as the difference between the major and minor principal stresses increases with the reduction in lateral stress, the diameter of Mohr's circle grows until the circle touches the rupture envelope. The lateral pressure has reached a *minimum* at this point; the stress conditions are no longer elastic; the soil mass behind the wall is in a state of shear failure; and further movement of the wall will just continue the failure with little change in pressure.

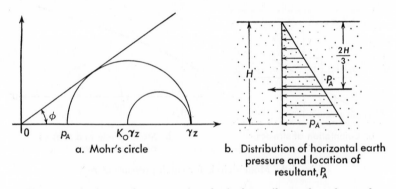

| a. Mohr's circle | b. Distribution of horizontal earth pressure and location of resultant, P_A |

Fig. 7:3   Active earth pressure in cohesionless soils, sands and gravels.

The minimum horizontal pressure p_A at any depth z for dry sands and gravels can be found from the Mohr diagram at failure (Fig. 7:3a) and is

$$p_A = \frac{\gamma z}{\tan^2 [45 + (\phi/2)]}, \tag{7:4a}$$

$$p_A = \gamma z \tan^2 \left(45 - \frac{\phi}{2}\right). \tag{7:4b}$$

The expression $\tan^2 [45 - (\phi/2)]$ is often called the *coefficient of active earth pressure* and is given the symbol K_A. The state of shear failure accompanying the minimum earth pressure is called the *active state*. The resultant force P_A per unit of width of wall for the dry sand can be found by integrating the expression for active pressure or from the area of the pressure diagram:

$$P_A = \frac{\gamma H^2 K_A}{2}. \qquad (7:5)$$

The action line is through the centroid at a depth of $2H/3$ (Fig. 7:3b).

If the sand is below water, neutral stress must again be considered. The effective active pressure is computed from the effective vertical pressure and K_A. The total is the sum of the effective and the neutral stress:

$$\bar{p}_A = (\gamma z - u)K_A, \qquad (7:6a)$$
$$p_A = (\gamma z - u)K_A + u. \qquad (7:6b)$$

When a dry cohesionless soil is inundated by a rising water table, the effective pressure is reduced to about half its original value. The total pressure, however, is approximately tripled. The location and magnitude of the resultant for a cohesionless soil below water is found by combining the effective and neutral stress diagrams.

Example 7:1   Compute the active earth pressure at a depth of 15 ft in a sand whose angle of internal friction is 37° and which weighs 97 lb per cu ft dry and 123 lb per cu ft inundated.

(1) The sand is dry throughout.
$$p_A = \gamma z \tan^2 [45 - (\phi/2)],$$
$$p_A = 97 \times 15 \times (0.5)^2,$$
$$p_A = 363 \text{ lb psf.}$$

(2) The water table is at a depth of 5 ft.
$$\bar{p}_A = (\gamma z - u) \tan^2 [45 - (\phi/2)],$$
$$\bar{p}_A = (5 \times 97 + 10 \times 123 - 10 \times 62.4) \times (0.5)^2,$$
$$\bar{p}_A = 1091 \times 0.25 = 273 \text{ psf,}$$
$$p_A = \bar{p}_A + u = 272 + 10 \times 62.4,$$
$$p_A = 897 \text{ psf.}$$

A similar analysis for saturated clay in undrained loading, using Mohr's circle, (Fig. 7:4a), gives the formula for the active pressure as

$$p_A = \gamma z - 2c. \qquad (7:7)$$

The total force per foot width of wall, P_A, is given by the expression

$$P_A = \frac{\gamma H^2}{2} - 2cH. \qquad (7:8)$$

According to this formula the resultant earth force will be zero when the height of the wall is $4c/\gamma$. This is why clay often stands unsupported in high, vertical banks. The pressure diagram (Fig. 7:4b) indicates that the clay is in tension to a depth of $2c/\gamma$. The tension causes vertical cracks and causes the clay to pull away from the wall. The tension part of the pressure diagram disappears, leaving a positive pressure against the bottom part of the wall. Thus a short wall up to the depth of $2c/\gamma$ should theoretically support the clay in spite of the cracking. However, water that accumulates in the cracks will add to the horizontal pressure and will require more support. The development of tension cracks explains why vertical cuts in clay sometimes fail without warning, weeks after they were made, and why many of the failures occur during wet weather.

Passive State   If, instead of moving away from the soil, the wall moves toward the soil, the pressure against the wall increases. The stress circles increase to the right of the vertical stress γz, which now

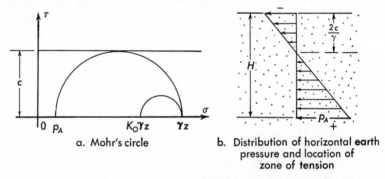

a. Mohr's circle

b. Distribution of horizontal earth pressure and location of zone of tension

Fig. 7:4   Active earth pressure in saturated cohesive soils, clays.

becomes the minor principal stress. The maximum pressure against the wall is reached as shear failure again occurs in the soil behind the wall.

For dry cohesionless soils the pressure at any depth can be found by Mohr's diagram (Fig. 7:5a) and is

$$p_P = \gamma z \tan^2\left(45 + \frac{\phi}{2}\right), \tag{7:9}$$

where p_P is the maximum or *passive earth pressure*. The expression $\tan^2[45 + (\phi/2)]$ is often called the *coefficient of passive earth pressure* and is given the symbol K_P.

The total force per foot width of wall of height H is found from the pressure diagram (Fig. 7:5b):

$$P_P = \frac{\gamma H^2}{2} K_P. \tag{7:10}$$

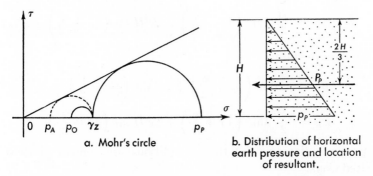

a. Mohr's circle

b. Distribution of horizontal earth pressure and location of resultant.

Fig. 7:5 Passive earth pressure in cohesionless soils, sands and gravels.

The action line is horizontal and is at a depth of $2/3H$.

Below the water table the effect of neutral stress is handled in the same way as for the active state.

For saturated clays in undrained loading, the passive pressure is found by Mohr's circle (Fig. 7:6a) to be

$$p_P = \gamma z + 2c. \tag{7:11}$$

The total force for a 1-ft width of wall is found from the pressure diagram (Fig. 7:6b) and is

$$P_P = \frac{\gamma H^2}{2} + 2cH. \tag{7:12}$$

For soils such as partially saturated clays whose shearing resistance is given by the formula $s = c' + p \tan \phi'$, the following formulas may be derived with the aid of Mohr's diagrams. For the active state:

$$p_A = \gamma z \tan^2 \left(45 - \frac{\phi'}{2}\right) - 2c' \tan \left(45 - \frac{\phi'}{2}\right), \tag{7:13}$$

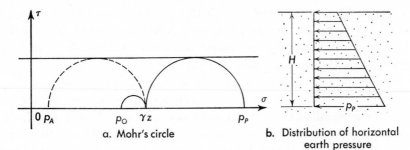

a. Mohr's circle

b. Distribution of horizontal earth pressure

Fig. 7:6 Passive earth pressure in saturated cohesive soils, clays.

$$P_A = \frac{\gamma H^2}{2} \tan^2 \left(45 - \frac{\phi'}{2} \right) - 2c'H \tan \left(45 - \frac{\phi'}{2} \right). \qquad (7:14)$$

For the passive state:

$$p_P = \gamma z \tan^2 \left(45 + \frac{\phi'}{2} \right) + 2c' \tan \left(45 + \frac{\phi'}{2} \right), \qquad (7:15)$$

$$P_P = \frac{\gamma H^2}{2} \tan^2 \left(45 + \frac{\phi'}{2} \right) + 2c'H \tan \left(45 + \frac{\phi'}{2} \right). \qquad (7:16)$$

The pressure diagrams for these conditions are similar to those for saturated clays.

The analytical approach to earth pressure is termed the *Rankine method* after that famous Scottish engineer who first applied such reasoning to soil masses.

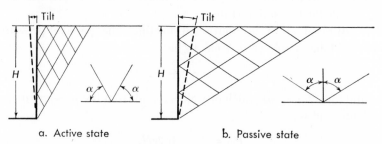

a. Active state   b. Passive state

Fig. 7:7   Failure planes and the soil wedges behind a frictionless wall.

7:2   Deformation and Boundary Conditions

In both the active and passive states the zones of soil adjacent to the frictionless wall that are in a state of shear failure form plane wedges (Fig. 7:7). Since the angle between a failure plane and the major principal plane is $\alpha = 45 + (\phi/2)$, the wedge is bounded in the active state by a plane making an angle of α with the horizontal, and in the passive state by a plane making an angle of α with the vertical. Within the wedges in both cases are an infinite number of failure planes making angles of α with the major principal plane.

The amount of horizontal movement of any point on the wall necessary to produce either the active or passive state is proportional to the width of the shear zone adjacent to that point. As can be seen from Fig. 7:7, the minimum movement consists of tilting about the base of the wall.[7:1] The amount of tilt is small and depends on the soil rigidity and wall height H, as given in Table 7:2.

Table 7:2 TYPICAL MINIMUM TILT NECESSARY FOR ACTIVE
AND PASSIVE STATES

Soil	Active State	Passive State
Dense cohesionless	$0.0005H$	$0.002H$
Loose cohesionless	$0.002H$	$0.006H$
Stiff cohesive	$0.01H$	$0 02H$
Soft cohesive	$0.02H$	$0.04H$

Soft cohesive soils do not remain in either the passive or active condition for long. Slow yield of the soil (often termed *creep*) tends to return the soil mass to the "at rest" state. In the case of walls supporting a soft clay backfill, this means that there will be a continual

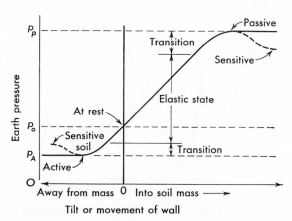

Fig. 7:8 Effect of deformation or tilt on the magnitude of earth pressure.

slow, outward movement of the wall if the wall is designed to support only active pressure.[7:2] Over a period of a few months, however, the change in pressure due to creep is usually negligible.

Incomplete Deformation The relation between deformation of the wall and earth pressure is shown in Fig. 7:8. The minimum and maximum limits (active and passive states) can be computed by the Rankine theory, and the point of no deformation (at rest) can be computed by the theory of elasticity. When the deformation is in between these limits, the pressure is also in between but cannot be computed by theoretical methods. Instead it must be estimated from the results of pressure measurements on structures correlated with limiting active, passive, or at-rest conditions.

When the deformation is small, the state of stress is elastic and the pressure is proportional to the tilt. When it is large, the stress is in a transition from elastic to plastic conditions and the pressure is no longer proportional to tilt. At very large deformations beyond that necessary for active (or passive) conditions, the pressure may again change toward the at-rest state, owing to a reduction in strength of sensitive soils from shear, as shown in Fig. 7:8.

Irregular Deformation: Arching   When the movement of the wall is different from the tilting required to establish the active or passive states, both the magnitude and the distribution of the earth pressure are changed. If a section of the wall deflects outward more than the neighboring sections, the soil adjacent to it will tend to follow, as

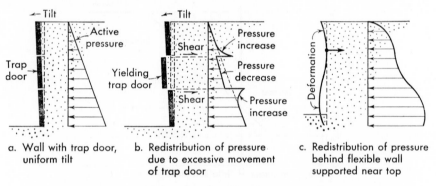

a. Wall with trap door,   b. Redistribution of pressure   c. Redistribution of pressure
   uniform tilt   due to excessive movement   behind flexible wall
                                     of trap door   supported near top

Fig. 7:9   Effects of irregular deformation, arching.

shown in Fig. 7:9a and b. Horizontal shear develops along the boundaries of this section of soil and this restrains it and transfers part of the lateral load it carried to the adjoining soil. The result is a *redistribution of pressure by shear*, sometimes called *arching*, and an irregular pressure distribution. Examples of the effect of arching on earth pressure against typical structures are shown in Fig. 7:9b and c. The magnitude of the redistribution must be estimated from observations of pressures and deflections of actual structures, since no valid theoretical analyses of arching have been developed.

Effect of Wall Friction: the Coulomb Analysis   The Rankine analysis is based on a smooth vertical wall that is frictionless. Actual walls are seldom vertical, and all develop friction with the soil. The result is a change in shape of the failure zone and the magnitude and direction of the resultant force. While the change is not serious for small, relatively smooth walls, it can be important when the wall height is over 30 ft or if the wall surface is rough.

In 1776 the French scientist Coulomb published a theory of earth pressure that includes the effect of wall friction and which can be applied regardless of the slope of the wall or its backfill. He discovered through many experiments with dry sand that a retaining wall tilts outward until earth pressure becomes a minimum—the active state. In this condition, the backfill is in a state of shear failure along a series of inclined, parallel, slightly curved surfaces (Fig. 7:10a). The wedge-shaped section of backfill, bounded by the shear surfaces, slides downward and outward as the wall moves outward. Coulomb approximated the shape of the failure wedge by assuming it to be sliding on a plane

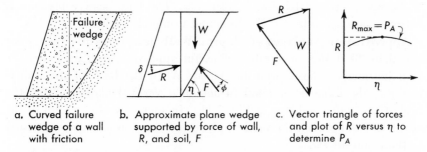

a. Curved failure wedge of a wall with friction

b. Approximate plane wedge supported by force of wall, R, and soil, F

c. Vector triangle of forces and plot of R versus η to determine P_A

Fig. 7:10 Coulomb's method for active earth pressure against a wall having friction.

surface, and derived the active earth pressure from the forces producing equilibrium in the wedge as it commences to move, as shown in Fig. 7:10b.

The weight W of the wedge of earth is computed by the assumed angle of the failure plane η, the soil weight, and the wall and backfill dimensions. Its direction is vertical. The resultant force F of the wedge on the soil is inclined at an angle ϕ with the normal to the shear plane, but its magnitude is unknown. The force of the wall on the wedge R is inclined at the angle of wall friction δ to the normal to the wall. Its magnitude is unknown.

The three forces form a vector triangle (Fig. 7:10c) from which the magnitude of R (and P_A) is obtained graphically. Of course the correct angle of the failure wedge η is unknown. It is found by computing values of R for several assumed values of η and plotting the results graphically. The peak of the curve represents the critical failure plane, and the maximum R is equal to but opposite in direction from P_A. If the soil has cohesion, the cohesive force c along the failure plane is added to the vector polygon. Graphical solutions of the Coulomb analysis and other more exact methods for computing earth pressure are available.[7:3,7:4]

The value of the angle of wall friction δ can be found by laboratory friction tests. For smooth concrete it is often $\frac{1}{2}\phi$ to $\frac{2}{3}\phi$, and for rough stone it is equal to ϕ.

The Coulomb analysis gives an active earth pressure equal to the Rankine for a frictionless vertical wall and a level backfill. When δ exceeds 0, the resultant pressure computed by the Coulomb method is as much as 10 per cent lower. The location of the resultant is the same.

The Coulomb analysis is still an approximation because it assumes a straight-line failure surface rather than a curve. For active conditions the error is negligible, but for passive pressure the error is considerable if the angle of wall friction is over $\frac{1}{2}\phi$. The true passive pressure is between that given by the Rankine and Coulomb analyses.

Approximate Analyses of Sloping Walls and Backfills For walls less than 30 ft high a number of useful approximations based on the Rankine analysis have been developed. When the back of the wall is inclined, the force is assumed to act on a vertical plane through the heel of the wall, as shown in Fig. 7:11a. In such cases the weight of the wedge of soil between the vertical plane and the wall is added vectorally to the resultant P_A.

If the backfill slopes at an angle β with the horizontal, the corresponding Rankine formula (derived in the same manner as the formula for a horizontal soil surface) is

$$P_A = \frac{\gamma H^2}{2} \cos \beta \, \frac{\cos \beta - \sqrt{\cos^2 \beta - \cos^2 \phi}}{\cos \beta + \sqrt{\cos^2 \beta - \cos^2 \phi}}, \qquad (7:17)$$

and P_A acts parallel to the backfill surface, as shown in Fig. 7:11c, at a depth of

$$z = \frac{2H}{3}, \qquad (7:3b)$$

where H is the height of a vertical plane through the heel of the wall.

Effect of Surcharge Loadings If a uniform surcharge load of q' acts on the soil behind the wall, as shown in Fig. 7:11b, it produces additional pressure on the wall. In the active state the resultant of this pressure P', in pounds per foot width of wall, is

$$P' = q'H \tan^2\left(45 - \frac{\phi}{2}\right). \qquad (7:18)$$

It acts midway between the top and bottom of the wall.

Sloping surcharges such as piles of materials on a level backfill can be approximated by a uniform surcharge equivalent to the average height of the material within the shear zone.

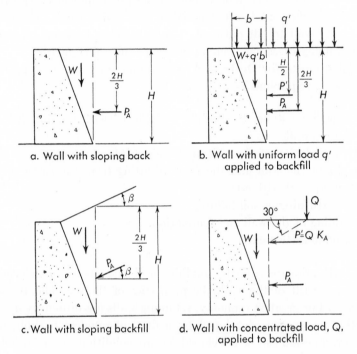

a. Wall with sloping back

b. Wall with uniform load q' applied to backfill

c. Wall with sloping backfill

d. Wall with concentrated load, Q, applied to backfill

Fig. 7:11 Approximate pressures for walls with cohesionless backfills.

If a concentrated load Q acts on the backfill in the active state, it exerts a force of P' at the location shown in Fig. 7:11d. The magnitude is approximately

$$P' = Q \tan^2 \left(45 - \frac{\phi}{2} \right). \qquad (7:19)$$

7:3 Retaining Walls

A retaining wall is a permanent, relatively rigid structure of cribbing, masonry, or concrete that supports a mass of soil. It substitutes the steep face of the wall for the gentle natural slope of the earth to provide usable space in highway and railroad cuts, in and around buildings, and in structures below ground level.

The wide use of retaining walls is accompanied by many failures and partial failures because of designs based on rules and formulas that fit only certain limited conditions. For example, the design of walls back-filled with soft clay is often based on analyses that apply only to sand, and the design of walls that support structures that will be cracked by foundation movement is often based on the active earth pressure that requires the wall to tilt outward. The only thing between success and failure in many cases has been an overgenerous safety factor.

Requirements for Design   A satisfactory retaining wall must meet the following requirements:

(1) The wall must be structurally capable of withstanding the earth pressure applied to it.
(2) The foundation of the wall must be capable of supporting both the weight of the wall and the force resulting from the earth pressure acting upon it without:
   a. Overturning or soil failure.
   b. Sliding of the wall and foundation.
   c. Undue settlement.

The earth pressure against a retaining wall depends on the deformation conditions or tilt of the wall, the properties of the soil, and the water conditions. For greatest economy, retaining walls are ordinarily designed for active pressure as developed by a dry cohesionless backfill, but if necessary, a design can be developed for any conditions of yield, soil, and water.

Organizations such as state highway departments[7:5] and railroads[7:6] who design many retaining walls have developed charts and tables that give earth pressures with a minimum of computation. Nearly all such charts and tables are based on the Rankine formula, with assumed values for the angle of internal friction and the unit weight of the backfill soil.

Some designers use the hydrostatic pressure developed by an imaginary fluid whose unit weight γ_f is termed the *equivalent unit weight*. This is a modification of the Rankine formula, where $\gamma_f = K_A \gamma$.

Retaining Wall Tilt   The earth pressure must be compatible with the wall tilt, which is limited by the rigidity of the wall, the foundation, and any connections with adjoining structures. The tilt for active pressure is given in Table 7:2. As a general rule the designer should allow at least 1 in. of tilt for each 10 ft of wall height $(0.008H)$ unless he is certain of the backfill quality and its installation. Ordinarily the tilt stops within a few days after the backfill is placed, although small movements sometimes continue in loose sands subject to vibration and in clays. For isolated straight walls on a soil foundation such tilting is no problem. For curved walls, long walls, or walls of widely varying height, it is necessary to provide joints that will permit movement. These can be sealed after the tilt stops.

Walls on piles are somewhat restrained, and the earth pressure is probably a little more than the active pressure. The difference is not great, and therefore the active pressure is used for design.

The foundations of walls resting on bedrock cannot deflect. If the wall itself is flexible, like a thin reinforced cantilever, it will probably deflect enough to establish active or near-active conditions. A massive wall, however, cannot tilt and must be designed for at-rest pressure. A cushion of sand between the wall foundation and the rock permits some movement and can result in a lower pressure on the wall.

The tilt is often limited by adjoining structures. If construction of such structures is delayed until after the wall is backfilled, little trouble should develop. Building walls resting on retaining walls often suffer from cracking, owing to retaining wall tilt. In one case the anchor bolts for columns resting on a 30-ft high wall were 2 in. out of line after the wall was backfilled, and in another case a brick wall on top of a retaining wall was split apart by the tilting.

Drainage Provisions   The most important problem of backfill design is keeping the soil dry. Two different methods may be used:

(1) Remove water from backfill.
(2) Keep water out of backfill.

In all cases the first method should be used, and in some cases both.

Removal of water from the backfill is accomplished by drainage, often by the simple expedient of *weep holes* through the wall (Fig. 7:12a). Weep holes should be spaced about 4 to 6 ft apart horizontally and vertically and should be at least 4 in. in diameter to permit easy cleaning. If the backfill is coarse sand, a few shovelfuls of peagravel over the inlet to each weep hole will act as a filter to prevent the hole from clogging with sand (Fig. 7:12b). Weep holes have the disadvantage of discharging water at the base of the wall where the foundation pressure is greatest. A better but more expensive drain consists of a 6-in. or 8-in. perforated pipe parallel to the wall at its base, lying in a filter trench (Fig. 7:12c). Manholes should be provided at the ends of this pipe so it may be cleaned.

For soils of lower permeability, such as silty sands and silts, more elaborate provisions are necessary. An inclined drainage blanket (Fig. 7:12d) drains the entire backfill and is simple to construct.

When clays that are likely to swell or soils that are difficult to drain must be used, it may be necessary to take steps to prevent water from entering the backfill. The first step is to locate the sources of water; the second is to divert the water away from the backfill. If surface infiltration is the source of water, the backfill may be paved with a flexible, impervi-

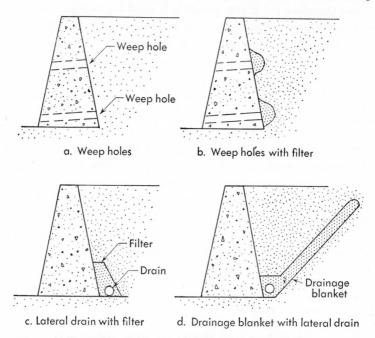

a. Weep holes   b. Weep holes with filter

c. Lateral drain with filter   d. Drainage blanket with lateral drain

Fig. 7:12 Drains for backfills of retaining walls.

ous blanket of asphalt or plastic clay. Surface drains must be provided to remove the water. Special attention should be paid to removing water from the inevitable crack between the top of the wall and the backfill. A small gravel blanket, drained with weep holes through the wall, will be sufficient. If underground seepage is the source of water, interceptor drains can be very effective in preventing water from entering the backfill.

Preventing Frost Action In northern climates frost action has caused many retaining walls to move so far that they have become useless. Since stone or concrete is a relatively good conductor of heat, the temperature along the back side of the wall is the same as in the air. If freezing temperatures prevail, if the backfill soil is susceptible to frost action, and if there is a plentiful supply of water, ice lenses will form parallel to the wall and can cause horizontal movements of up to 2 or 3 ft in a single season.

Frost action can be prevented by substituting a thick blanket of relatively coarse, cohesionless soil such as sand or gravel for the portion of the backfill adjacent to the wall. This blanket should be as thick as the depth of frost penetration in the region. It can be constructed by dumping small loads of sand or gravel against the wall as the backfill is being placed.

Serious frost action can be prevented by cutting off the source of water supply to the ice lenses. A blanket of gravel 8 in. thick is placed below the backfill and provided with a drain. Such a blanket can serve the dual purpose of keeping water pressure out of the backfill and also preventing frost heave.

Backfill Material The best backfill is rigid, free draining, and with a high angle of internal friction so as to develop minimum earth pressure with the least movement. Table 7:3 rates the soils of the Unified Classification for selection.

Table 7:3 RETAINING WALL BACKFILL

GW, SW, GP, SP	Excellent, free-draining backfill.
GM, GC, SM, SC	Good if kept dry but require good drainage. May be subject to some frost action.
ML	Satisfactory if kept dry but requires good drainage. Subject to frost. Neglect any cohesion in design.
CL, MH, OL	Poor. Must be kept dry. Subject to frost. Wall deflection likely to be large and progressive unless at-rest pressure is used.
CH, OH	Should not be used for backfill because of swelling.
Pt	Should not be used.

Artificial materials such as cinders and crushed slag often make good backfill. All the cohesionless backfills are best when well compacted because the higher internal friction angle and the resistance to vibration offset the higher weight.

A wedge-shaped backfill of sand, gravel, or slag at least 50 per cent wider than the failure wedge makes it possible to design the wall for the low pressure of a cohesionless soil even though the remainder of the backfill is clay.

Retaining Wall Design The design of a retaining wall is based on the materials available, appearance, the space required, the forces acting, and finally, cost. The materials for wall construction are stone masonry, plain concrete, reinforced concrete, and earth or broken stone. The choice is based partly on appearance. Walls used in conjunction with stone-faced buildings or in residential areas and parks are often of brick or stone masonry. Walls in industrial areas or adjacent to bridges and dams are usually concrete. Cost and availability of materials and labor are important factors in the choice of wall materials. Stone masonry is expensive in the United States and requires skilled workmen; plain concrete is relatively easy to form and requires no steel but may use excessively large quantities of concrete; reinforced concrete is economical for large structures but requires accurate fabrication of the steel and forms and controlled-quality concrete.

Space is an important factor in wall design, since the function of retaining walls is to make more usable, level space than a natural slope will provide.

In addition to having an important bearing on choice of wall materials, appearance often governs the shape of the wall face. Walls should not be designed with vertical faces because the inevitable slight tipping will cause them to lean outward and appear unstable, even though they actually may be quite safe. To give the appearance of stability, it is better to provide the face of the wall with an inward batter of at least 1 (horizontal) to 10 (vertical).

Gravity walls (Fig. 7:11a) resist earth pressure by their weight. They are constructed of stone and concrete that can resist compression and shear but no appreciable tension, and so the design is mainly concerned with preventing tension. Tentative dimensions are selected: a top width of 1 to 2 ft and a bottom width of about half the height are typical trial values. Sections are taken through the wall at the base and at one or two intermediate levels. The resultant of all the forces acting above the section, including the resultant of earth pressure, the weight of the wall, and any load acting on the top of the wall, must pass through the middle third of the section to avoid tension.

Two types of reinforced concrete walls are used: *cantilever* (Fig. 7:13a) and *buttress* or *counterfort* (Fig. 7:13b). Cantilever walls are used for heights up to 30 ft, and buttress walls are commonly used for heights greater than 25 ft. Structurally the cantilever wall is a wide cantilever beam acted upon by pressure that increases uniformly to a maximum at the point of restraint. It is reinforced in the vertical direction to withstand the bending moments and in the horizontal direction to prevent cracking.

The buttress or counterfort wall consists of a vertical, flat slab supported on two sides by the buttresses and on the bottom by the wall foundation. Ordinarily the support furnished by the wall foundation is neglected and the slab is designed as though it were continuous over the vertical buttress supports. Counterforts are buttresses on the back side of the wall in order to provide more usable space in front. This increases the cost of the wall, since they are in tension and require considerable reinforcing; but on the other hand, a lower wall is usually possible.

The crib retaining wall consists of a hollow rectangular cribwork of logs, timbers, reinforced concrete beams or steel beams filled with soil or rock. The cribwork can be vertical or tilted toward the backfill for greater stability. Crib walls are relatively cheap and are usually flexible

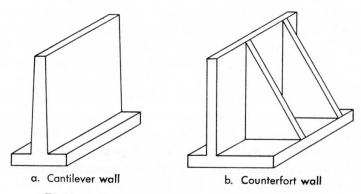

a. Cantilever wall   b. Counterfort wall

Fig. 7:13   Types of reinforced concrete retaining walls.

enough to be used where settlement is a serious problem. Structurally the crib is a gravity wall and is designed so that its width is sufficient to keep the resultant within the middle third. In addition the shear at any cross-section must not exceed the shear strength of the soil.

Wall Foundation   Faulty foundations are a frequent cause of retaining wall failures, and so extra care should be taken to see that the foundations are adequate. As stated before, the wall foundation must be safe against sliding, safe against overturning and bearing-capacity failure, and free from excessive settlement. The procedure for meeting these requirements is essentially one of trial and error. A tentative design is selected, the soil pressure over the base of the foundation is computed, the safety against sliding determined, and the safety of the point of maximum soil pressure (usually the toe of the foundation) with respect to soil bearing capacity is determined. Settlement of the wall may be calculated if the soil is soft or compressible.

The point at which the resultant of the earth pressure and weight of the wall and foundation intersect the base of the foundation is found, and the pressure is calculated by methods of statics, assuming a straight-line distribution. If the resultant passes through the third point of the base, the pressure distribution will be triangular; if it passes through the center, the pressure distribution will be uniform. If the foundation rests on soil, the resultant must be within the middle third, and the maximum pressure at the toe must not exceed the safe bearing capacity of the soil. If the foundation rests on rock, the resultant can be outside the middle third, which means that the heel of the wall will rise up. In this case the safety factor against overturning governs: The ratio of the overturning moments about the toe due to the horizontal component of earth pressure must be no greater than two-thirds the resisting moments about the toe due to the wall weight, vertical earth pressure, and loads from any superimposed structure (a safety factor of 1.5).

The resistance to sliding is equal to either the adhesion and friction of the wall on the soil or the shear resistance in the soil beneath the base, whichever is the smaller. For safety it should be at least 1.5 times the horizontal component of the resultant of earth pressures. If the soil surface is rough but sound and undisturbed, the soil strength governs. If it is smooth, a coefficient of friction from 0.35 for silt to 0.6 for sand can be used.

If the sliding resistance is insufficient, the base can be widened. In some cases a shear key placed near the toe will add some passive pressure. However, this may bring about a false sense of security because the passive pressure could be destroyed by a shallow excavation at the toe. A sloping base on the foundation will help in some cases by increasing the pressure on the sliding surface.

The passive pressure of soil on the outside vertical edge of the foundation may contribute materially to its resistance against sliding. In many cases, however, the soil is so badly cracked from seasonal volume changes that the amount of passive pressure cannot be calculated. Unless the soil is dense and sound and any excavation at the toe prevented, the passive pressure should be considered as an extra safety factor and ignored in design.

Settlement of retaining walls is calculated in the same manner as for other structures. However, contact settlement is almost impossible to compute. Non-uniform contact settlement that would result in excessive tipping of the wall can be prevented by designing the foundation so that the resultant of the earth pressure and the weight of the wall and the foundation passes through the center of the foundation.

If the soil is not capable of supporting the wall with sufficient safety against sliding, bearing-capacity failure, and undue settlement, then pile foundations will be required. In many cases where the surface soil is so soft that it will not support the wall, the soil is also so soft that it will not provide resistance to horizontal movement of the piles. Therefore the piles should be given sufficient batter (Fig. 7:14a) to enable them to resist the horizontal forces acting on the wall. The piles are placed so that the intersection of the axis of the batter piles and the axis of one line of

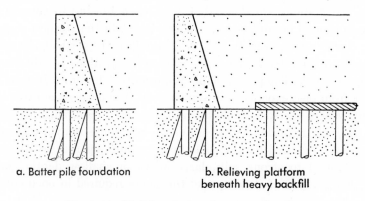

a. Batter pile foundation   b. Relieving platform
                                   beneath heavy backfill

Fig. 7:14   Wall foundations for very soft soils.

vertical piles is about 6 in. above the base of the foundation. When batter piles are used, little movement of the wall can take place, and the earth pressure will be somewhat more than the active pressure. When only vertical piles are used, the earth pressure will be active.

When the foundation soil is soft clay, the pressure of the backfill on the soil beneath may cause it to deform elastically outward. Actually this is a movement of the entire soil mass that carries the wall with it. Even batter piles may not be able to prevent movement of this type. The only solution in some cases is to use a lightweight backfill or to construct a relieving platform to support the weight of the backfill (Fig. 7:14b).

7:4   Excavation Bracing

In many construction jobs deep excavations must be made before the structure can be built. Often the planning of the excavation is left to the excavation superintendent or to a shovel operator. When expensive excavations or those that may endanger lives or adjacent property are involved, however, the bracing must be designed as is any other important structure.

Since an excavation is an opening in the soil for some specific purpose, the design of the excavation depends on two factors: the nature of the soil and the size of the opening desired. In most cases the primary factor is size, including depth, area, yardage, and the working space required for equipment and the structure within the excavation. The soil strength and its ease of excavation, the depth of ground water and the ease by which it travels through the soil influence both the excavation method and the excavation design.

Open excavations are those that require no bracing to support the soil or to control ground water. The soil is cut to the steepest slope on which it will stand, usually 1½ (horizontal) to 1 (vertical) for sandy soils, and up to vertical slopes for shallow excavations in stiff clay or decomposed rock. The proper slopes are usually determined by trial and error or from past experience in similar soils. The deeper the excavation and the weaker the soil, the flatter are the slopes required. Flat slopes, small size, and great depths all result in considerable excavation beyond that actually required for the structure; therefore open excavations are usually limited to strong soils, large areas, or shallow depths (under 20 ft). For analysis of stability and the slopes required in open cuts see Chapter 9.

Cut Bracing   When it is uneconomical or impossible to use open excavations, bracing must be employed to support the soil. Many methods of bracing have been devised, and some have been even standardized by organizations (such as sewer contractors) who must do considerable trench excavation work. Unfortunately, however, even excavation contractors spend little or no time designing their bracing, and as a result there have been numerous failures. Almost every year workmen are crushed to death by the failures of inadequately designed bracing, which occur even in shallow excavations.

The simplest type of bracing is the strut (Fig. 7:15b), a horizontal timber whose ends are jammed against the soil. Struts are commonly applied in shallow cuts in cohesive soils where the soil can stand unbraced for a short time. The struts, applied near the top of the cut, relieve the tension in the soil that occurs above the depth $z = 2c/\gamma$ and prevent the formation of tension cracks (Fig. 7:15a) that would lead to a collapse of the walls of the excavation. If two rows of struts are required, they may be set against vertical timbers known as *soldier beams*.

When more extensive bracing is required, two methods may be employed:

(1) Vertical sheeting
(2) Horizontal lagging

When the soil is very soft and runny, the time-honored method of vertical sheeting is employed, as shown in Fig. 7:15c. Vertical sheeting (either wood or steel sheet piling) is driven along the line of the excavation before the soil is removed. As excavation proceeds, horizontal members known as *wales* are placed along the inside of the sheeting and braced with struts. In small excavations the struts may react against an opposite wale; in large excavations the struts are placed at an angle and may react against portions of the completed structure or against special anchors in

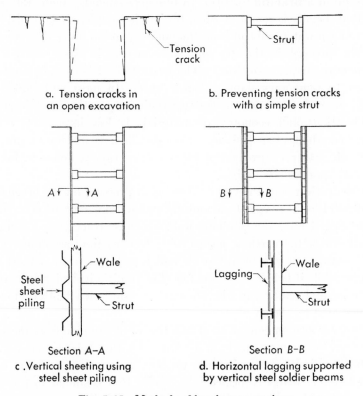

a. Tension cracks in an open excavation

b. Preventing tension cracks with a simple strut

Section A–A
c. Vertical sheeting using steel sheet piling

Section B–B
d. Horizontal lagging supported by vertical steel soldier beams

Fig. 7:15 Methods of bracing excavations.

the bottom of the excavation. In large excavations very complicated systems of struts and cross-bracing may be employed to prevent damage to the struts by construction equipment. If the depth of excavation is greater than the length of the sheeting, a second row of sheeting may be driven inside the first after excavation has extended near the bottom of the first row.

When the soil is not runny, horizontal lagging (Fig. 7:15d) may be used. If the cut will stand without bracing for a few hours, it is excavated without supports and then horizontal boards known as *lagging* are placed against the soil. These are held in place by vertical soldier beams supported by struts. If the soil requires support at all times but does not run, the soldier beams, consisting of steel W sections are driven into the soil, and the lagging is wedged tightly against the soil to prevent any excessive movement. The vertical beams are supported by a wale and strut system in the same manner as vertical sheeting.

Design of a Bracing System   A bracing system is a temporary structure that usually is removed when the job is completed. Actually it is a dam to keep water and soil from the building site in order that construction can proceed in the dry and consequently is often called a *land cofferdam* or simply a *cofferdam*. The latter term, however, is more often applied to temporary dams in open water. In most situations, since safety, ease of construction, and convenience are the most important considerations and economy of materials is less important, refined, accurate methods of analysis are seldom justified. An understanding of the nature of earth pressure against bracing is necessary, however, for even the most approximate design.

Deformation and Pressure   The earth pressure on the bracing system depends on the type of soil and the amount of deformation or yield of the bracing. Unlike the retaining wall, which is structurally a rigid unit against which the earth is placed after construction is completed, the bracing system is somewhat flexible and is called upon to support earth pressure while it is being constructed. The result is irregular deformation conditions and erratic variations in earth pressure with depth that cannot be calculated by theory alone.

A bracing system consisting of one row of struts placed at the top of the excavation deforms with an inward bulge that becomes greater with depth. The limiting or minimum pressure under this condition occurs when a sliding wedge is formed (Fig. 7:16a) that is similar to the wedge associated with active earth pressure but which has narrower, steeper boundaries. The resultant earth force under such conditions is about 10 per cent greater than the active earth pressure, and the pressure distribution, instead of being linear with respect to depth, is parabolic, as shown in Fig. 7:16b. When the bracing is prevented from deforming enough to produce this minimum pressure, the resultant earth force is indeterminate. If the bracing is tight enough to keep the soil in exactly its original position, earth pressure will be approximately that of the at-rest condition; if the bracing allows some deformation, the resultant force will be somewhere between that of the at-rest and active conditions; if the bracing is forced into the soil, forces greater than those of the at-rest condition may develop.

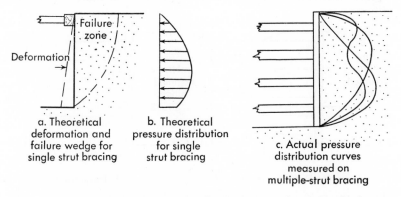

a. Theoretical deformation and failure wedge for single strut bracing

b. Theoretical pressure distribution for single strut bracing

c. Actual pressure distribution curves measured on multiple-strut bracing

Fig. 7:16 Theoretical and actual pressures on a bracing system.

When a bracing system consists of many rows of struts, the pressure becomes more indeterminate, as shown in Fig. 7:16c. The general pressure distribution is parabolic, but between each strut the pressure is lower and at the struts, higher. This is due to arching of the soil between points of rigid support. Unfortunately the effects of arching can only be estimated on the basis of field measurements and cannot be calculated accurately. Measurements of actual pressure against bracing systems have been made on several large construction jobs. These measurements have in general verified theoretical predictions of the magnitude and distribution of pressure and also of the effects of bracing deformation and soil arching. They have provided valuable information for the design of bracing systems in similar situations.

Design of Bracing in Sand   A semiempirical method was developed during subway construction in Berlin, Germany, to approximate meas-

ured earth pressures against excavation bracing in dense sand. A trapezoidal pressure diagram (Fig. 7:17a) was found to represent very closely
the actual earth pressure and to be compatible with theory.[7:1] The
resultant force of the assumed trapezoid is about 28 per cent greater than
the active earth pressure. For loose sands a similar pressure diagram
(Fig. 7:17b) has been suggested.[7:7] The resultant force in this case is 44
per cent greater than that of active conditions.

For design purposes the trapezoidal pressure is assumed to be acting
over each vertical section of the bracing. Strut loads may be calculated
by assuming the vertical members to be hinged at each strut except the
topmost and to be supported by a concentrated force at the bottom of
the cut. Moments in the vertical members can be calculated by assuming

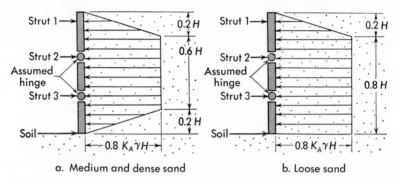

Fig. 7:17   Design pressures for bracing in sand. Vertical members assumed
to be hinged at each strut except the topmost, for computing
strut loads. (After Terzaghi and Peck.[7:7])

them to be acting as simple beams between the assumed hinges. Ordinarily, members subjected only to bending can be designed with a low
factor of safety, since bracing is temporary and excessive bending can
usually be corrected long before an actual failure takes place. On the
other hand, a very high factor of safety with respect to strut buckling
should be used, since struts are occasionally damaged through careless
installation or subsequent construction work and since buckling, unlike
bending, occurs suddenly and can precipitate a chain reaction of buckling
failures. Steel struts should be designed for two-thirds of the compressive
stress allowed by the customary column formulas; and wood struts
should be designed with one-third the customary compressive stress.
Struts must be carefully cross-braced to prevent damage from impact of
construction equipment.

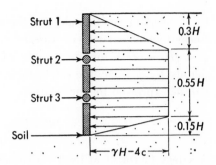

Fig. 7:18 Design pressures for bracing in soft to firm clay.
Vertical members assumed
to be hinged at each strut
except topmost for com-
puting strut loads. (After
Terzaghi and Peck.[7:7])

Design of Bracing in Clay During the construction of the Chicago subway, pressure measurements were made on the excavation bracing in clay, and on the basis of those measurements an empirical design pressure diagram (Fig. 7:18) was developed.[7:8] It is similar to the diagram for dense sands. The resultant force is 55 per cent greater than that developed in the active state. This pressure diagram applies to medium plastic, inorganic clays such as those found in the Chicago area and should be used in other situations only with caution. For soft clays the at-rest pressure with $K_0 = 0.6$ to 0.8 should be used. The struts and other members should be designed in the same manner as described for bracing in sands.

Stability of Bottom of Excavation When the bottom of the excavation extends into soft clay, there is danger of a failure by bulging upward. The weight of the soil adjacent to the excavation bears on the soil stratum at the level of the bottom of the excavation, and if the bearing capacity of that soil is not great enough to support the weight, a failure will occur. The failure zone can be approximated by drawing a 45° line from one bottom corner of the excavation and connecting it to a circular arc whose center is the opposite bottom corner as in Fig. 7:19. The zone of soil contributing to the failure has a width of 0.7 times the width of the excavation in this case. The downward force of this mass of soil is reduced

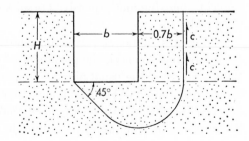

Fig. 7:19 Stability of bottom
of an excavation in
soft clay.

by shear along the boundary of the mass, so its effective vertical force per linear foot of cut is $Q = 0.7b\gamma H - cH$. The pressure per square foot is $q = \gamma H - cH/0.7b$. Since the bearing capacity of clay is given approximately by $q_0 = 5c$, the safety factor SF of the bottom of the excavation can be expressed by the relation

$$SF = \frac{5c}{\gamma H - cH/0.7b}.$$ (7:20)

A safety factor of at least 1.5 should be used. If sheeting extends below the bottom of the cut, the effective load is reduced by the shear along both sides of the imbedded portion of the piling.

Excavation bottoms in sand are ordinarily stable so long as the water level inside the excavation is not lower than the ground water level outside. As soon as the level inside is lowered by pumping, an upward seepage of water is created. If the difference in water levels is excessive, the bottom will heave, then become quick, and sand boils will appear. Seepage erosion can cause subsidence of adjoining structures. The analysis of seepage stability is given in Art. 4:2.

Preventing Lost Ground   Both deformation of the bracing and heave of the excavation bottom are accompanied by a subsidence of the soil adjacent to the excavation. This is known as *lost ground*. While in many instances a moderate subsidence is of no consequence, in others even a slight movement of the soil can result in damage to adjacent buildings. In some instances lost ground results from running of sands in a "quick" condition, owing to excessive neutral stresses; in still other cases it may be caused by the slow, plastic creep of clays that are strong enough to stand in open excavations with no bracing at all.

Before any excavation that could cause damage to adjacent structures is begun, a survey should be made to determine the condition of those structures. The location, elevation, and size of all building cracks should be recorded and photographs secured. This information can do much to prevent annoying and expensive lawsuits that often arise during excavation work.

During construction, level readings should be made on points adjacent to the excavation to check the possibility of subsidence that might go unnoticed because of the usual din and confusion within the excavation. The bench mark should be located far enough from the excavation so that it will not subside and produce erratic level readings. A distance of at least five times the depth of the excavation from the excavation should be sufficient.

If subsidence is caused by deformation, it can be corrected by tightening the bracing system or by forcing it tightly against the soil. If the bottom heaves, it can be prevented by driving the sheeting deeper and by loading the portions of the bottom of the excavation not actually involved in construction with excavation waste or piles of sand. If creep of unbraced soil is the cause, it can be prevented by bracing. If running of sands is the cause, it can be prevented by drainage to relieve the neutral stress or by a water and sandtight bracing system.

7:5 Anchored Bulkheads

An *anchored bulkhead* is a special form of retaining wall of sheet piling that is widely used in waterfront construction. Because it is built from the surface down by driving the sheets, it is adapted to sites where the water level is so high or the soil immediately beneath is so soft that the cost of constructing a retaining wall of masonry or concrete would be prohibitive.

Bulkhead Construction   The components of an anchored bulkhead are shown in Fig. 7:20a. The wall itself is of interlocking sheet piling. For very low walls, laminated creosoted timbers are occasionally used. Reinforced concrete sheets (often prestressed) 6 to 8 in. thick and 12 to 18 in. wide are sometimes employed in salt water locations because of their resistance to corrosion. The concrete must be dense and free of honeycombing in order to protect the reinforcement. Steel sheet piling is the most widely used because of its ease of handling and driving. Protection against corrosion, by coatings or by electrochemical methods (cathodic protection) is desirable, particularly in salt water.

The sheets are driven into the ground to provide lateral support at the bottom. The upper end is supported by the anchor system, consisting of the *wale, anchor rod,* and *anchor.* The wale is a continuous beam, usually a pair of channels or a W⁻ section, that ties the sheets together and carries their load to the anchor rod. Structurally it is simpler to place it on the outside of the wall. However, since it is vulnerable to damage from ships in that position, it is often placed on the inside. The anchor, or tie, rod connects the wale to the anchor. It is threaded for a nut at the bulkhead end or provided with a turnbuckle so its length can be varied and the sheeting aligned after installation. The anchor can take many forms, as shown in Fig. 7:20. The simple concrete *deadman* and the sheet pile deadman are used when the soils are strong enough and there is sufficient space. The A-frame and the single batter pile are employed when space is limited or when the upper soils are weak.

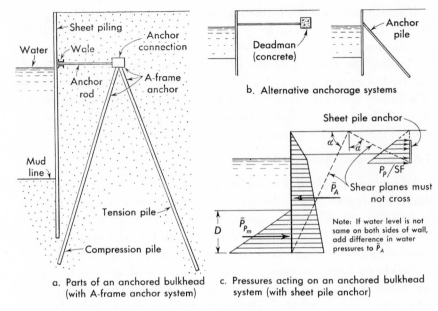

a. Parts of an anchored bulkhead (with A-frame anchor system)

b. Alternative anchorage systems

c. Pressures acting on an anchored bulkhead system (with sheet pile anchor)

Fig. 7:20 Anchored bulkhead system.

Two general methods of construction are found. When the bulkhead is built in open water and then the fill placed behind it, it is a *fill bulkhead*. When it is constructed in natural ground and then the earth removed from its face, it is a *dredged bulkhead*.

The wale and anchor rod are ordinarily placed as low as possible to minimize bending moments in the sheeting. Their depth is limited by low water; otherwise, their cost of installation becomes excessive.

Bulkhead Design[7:9,7:10,7:11] The forces acting on a bulkhead are shown in Fig. 7:20c. The inner face of the sheeting supports active earth pressure. This is resisted by the wale and anchor near the top and by passive earth pressure distributed along the outside of the sheeting at the bottom. Such a condition is termed *free earth support* because the embedded section of the pile is free to rotate as the unsupported section bulges outward under load. If the sheeting penetrates deeply into a rigid soil, it is fixed against rotation, and the condition is termed *fixed earth support*. The free support analysis described below is satisfactory for many design problems. The more complex fixed earth support analysis is described elsewhere.[7:12]

The pressure acting on the inner face of the bulkhead is essentially the effective active earth pressure. Although the pressure distribution is probably distorted by arching, as shown in Fig. 7:9c, the magnitude and location of the resultant $\bar{P}_A$ are probably not changed enough to affect the analysis.

In addition to the earth pressure there may be a difference in water pressure between one side of the sheeting and the other, caused by tidal fluctuations or rainfall infiltration. The unbalanced head can also cause a reduction in the passive pressure in the zone of embedment. Weep holes are sometimes installed to equalize the pressures but can lead to erosion of the backfill.

The depth of embedment is determined by the passive pressure required to support the toe. The effective resultant of passive pressure $\bar{P}_P$ is divided by the safety factor, usually 2 to 3, to obtain a *mobilized* or *working* resistance $\bar{P}_{Pm}$. The depth of embedment, D, is found, so that the algebraic sum of the moments of the active resultant and the mobilized passive resultant is zero.

The wale reaction per foot is the difference between the active resultant and the mobilized passive pressures. The wale is designed as a uniformly loaded beam with support at the anchor rods. The anchor rod pull is determined by the accumulated wale load. The rod is designed conservatively because corrosion and physical damage can reduce its capacity.

The moments in the sheeting are determined from the distributed loading (Fig. 7:20c). The working stresses in bending for design of the sheet piling are ordinarily 10 to 20 per cent greater than for other structures, since the real bending moments are less than those computed because of arching.

The deadman anchor is essentially a second wall with passive pressure acting on its face. The working passive pressure is one-third to one-half the maximum. The anchor and the bulkhead must be separated a sufficient distance so that their shear zones do not interfere. The anchor wale is located at the depth of the resultant, which sometimes means a sloping anchor rod. If a concrete deadman is employed, its friction with the soil beneath provides added resistance. The A-frame anchors are designed on the assumption that the heads and tips of the piles are hinged. All anchor systems must be structurally flexible so that rotation and deflection of either the sheeting or the anchor will not develop secondary stresses that lead to failure.

Most bulkhead failures can be traced to inadequate depth of penetration of the sheeting or to insufficient anchor resistance; therefore special attention should be paid to these aspects of design.

REFERENCES

7:1 K. Terzaghi, "General Wedge Theory of Earth Pressures," *Transactions, ASCE*, Vol. 106, 1941, p. 68.

7:2 K. Terzaghi, "The Mechanics of Shear Failures on Clay Slopes and the Creep of Retaining Walls," *Public Roads*, Vol. 10, December, 1929.

7:3 K. Terzaghi, *Theoretical Soil Mechanics*, John Wiley & Sons, Inc., New York, 1943, p. 48.

7:4 J. Brinch Hansen, *Earth Pressure Calculation*, Danish Technical Press, Institution of Danish Civil Engineers, Copenhagen, 1953.

7:5 *Specifications for Design of Highway Structures*, State of Ohio, Department of Highways, 1948.

7:6 *Manual of the American Railway Engineering Association*, Chicago, 1946, pp. 8–82, 8–86.

7:7 K. Terzaghi and R. B. Peck, *Soil Mechanics in Engineering Practice*, John Wiley & Sons, Inc., New York, 1948, pp. 348–350.

7:8 R. B. Peck, "Earth Pressure Measurements, Chicago Subway," *Transactions, ASCE*, Vol. 108, 1943, p. 1008.

7:9 K. Terzaghi, "Anchored Bulkheads," *Transactions, ASCE*, Vol. 114, 1954, p. 1243.

7:10 G. Tschebotarioff, "Design of Flexible Anchored Sheet Pile Bulkheads," 12th International Navigation Congress, Lisbon, 1949.

7:11 *U.S. Steel Sheet Piling*, Carnegie Illinois Steel Corporation, Pittsburgh.

7:12 F. E. Richart, Jr., "Analysis for Sheet Pile Retaining Walls," *Transactions, ASCE*, Vol. 122, 1957, p. 1113.

Suggestions for Added Study

1. References 7:1, 7:4, 7:9.
2. G. P. Tschebotarioff, *Soil Mechanics, Foundations, and Earth Structures*, McGraw-Hill Book Co., Inc., New York, 1951.
3. L. White and E. A. Prentis, *Cofferdams*, 2d ed., Columbia University Press, New York, 1950.
4. M. G. Spangler, "Underground Conduits—An Appraisal of Modern Research," *Transactions, ASCE*, Vol. 113, 1948, p. 316.

PROBLEMS

7:1 A vertical wall 20 ft high has a backfill of sand whose $\phi = 39°$, that weighs 110 lb per cu ft dry and 131 lb per cu ft saturated.

   a. Compute the active earth pressure diagram and the resultant, assuming the backfill to be dry.

   b. Compute the active pressure, assuming the water table in the backfill rises to the top of the wall. Compare with (a).

7:2 A vertical wall 30 ft high moves outward enough to establish the active state in a dry sand backfill.

    a. Draw the pressure diagram and compute P_A if the sand $\phi = 37°$ and it weighs 104 lb per cu ft dry.

    b. Compute the pressure and the resultant on the assumption that the wall does not move at all.

7:3 A wall 40 ft high retains sand. In the loose state the sand has a void ratio of 0.67 and a ϕ of 34°. In the dense state the sand has a void ratio of 0.41 and a ϕ of 42°. Which would produce the lesser resultant of active pressure, the loose or the dense state? Which would produce the greater resultant of passive pressure? How much difference is there in the resultants for both conditions?

7:4 A wall 25 ft high retains sand weighing 98 lb per cu ft dry and 123 lb per cu ft saturated. The water table is permanently 10 ft below the top of the wall. Estimate ϕ of 38°.

    a. Compute the effective and total active earth pressure diagrams.

    b. Find the location of the resultant.

    c. How much reduction in overturning moment about the base of the wall would occur if the ground water level could be lowered to the bottom of the wall?

7:5 A vertical wall 25 ft high has a soft clay backfill. The clay weighs 110 lb per cu ft and its strength c is 750 psf.

    a. Compute the at-rest pressure, draw the pressure diagram, and find the resultant.

    b. Compute the active pressure and draw the pressure diagram. Find the resultant, neglecting the tension because of cracks.

    c. How much is the overturning moment caused by earth pressure reduced by allowing the wall to yield enough to establish the active state, neglecting tension?

    d. How much increase in overturning moment would occur if water got in the tension cracks?

7:6 Derive the expressions for active and passive pressures of a partially saturated clay whose shear strength is expressed by $s = c' + p \tan \phi'$.

7:7 An anchor consisting of a sheet pile wall 10 ft high is embedded in a partially saturated clay whose $\phi = 19°$, $c = 1800$ psf, and $\gamma = 112$ lb per cu ft. The top of the wall is at the ground surface.

    a. Compute the passive pressure, draw the pressure diagram for a 1-ft width section of wall, and find the resultant force.

    b. Determine the depth below the top of the wall at which the anchor rod should be attached.

7:8 Compute the active, passive, and at-rest pressures for a sand having a unit weight of 125 lb per cu ft, and $\phi = 39°$. The sand is placed behind a bridge abutment that is 20 ft high. Draw the pressure diagrams for each condition, and find the resultant.

7:9 A retaining wall 12 ft high supports a level backfill of sand whose $\phi = 37°$ and $\gamma = 120$ lb per cu ft. The back of the wall has a batter of 1 (horizontal) to 4 (vertical). Trucks park with their rear wheels 3 ft from the wall. Each truck's rear wheels carry 3000 lb, and there is one truck for every 10 ft of wall. Compute the moment of earth pressure about the heel of the wall per foot of wall.

7:10 A retaining wall 25 ft high supports a dry sand fill whose $\phi = 34°$ and $\gamma = 117$ lb per cu ft. The top of the fill rises on a slope of 3 (horizontal) to 1 (vertical). The back of the wall slopes at an angle of 75° with the horizontal.

    a. Compute the resultant of the active earth pressure and its direction and line of action.

    b. Find the base width required to place the resultant at the third point of the base of a stone gravity wall with a top width of 18 in. and a masonry weight of 155 lb per cu ft.

7:11 A gravity retaining wall 19 ft high supports a level sand backfill. The top of the wall is 2 ft wide and the front face has a batter of 1 (horizontal) to 6 (vertical). Find the base width required so that the resultant of the earth pressure and the weight of the wall will pass through the outside third point of the base. Assume that ϕ is 35°, the unit weight of the sand is 120 lb per cu ft, and the unit weight of the concrete is 150 lb per cu ft.

7:12 A concrete cantilever retaining wall is 15 ft high and supports a sand backfill that rises on a slope of 2 (horizontal) to 1 (vertical). The sand $\phi = 32°$ and $\gamma = 113$ lb per cu ft. The wall is 18 in. thick at the top and 30 in. at the base; its back side is vertical. The wall foundation is 2 ft thick and extends 2 ft back of the back face of the wall. The foundation soil is clay, with $c = 1500$ psf. The concrete weighs 150 lb per cu ft.

    a. Compute active earth pressure diagram and the resultant.

    b. Compute width of foundation so that resultant is within middle third.

    c. Check foundation for safety against bearing failure and against sliding. A sand cushion is placed between the foundation and the clay.

7:13 Recompute the resultants of problems 7:10, 7:11, 7:12, using the Coulomb analysis with $\delta = \frac{2}{3} \phi$ and assuming that the resultant meets the wall at a depth of $2H/3$ below the top. Find the base width required and compare with that required for the wall, based on the Rankine analysis.

7:14 An excavation 30 ft deep and 40 ft square is to be made in sand with $\phi = 40°$ and $\gamma = 122$ lb per cu ft. The bracing system is to consist of horizontal wood lagging supported by vertical 8-in. soldier beams.

    a. Determine the pressure diagram.

    b. Determine thickness of lagging if the soldier beams are 6 ft apart. Wood is southern shortleaf pine (dense structural select).

    c. The uppermost wale is at a depth of 4 ft and the others are spaced 10 ft apart. Design wales and struts, assuming only one strut in each direction at each elevation. Struts to be tied vertically at intersection in center of excavation.

7:15 A long excavation 35 ft deep and 25 ft wide in soft clay is supported by steel sheet piling. The clay $c = 600$ psf, and $\gamma = 110$ lb per cu ft. Three sets of wales are used. The uppermost is 6 ft below the ground and the other two are 12 ft and 24 ft below the first.

    a. Compute the pressure diagram.

    b. Select the steel sheet piling (see manufacturer's catalogs).

    c. Determine the size wales and the strut size and spacing. The struts are braced vertically at their centers.

    d. Check the stability of the bottom of the excavation if the sheet piling extends just below the bottom of the excavation. The clay extends 50 ft below the bottom of the excavation.

7:16 An anchored bulkhead retains sand weighing 120 lb per cu ft saturated and 110 lb per cu ft damp, with an angle of internal friction of 36°. Below the dredge line is sand weighing 130 lb per cu ft, with an angle of internal riction of 39°. Low tide is 26 ft above the dredge line, the tidal fluctuation is 6 ft, and the top of the bulkhead is 15 ft above low tide.

    a. Compute the active and working passive pressure diagrams, using a safety factor of 2 for passive pressure and assuming a maximum difference in water levels of 2 ft, front to back of the wall.

    b. Compute the minimum embedment, assuming the wale to be 2 ft above low tide.

    c. Determine the wale reaction per foot.

    d. Determine the sheet pile section to be used if the maximum bending stress is 24,000 psi.

    e. Determine the wale size and anchor rod diameter if one rod is used for every six sheets.

7:17 Design a sheet pile anchor system for problem 7:16, including the sheeting length, the anchor location, the anchor rod length, and the wale size.

8 ... SOIL CONSTRUCTION—
COMPACTION and STABILIZATION

Soil is the oldest of construction materials. Man found that he could mold earth into blocks which he dried in the sun and laid up in walls for his house, and he learned how to mound earth up to bury his dead or to form an elevated platform for worship long before he discovered how to read or write. Soil is an enduring construction material, which is demonstrated by the prehistoric mud-walled cities and ancient mounds found in many parts of the world today. The scientific approach to the use of soil as a construction material began in the 1930's and has revolutionized earthwork. Now it is possible to utilize soil in the construction of dams, fills to support buildings and transportation avenues, and subgrades to resist concentrated wheel loads under conditions that were once thought to be unsuitable.

8:1 Soil as a Construction Material

When soil is used as a raw material for construction, it undergoes so many changes that it ultimately has little resemblance to its undisturbed state. Excavation is the first step in the process of change: The soil structure is broken down by the action of a shovel or scraper; the different strata become mixed; and the water content increases or decreases, depending on the weather. In some instances a soil is purposely modified to improve its characteristics: It can be mixed with other soils; it can be supplied with chemical admixtures that change its chemical and physical properties; or it can be bound together by a cementing agent. The final step of placing the soil in the structure involves still more changes:

276

Mixing brings about a relatively uniform composition, and compaction produces a controlled void ratio that is often considerably less than that of the original soil. Each step, from the undisturbed soil deposit to the finished structure, should be considered an engineering operation that is a part of a manufacturing process; each should be carefully planned and adequately controlled to ensure a satisfactory product.

Uses of Soil in Construction The most important use of soil is in the construction of fills. A *fill* is a man-made deposit used to raise the existing ground surface or sometimes used to dispose of waste such as garbage or rubbish. The soil from which it is constructed is termed *fill, fill material,* or *borrow.* Fills serve many purposes. Long narrow fills, termed *embankments,* carry railroads and highways across low areas or act as dams and levees to impound or confine water. Fills are used in building construction to provide level sites in hilly country. If properly constructed, they can support heavy structures with safety and only nominal settlement. Fills are placed behind retaining walls and bulkheads to secure the required ground surface contour and to bridge the gap between the wall and the original soil.

The foundation or supporting soil for a highway or airfield pavement is the *subgrade.* Subgrades can be the surface of the virgin soil or specially prepared, artificially compacted layers.

Pavements themselves are sometimes constructed of soil. In such cases the soil often must be modified with admixtures and binders to give the pavements sufficient strength and resistance to deterioration.

In many countries earth is used for the walls of structures. Sun-dried bricks have been used for thousands of years in arid regions, while in regions of more moisture, walls of earth are built by ramming the soil between temporary forms. Earth buildings are practical in areas where cheap construction labor and abundant supplies of clays and sands are available. They are durable when well constructed and protected from rain wash and flooding.

Construction with Soil Building structures of soil requires a different approach from building structures of other materials. First, local materials must be used because it would cost too much to transport large quantities of suitable soil from a long distance away. For instance, in planning a highway, either a fill or a long bridge could be used to carry the roadway across a valley. Compared with the bridge, the fill would require enormously greater quantities of materials to do the same job, but if those materials were available locally at little cost, the fill would be cheaper than the bridge. If the fill soil had to be hauled a long distance, the cost would be so great that a bridge would be cheaper. The same reasoning often applies to the choice between an earth or concrete dam.

Second the design of the structure that is to be made of soil must be very closely keyed to the construction. Ordinarily an engineer designs a structure with assumed values for strength and other material characteristics and then writes specifications that will ensure his getting what he assumed. When he contemplates using an earth structure, however, he first must investigate the materials available, determine their suitability for construction, and then design the structure to suit the actual characteristics of available soils. Often the design must be modified after construction has started in order to compensate for some unforeseen changes in the soils. The design of the structure, in the case of soils, is a secondary process that must be subordinated to the engineering problem of manufacturing a suitable, economical material for the structure. The engineering problems of soil selection and processing are discussed in this chapter; the structural design of soil structures, such as embankments and dams, is discussed in Chapter 9.

Finally the constructor must exercise engineering initiative in processing the soil, from excavation to compaction. He must guard against using methods that he found satisfactory on one job but which may not be suitable for handling the soils on a new project. For example, a contractor who has found that flooding helps to compact a damp sand too often wants to flood all fills with water. The result, if the soil is clay, is likely to be a soupy mass that will not support anything for years.

Objectives in Soil Construction   The product of soil construction, whether it be a fill for a highway, an embankment for a dam, the support for a building, or the subgrade for a pavement, must meet certain requirements:

(1) It must have sufficient strength to support safely its own weight and that of the structure or wheel load on it.
(2) It must not settle or deform under load so much that it damages the soil or the structure on it.
(3) It must not swell or shrink excessively.
(4) It must retain its strength and incompressibility permanently.
(5) It must have the proper permeability or drainage characteristics for its function.

Strength is a major factor in the use of soil in dams, high embankments, and subgrades. It depends on the nature of the soil material, the water content, and void ratio. In general, for any given soil material, the strength increases with a decrease in water content and with a decrease in void ratio (or increase in density). When the quality of the available soil material is poor, it is frequently possible to compensate for the deficiency by increased density.

Settlement from consolidation and elastic deformation is important in all applications of soil construction but particularly critical in subgrades and embankments that support pavements or structures. Settlement in the fill itself depends on the nature and density of the soil of which it is composed. For any given soil, the elasticity increases and the compressibility decreases with increased density. By preconsolidation to a sufficiently high density through compaction, nearly every soil can be made to support reasonable loads without undue settlement.

Shrinkage can be a factor in the settlement of pavements and structures on fill and is sometimes a serious hazard in the leakage of earth dams. The amount depends on the soil character, the density, and the loss in water content after construction; the greater the density and the less the water content change, the less the shrinkage.

Swelling is extremely hazardous because it disrupts the shape of the fill, damaging pavements and structures, and also because it is accompanied by a loss in strength. Swelling depends on the mineralogy of the soil, the density, and the increase in moisture after construction. In general, the tendency to swell is increased with increased density and can be controlled best by the proper choice of soils and by preventing (where possible) increasing water contents.

Loss of strength is ordinarily the result of increased moisture in soils containing clay minerals. It can be controlled by the choice of the soil and by preventing moisture increases. Frequently the loss of strength from increased moisture can be offset by making the soil so dense that its strength is adequate even in a weakened condition. This, of course, is not possible in soils having a tendency to swell.

Permeability is a factor in fills subject to temporary inundation, subgrades which must drain, and in dams. It is a function of the character of the soil and must be controlled by the proper selection of the soil material.

Obtaining the Required Soil Characteristics In order to obtain the required properties in the end product of soil construction the engineer must control the character of the soil material, the moisture, and the density. Control of the moisture is ordinarily possible during the construction period. Afterwards, however, the moisture is largely dependent

on the environment and the use to which a structure is put, and often is
not subject to control no matter how desirable it may be. The soil in some
uses, such as the upstream face of a dam, is certain to become saturated.
In other applications, such as a subgrade, the soil can ordinarily be
protected by drainage, but there is still danger (however remote) that
the soil could be saturated by abnormal rainfall. Proper water control by
drainage (Chapter 4) is essential in the design of structures of earth in
order to maintain the best soil properties under normal conditions.
However, unless the engineer is certain that the drainage will always be
effective, it is necessary to design earth structures on the basis that the
soil moisture could increase to the point of saturation.

Control over the character of the soil is ordinarily limited by the
materials available and the cost of their excavation and hauling to the
job site. Too often, only a limited range of materials is present in any
locality, and the engineer must select the best of what there is. It is sometimes possible to alter the soil by processing, such as mixing two soils to
improve the gradation of both, or by adding a material that alters the
physical or chemical nature of the soil. Such a change to improve the soil
material is termed *stabilization* and will be described in Art. 8:5.

The greatest control of the soil properties is through densification. By
densification it is usually possible to compensate for deficiencies in soil
quality and for the deterioration in properties that results from increased
moisture. The only property that is not improved by densification is the
tendency to swell, and that must be controlled by proper soil selection.

8:2   Theory of Soil Compaction

From prehistoric times builders have recognized the value of compacting the soil to produce a strong, settlement-free, water-resistant soil mass.
Earth has been tamped by heavy logs, trampled by cattle, or compacted
by rolling for more than 2000 years, but the cost of such crude work was
often more than the value of the compaction. On the other hand, earth
that was merely dumped in place without compaction frequently failed
under load and continued to settle for decades. It remained for R. R.
Proctor to point the way to low-cost, effective densification[8:1].

Mechanics of Densification   Densification, or a reduction in the
void ratio, occurs in a number of ways: reorientation of the particles;
fracture of the grains or the bonds between them, followed by reorientation; and bending or distortion of the particles and their adsorbed layers.
Energy consumed in this process is supplied by the *compactive effort* of the

compaction device. The effectiveness of the energy depends on the type of particles of which the soil is composed and on the way in which the effort is applied. In a cohesive soil the densification is primarily accomplished by distortion and reorientation, both of which are resisted by the interparticle attractive forces of "cohesion." As the water content of the soil is increased, the cohesion is decreased, the resistance becomes less, and the effort becomes more effective. In a cohesionless soil the densification is primarily attained by reorientation of the grains, although fracture of the grains at their points of contact is sometimes a secondary factor. The reorientation is resisted by the friction between the particles. Capillary tension in moisture films between the grains increases the contact pressures and increases the friction. As the moisture content increases, the capillary tension decreases and the effort becomes more effective.

If the moisture content is very high, however, the densification and decrease in void ratio of both cohesionless and cohesive soils leads to saturation. The buildup of neutral stress prevents further reduction in void ratio so that additional effort is wasted. Saturation, therefore, is the theoretical limit for compaction at any given water content unless the soil permeability is so high that water can escape from the voids during compaction.

Moisture–Density Relation The importance of soil moisture in securing compaction is illustrated by the following experiments. A sample of soil is separated into six or eight portions. Each portion is mixed thoroughly with a different quantity of water so that each has a different water content, ranging from nearly zero to about midway between the liquid and plastic limits. Each portion is compacted in a container with *exactly the same compactive effort;* its water content and weight of solids per cubic foot of compacted soil, usually termed the *dry density* and denoted γ_d, are determined:

$$\gamma_d = \frac{W_s}{V}, \tag{8:1a}$$

$$\gamma_d = \frac{\gamma}{1 + w}. \tag{8:1b}$$

If a graph is plotted with water content as the abscissa and the dry density as the ordinate, the resulting curve will be similar to Fig. 8:1. It will be seen that there is a particular water content, known as the *optimum moisture*, that results in the maximum dry density for the particular compaction method used. For a given soil, the greater the dry density, the smaller the void ratio, regardless of water content; so, maximum dry density is just another way of expressing the minimum void ratio or the minimum porosity.

For any given water content, perfect compaction would expel all air from the soil and produce saturation. If the dry densities corresponding to saturation at different water contents are plotted on the graph, the result will be a curve that lies completely above the first. This is known as the *zero air voids* curve and represents the theoretical densities obtained by perfect compaction at different water contents. The theoretical maximum

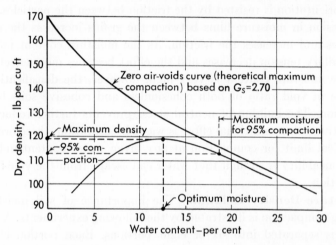

Fig. 8:1 Moisture-density curve for one method of compaction and maximum moisture for specified degree of compaction.

density of the zero air voids curve γ_z is computed from the specific gravity of the solids for each given moisture:

$$\gamma_z = \frac{\gamma_w}{w + (1/G_s)} \qquad (8:2)$$

At high water contents the theoretical dry density is low because much of the volume of the soil is occupied by water. At low water contents the theoretical density increases until at a water content of zero it becomes equal to $\gamma_w G_s$, the weight of the soil grains.

The compacted density increases with increasing moisture, as would be expected from the mechanics of the process previously described. The increase is limited by saturation—the zero air voids curve—where neutral stress prevents a further reduction in void ratio without a reduction in moisture. If the moisture increases, the density must therefore decrease, the slight difference between the actual curve and the theoretical maximum being caused by air trapped in the voids. The optimum moisture is a compromise where there is enough water to permit the soil grains to distort and reposition themselves but not so much water that the voids are filled.

Compactive Effort   If a second set of soil samples is made up with different water contents, as previously described, and then compacted by a different effort, a similar moisture–dry-density curve will be produced but with a different optimum moisture and maximum density. The greater the effort, the higher the maximum density and the lower the optimum moisture.

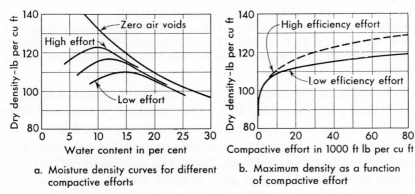

a. Moisture density curves for different compactive efforts

b. Maximum density as a function of compactive effort

Fig. 8:2   Effect of compactive effort on moisture-density curves and maximum density.

The relation between effort and maximum density is shown in Fig. 8:2. It is not linear, and a large increase in effort is required to produce a small increase in density. The way in which the effort is applied has a significant effect on the density. In cohesionless soils, vibration, which reduces the friction between the grains, is particularly effective. In cohesive soils, pressure that bends and forces the grains into new positions is better. A large number of applications of small pressure is not so effective as the same total effort applied in a single application, because a small force cannot overcome the cohesive resistance to grain movement no matter how often it is applied. The duration of the effort is sometimes a factor in the density obtained. In coarse-grained soils the neutral stress that resists compaction at high moisture contents will not build up if the effort is applied so slowly that the water can drain away. In some clays a rapidly applied effort appears to mobilize viscous resistance in the water and is less effective than a slowly applied effort.

Compaction Tests   A number of arbitrary standards for determining the optimum moistures and maximum densities have been established to simulate different amounts of effort as applied by the full-sized equipment used in soil construction. The simplest and the most widely used are the "Proctor tests" named for R. R. Proctor, who first developed the optimum-moisture–maximum-density concept.[8:1]

Standard Proctor (ASTM D 698–58T, AASHO T 99–38. British Standard 1377: 1948):
Twenty-five blows of a 5.5 lb hammer falling 12 in. on each of 3 equal layers in a 4 in. diameter $\frac{1}{30}$ cu ft cylinder.* The effort is 12,400 ft-lb per cu ft which is comparable to light rollers or thorough tamping.
Modified Proctor (ASTM D 1557-58T, Modified AASHO):
Twenty-five blows of a 10 lb hammer falling 18 in. on each of 5 equal layers in a 4 in. diameter $\frac{1}{30}$ cu ft cylinder.* The effort is 56,200 ft-lb per cu ft which is comparable to that obtained with the heaviest rollers under favorable working conditions.

In most soils the maximum density by the Modified method is from 3 to 6 lb per cu ft greater than that by the Standard. A number of other procedures for obtaining optimum moistures and maximum densities have been developed, such as static pressures and kneading pressures, more closely to simulate field conditions. Their use is not widespread, however, because the test equipment is more complex and the results not sufficiently different in many soils to justify the added expense.

8:3   Evaluation of Materials

The evaluation of the materials includes the determination of the quantity and quality of the materials available, the testing of the soils to find their physical properties when compacted, and the selection of the material and the degree of compaction to be used in construction.

Field Survey   The first step is a survey of all the soil deposits that can be used. The depth and extent of the different soil strata are determined by auger boring on a grid pattern, as described in Chapter 10. Samples weighing about $\frac{1}{2}$ lb are secured of each different material in each boring to the depth that it appears likely the soil will be removed.

Preliminary Evaluation   A preliminary evaluation of the soil samples is made on the basis of past experience. For this purpose, classification by the Unified System[8:2] or the Public Roads System[8:3] (Chapter 3)

* If the soil contains many particles larger than a No. 4 sieve, a 6-in. diam cylinder of the same height is used and the blows increased to 55 per layer.

is helpful because both have been supplemented by performance ratings, such as Table 8:1.[8:2] A number of state highway departments have developed systems that are applicable to their own peculiar soil problems. Since these ratings have been based on field behavior, classification is a cheap, rapid method for estimating the properties of the compacted soil and determining its promise of suitability for construction.

Compaction Studies Soils whose availability and suitability for fill purposes have been found satisfactory by the field survey and classification are sampled again to secure enough material (50 to 100 lb) for more extensive testing. In order to avoid two sampling operations, representative large samples are often made in the first place, but the handling and transportation of many samples weighing 50 lb to 100 lb is a problem.

Tests are made of each sample to determine its natural or *field moisture* and to obtain its moisture density curve by one of the standard procedures. Samples are then prepared at different percentages of the maximum density, such as 92, 95, and 97 per cent, usually at the highest moisture consistent with the degree of compaction.

Swelling and shrinking tests can be made by soaking compacted samples in water and determining their percentage volume increase and by drying samples to determine the percentage volume decrease. The sum of the volume increase and the volume decrease is called the *percentage volume change*. Fills made of soil having a volume change over 5 per cent may require special provisions to prevent their moisture content from changing enough to cause damage by swelling and shrinking.

Strength and consolidation tests can be made of the compacted samples, simulating the worst possible field conditions. Unless it is certain that the soil will never become saturated, the tests are made after soaking the compacted soil in water under the future confining load or saturating the soil under pressure. The results of the tests can be presented on moisture–density coordinates in terms of "contours" of settlement under a given load or contours of strength under a given confining pressure, as shown in Fig. 8:3.

Strength and Compressibility of Compacted Cohesive Soils[8:4,8:5,8:6,8:7] The physical properties of a compacted soil depend largely on the soil material, moisture, and density. In addition the structure and the conditions of compaction that produced it are important in cohesive soils. When the cohesive soil is compacted at moisture contents less than optimum, an aggregated structure is formed; when the soil is compacted at high moisture contents, a dispersed structure is formed, with the flakey particles aligned in parallel.

Table 8:1   CHARACTERISTICS AND RATINGS OF UNIFIED

Class (1)	Compaction Characteristics (2)	Maximum Dry Density Standard Proctor (pcf) (3)	Compressibility and Expansion (4)	Drainage and Permeability (5)
GW	Good: tractor, rubber-tired, steel wheel, or vibratory roller	125–135	Almost none	Good drainage, pervious
GP	Good: tractor, rubber-tired, steel wheel, or vibratory roller	115–125	Almost none	Good drainage, pervious
GM	Good: rubber-tired or light sheepsfoot roller	120–135	Slight	Poor drainage, semipervious
GC	Good to fair: rubber-tired or sheepsfoot roller	115–130	Slight	Poor drainage, impervious
SW	Good: tractor, rubber-tired or vibratory roller	110–130	Almost none	Good drainage, pervious
SP	Good: tractor, rubber-tired or vibratory roller	100–120	Almost none	Good drainage, pervious
SM	Good: rubber-tired or sheepsfoot roller	110–125	Slight	Poor drainage, impervious
SC	Good to fair: rubber-tired or sheepsfoot roller	105–125	Slight to medium	Poor drainage, impervious
ML	Good to poor: rubber-tired or sheepsfoot roller	95–120	Slight to medium	Poor drainage, impervious
CL	Good to fair: sheepsfoot or rubber-tired roller	95–120	Medium	No drainage, impervious
OL	Fair to poor: sheepsfoot or rubber-tired roller	80–100	Medium to high	Poor drainage, impervious
MH	Fair to poor: sheepsfoot or rubber-tired roller	70– 95	High	Poor drainage, impervious
CH	Fair to poor: sheepsfoot roller	80–105	Very high	No drainage, impervious
OH	Fair to poor: sheepsfoot roller	65–100	High	No drainage, impervious
Pt	Not suitable		Very high	Fair to poor drainage

* Adapted from Reference 8:2.
† Not suitable if subject to frost.

SOIL SYSTEM CLASSES FOR SOIL CONSTRUCTION*

Value as an Embankment Material (6)	Value as Subgrade when Not Subject to Frost (7)	Value as Base Course (8)	Value as Temporary Pavement	
			With Dust Palliative (9)	With Bituminous Treatment (10)
Very stable	Excellent	Good	Fair to poor	Excellent
Reasonably stable	Excellent to good	Poor to fair	Poor	
Reasonably stable	Excellent to good	Fair to poor	Poor	Poor to fair
Reasonably stable	Good	Good to fair†	Excellent	Excellent
Very stable	Good	Fair to poor	Fair to poor	Good
Reasonably stable when dense	Good to fair	Poor	Poor	Poor to fair
Reasonably stable when dense	Good to fair	Poor	Poor	Poor to fair
Reasonably stable	Good to fair	Fair to poor†	Excellent	Excellent
Poor stability, high density required	Fair to poor	Not suitable	Poor	Poor
Good stability	Fair to poor	Not suitable	Poor	Poor
Unstable, should not be used	Poor	Not suitable	Not suitable	Not suitable
Poor stability, should not be used	Poor	Not suitable	Very poor	Very poor
Fair stability, may soften on expansion	Poor to very poor	Not suitable	Very poor	Not suitable
Unstable, should not be used	Very poor	Not suitable	Not suitable	Not suitable
Should not be used	Not suitable	Not suitable	Not suitable	Not suitable

The typical undrained strength of a cohesive soil, as compacted, at a constant confining pressure is shown in Fig. 8:3a. At constant density the strength decreases with increasing moisture; at constant moisture the strength increases with increasing density. An exception to the latter occurs as the zero air voids curve or saturation is approached. The increasing density brings about increased pore pressure and thereby decreased strength. This sometimes occurs when a soil is compacted at a moisture content well above the optimum and can result in shear failure during construction. This is termed "overcompaction" and is prevented by proper moisture control.

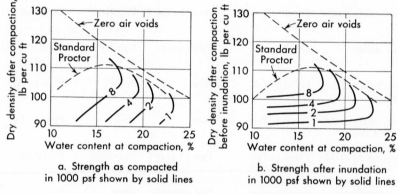

a. Strength as compacted
in 1000 psf shown by solid lines

b. Strength after inundation
in 1000 psf shown by solid lines

Fig. 8:3 Relationship of unconfined compressive strength (undrained shear strength) of a compacted cohesive soil to water content and dry density. Solid lines are curves of equal strength *c*. (After Seed and Chan.[8:6])

The undrained strength of a compacted cohesive soil after inundation (under a constant confining pressure) is shown in Fig. 8:3b. Although the moisture content after inundation is nearly the same for equal densities, the strength decreases slightly with increasing initial (compaction) moisture, probably because the soil structure changes from the stronger aggregated to the weaker dispersed form. As before, close to the zero air voids curve the strength drops rapidly with increasing density because of the greater buildup of neutral stress in the dispersed structure.[8:6]

Structure also plays a part in the compressibility of compacted soils. In general, cohesive soils compacted at moistures less than optimum are less compressible than those compacted at moistures higher than optimum because the aggregated structure is more tightly bound than the oriented structure. At very high pressures, however, which tend to break down the aggregated structure, the oriented structure is less compressible.

Selection of Soil and Degree of Compaction The final selection of the soil depends on its availability and compacted characteristics, and the cost of excavation, hauling, and compaction. The density specified is the minimum percentage of the maximum dry density that will provide the necessary strength and incompressibility under the worst possible future moisture conditions. Table 8:2 will serve as a guide for estimates where soil test data are not available.

The amount of soil moisture to be used in construction must be consistent with the percentage of compaction specified. Some indication of the range can be seen in the moisture density curve: If a high percentage is required, the range in moistures is small; if a low percentage is required, the range is wider. The maximum possible moisture is the intersection of the horizontal line corresponding to the required compaction with the leg of the moisture density curve adjacent to the zero air voids curve. This point, for 95 per cent compaction, is shown on Fig. 8:1. This limit, or a moisture content 1 or 2 per cent below it, is sometimes specified to prevent useless attempts at compaction when the soil is too wet. Still lower limits for maximum moisture, such as the optimum, are sometimes specified to prevent the buildup of neutral stress by compaction.

Table 8:2 REQUIREMENTS FOR COMPACTION, UNIFIED SOIL SYSTEM CLASSES

Soil Class	Required Compaction—Percentage of Standard Proctor Maximum		
	Class 1	Class 2	Class 3
GW	97	94	90
GP	97	94	90
GM	98	94	90
GC	98	94	90
SW	97	95	91
SP	98	95	91
SM	98	95	91
SC	99	96	92
ML	100+	96	92
CL	100	96	92
OL	—	96	93
MH	—	97	93
CH	—	—	93
OH	—	97	93

Class 1	Upper 8 ft of fills supporting 1- or 2-story buildings
	Upper 3 ft of subgrade under pavements
	Upper 1 ft of subgrade under floors
	Earth dams over 100 ft high
Class 2	Deeper parts of fills under buildings
	Deeper parts (to 30 ft) of fills under pavements, floors
	Earth dams less than 100 ft high
Class 3	All other fills requiring some degree of strength or incompressibility

8:4   Excavation, Placement, and Compaction[8:8,8:9]

Excavation of the raw materials, processing, hauling, placement, and compaction are important from the standpoint of cost and the time required for construction. All, and particularly compaction, are also vital in determining the quality of the completed structure.

Excavation Method   The excavation procedure is usually selected by the constructor on the basis of the type of material and the layout of the borrow pit. However, since the excavation method affects the breaking of the material into small pieces and the way the material is mixed, it is sometimes necessary for the engineer to specify the methods to be used, to ensure the desired result.

Hand excavation has been used throughout history and is still important in areas of cheap labor. Most soils can be excavated, but coarse gravel, boulders, and rock cannot be handled efficiently. Stratified materials can be either mixed or segregated by layers with equal ease, and small pockets of objectionable materials can be removed with little added expense. The soil is well broken up and usually requires little additional pulverization.

The *power shovel* is adapted to a wide variety of materials, from soft soil to boulders and layered or soft rock. It is also suitable for hard rock that has been broken by explosives. Stratified materials are easily mixed because the shovel makes a nearly vertical slice; but segregation by layers is difficult and expensive. At its most efficient output, the shovel is likely to excavate soil in large chunks, but it can be made to break the soil thoroughly, although there is some sacrifice in efficiency. The shovel is best adapted to deep borrow pits above the water table.

The *dragline* is adapted to most soils except tough clays and hard or cemented materials. Stratified materials can be either mixed or segregated if the layers are not thin. The soil is well broken up and mixed by the boiling action in the bucket. The dragline is most efficient when it excavates below its own base level, and for that reason it can excavate satisfactorily below water. Of course the materials would be waterlogged in that case.

The *scraper* or *pan* is adapted to most soils except very soft or sticky clays. Hard materials such as cemented soil and soft layered rock can frequently be broken up by a tractor-drawn *rooter* (similar to a giant hooked plow) and then excavated with a scraper. Stratified materials are easily segregated because the scraper can excavate layers as thin as 6 in.

Some mixing of strata is possible by making a deep cut or by making a sloping cut across several strata. The soil is broken up by the cutting blade and by the boiling action in the scraper bowl. The scraper is best in long borrow pits because it must travel in a straight line during excavation.

The *elevating grader* is similar to the scraper in the types of materials handled, but it tends to provide more pulverizing. A long level pit is required for best operation.

Borrow Pit Control Moisture control is often necessary in the borrow pit to obtain efficient operation of the excavation equipment and to condition the soil for future excavation. Predrainage is necessary in low, wet pits. Plowing and exposure to air and sunshine are often required to help dry the soil. Moisture addition makes it easier to excavate hard, dry soils. If the soil is drier than optimum, water addition is necessary for compaction; and when the moisture is added at the borrow pit, the moisture is mixed by the subsequent handling and is likely to be uniformly distributed.

Supervision of the borrow pit is necessary to ensure the quality of the materials. This requires experienced technicians who can recognize the specified soils, and sometimes even a field laboratory for checking moisture, gradation, and plasticity.

Placement and Processing The placement of the fill materials depends on the method of hauling, the processing that is necessary before compaction, and the size of the area to be filled. The materials excavated by shovels, draglines, and elevating graders are hauled by trucks and wagons and *end-dumped* from the rear of the hauling unit in uniformly spaced piles, or *side-dumped*, or *bottom-dumped* from special units while moving to form long, narrow windrows. The scraper spreads the materials in ribbon-like layers the width of the blade.

The piles and windrows are spread out into uniform layers with a bulldozer or road grader. Some leveling of the layers spread by the scrapers is usually needed. At the same time objectionable materials such as roots, clumps of grass, and large stones are removed.

If the materials are too wet, they are cut and turned with a disk plow so that they will aerate and dry in the sun. Cutting is also necessary if the soil is in lumps that are too large to compact. If the soil is too dry, the correct amount of water (plus an allowance for evaporation) is added by sprinkling and mixed into the soil by plowing.

In some cases it is necessary to mix different soils, such as a wet and a dry soil, to obtain optimum moisture, or a sand and a clay to secure a sandy clay. If the materials are hauled by trucks, they are placed in alternate piles or windrows. They are then mixed by blading them across each other before spreading. Materials hauled by scrapers are placed in thin layers, one on top of the other, and are mixed vertically by plowing. Different types of traveling mixers are available to pick up the soils, mix and pulverize them, and place them back, ready for compaction.

Compaction Characteristics of Soils Compaction occurs by the reorientation of the particles or the distortion of the particles and their adsorbed layers. In a cohesionless soil, compaction is largely by reorientation of the grains into a more dense structure. Static pressure is not very effective in this process, for the grains wedge against each other and resist movement. If the grains can be momentarily freed, then even light pressure is effective in forcing them into a more dense arrangement. Both vibration and shock are helpful in reducing the wedging and aiding compaction. Flowing water will also reduce the particle friction and permit easier compaction. However, water in the voids also prevents the particles from assuming a more dense arrangement. For this reason flowing water can be used to aid compaction only when the soil is so coarse-grained that the water can leave the voids quickly.

In cohesive soils the compaction occurs by both reorientation and distortion of the grains and their adsorbed layers. This is achieved by a force that is great enough to overcome the cohesive resistance or interparticle forces. Vibration and shock are of little help, for although they provide a dynamic force in addition to the static, this is largely offset by the increased cohesive resistance that accompanies dynamic loading.

For greatest efficiency the compaction force should be as high as possible, but it must not exceed the soil bearing capacity. In cohesionless soils the bearing capacity is dependent on the width of the loaded area, b; and a high pressure requires a wide area of application. In cohesive soils the bearing capacity is not greatly dependent on b, and therefore high pressures can be applied over relatively small areas.

Compaction Methods Many different compaction methods are in use, each with its adaptations and limitations that must be understood by the engineer. In many jobs the constructor claims that the specified degree of compaction is impossible, whereas it is only the wrong equipment or the wrong use of equipment that is responsible for the lack of density. Too often the available performance data on compaction equipment do not define the job conditions or the character of the soil accurately enough for the engineer to decide if the equipment will work in the new application. Therefore the engineer must study the mechanical behavior of the equipment and, if uncertain, conduct his own performance tests.

Tamping is the oldest method of compaction. It provides momentary pressure at the instant of impact and some vibration, and because of this dual action it is effective in both cohesive and cohesionless soils. The hand tamper, a block of iron or stone weighing 6 to 9 lb, is the simplest, but the compactive effort is so small that the soil must be tamped in 1- to 2-in. layers at a moisture 2 to 4 per cent above the Standard Proctor optimum. Furthermore, it is slow. Pneumatic tampers are much faster but only slightly more effective in producing high compaction.

Jumping tampers are actuated by gasoline-driven pistons that kick them into the air to drop back on the soil. The Barco Rammer (Fig. 8:4a) weighs 210 lb, jumps as high as 18 in., and delivers a blow capable of compacting soils in layers 6 to 12 in. thick to the Standard Proctor maximum density at optimum moisture.

Rolling produces pressure that is applied for a relatively short time, depending on the roller speed. The *sheepsfoot roller* (Fig. 8:4b) consists of a steel drum with projecting lugs or feet.[8:11] It applies a high static pressure to a small area of 7 to 9 sq in. or an equivalent diameter of 3 to $3\frac{1}{2}$ in. The pressure exerted depends on the number of feet in contact with the ground at any one time and on the roller weight (which can be varied by changing the water or wet sand ballast in the drum). Although pressures as low as 100 psi and as high as 1200 psi are available, most equipment now in use falls into two categories: light, with pressures of 150 to 300 psi; and medium, with pressures of 350 to 700 psi.

Because of the small width of the loaded area, the sheepsfoot roller is adapted best to cohesive soils such as clays. The medium rollers are capable of producing densities greater than the Standard Proctor maximum in layers 6 to 12 in. thick (after compaction) and at moistures slightly below the optimum in six to eight passes over the surface. The light roller can produce 95 per cent of the maximum at optimum moisture with 4- to 6-in. layers.

A modified sheepsfoot roller with wider feet, up to 8 or 10 in. across, is far better for silty soils of low cohesion because the increased width of the loaded area produces greater bearing capacity. This device, termed the *elephant's foot roller* by the authors, is made by removing some of the feet from the ordinary sheepsfoot and welding flat plates on those remaining.

*b. Sheepsfoot roller. (Courtesy of Le Tour-
neau Westinghouse, Inc.)*

*a. Soil rammer. (Courtesy Barco Manu-
facturing Company.)*

c. Fifty-ton rubber-tired roller. (Courtesy Bros, Inc.)

*d. Surface vibrator. (Courtesy Baldwin-
Lima Hamilton, Inc.)*

Fig. 8:4   Soil compacting equipment.

The pneumatic tire has proved to be an excellent compactor for cohesionless and low cohesion soils, including gravels, sands, clayey sands, silty sands, and even sandy clays. It applys a moderate pressure to a relatively wide area so that enough bearing capacity is developed to support the pressure without failure. The *light rubber-tired roller*, also known as the *traffic roller*, employs from 7 to 13 wheels mounted in two rows and spaced so that the wheels of the rear row track in the spaces between those of the front row. The wheels are mounted in pairs on oscillating axles so that they can follow the ground irregularities. The tires are similar in size to those used on pickup trucks, and each exerts a load of up to 2000 lb on the soil, depending on the ballast in the box mounted above the wheels. With a tire contact pressure of 35 psi the load is applied to an area with an equivalent diameter of nearly 9 in.

The *heavy rubber-tired roller* (Fig. 8:4c) consists of four large tires mounted side by side on a suspension system that permits them to follow the ground irregularities. The load is provided by a ballast box, which is filled with earth, water, or even steel billets. A number of sizes are available, from a 35-ton maximum load to a 200-ton maximum load, with tire pressures of from 75 to 150 psi. The widely used 50-ton roller applies its 25,000-lb wheel load at 100 psi to an equivalent circle having an 18-in. diam.

The light rollers are capable of compacting soils in 4 in. thick layers to densities approaching the Standard Proctor maximum at optimum moisture in three or four passes. The heavy rollers can obtain densities far greater than the Standard Proctor maximum (as high as 105 per cent of the Modified Proctor maximum in one case) in layers up to 18 in. thick with four to six passes, with moistures slightly less than optimum.

The smooth-drum paving roller is sometimes used for compacting cohesionless soils. It is satisfactory if the layers are thin and well leveled, but it tends to bridge over low spots. A drum-type roller with a surface of circular segments with space between, called the *Kompactor*, provides low pressure over a wide area and is useful in compacting sand, gravel, and crushed rock. The grid roller employs a heavy steel grid in place of the smooth steel drum. It develops a relatively high pressure over small areas and has been found useful in compacting cohesive soils in thin layers.

Vibrators in a number of forms have been developed for compacting cohesionless soils. The surface plate form (Fig. 8:4d) consists of a curved metal plate or shoe on which is mounted the vibrator. Within the vibrator are eccentric weights that rotate at speeds of from 1000 to 2500 rpm, depending on the particular design, and produce an up-and-down vibrat-ing impulse. These are available in single units that propel themselves slowly across the surface and in multiple units, such as shown in Fig. 8:4d, mounted on a self-propelled chassis. They are capable of compacting cohesionless soils to densities as high as the Standard Proctor maximum in layers 6 to 12 in. thick.

Vibrating rollers have been developed to provide both greater weight and greater intensity of vibration. One form consists of a steel drum 4 ft in diameter and weighing $3\frac{1}{2}$ tons. A vibrating unit driven by a gasoline engine is mounted on the roller and delivers the impulse to the drum. A second form consists of a two-wheel rubber-tired roller. A gasoline-engine-driven vibration unit is attached to the axle, and the ballast box is spring-suspended so that the axle is free to vibrate unhampered by the mass above. Both types are capable of compacting cohesionless soils in layers from 1 to 3 ft thick to the Standard Proctor maximum in two or three passes.

The *vibroflotation* process employs a giant cylindrical vibrator that is suspended from a crane. Water jetted from within the vibrator loosens the soil and permits the vibrator to penetrate as deep as 40 ft. The vibra-tion, which is in the horizontal direction, compacts the soil in a cylindrical column 8 to 10 ft in diameter. The device is slowly withdrawn and at the same time sand is placed in the annular space between the vibrator and the soil, filling the hole left behind. The water opens the hole for the vibrator and in some cases helps the particles reorient themselves. The method is suitable only for free-draining soils where the water in the voids will not hamper compaction. It can be used below the water table.

Pile driving is a very effective way of compacting loose, cohesionless soils throughout great depths. The hammer vibration coupled with the displacement force of the pile is ideal, but the method is slow and expen-sive. The method ordinarily used is the same as for driving uncased con-crete piles, but instead of concrete, sand can be used. The resulting piles are called *sand piles*.

The treads of a crawler tractor are efficient compactors of cohesionless soils placed in layers no thicker than 3 or 4 in. The action produced is light, static pressure combined with vibration.

Explosives, placed at the surface or a few feet below, have been used to compact loose cohesionless soils through shock and vibration. The results are unpredictable and usually erratic.

The *vibratory tampers* consist of a curved shoe mounted with an eccentric weight vibrator and powered by a small, one-cylinder gasoline engine. These provide vibration and high-speed tamping and are useful in compacting cohesionless and slightly cohesive soils. Although theoretically they should produce large impulse forces, much of their energy is dissipated in elastic rebound, and they can produce up to 95 per cent of the Standard Proctor maximum in layers 2 to 3 in. thick.

Jetting and flooding have been used with some success in cohesionless soils of high permeability. Flooding destroys the capillary tension, which prevents the grain from moving into more compact arrangements. Jetting with water under pressure in some cases provides flooding and a little vibration that helps to compact medium sands, but the results are ex-

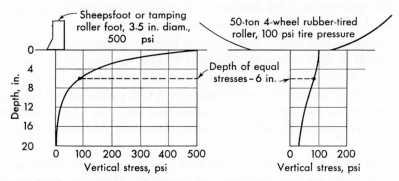

Fig. 8:5 Comparison of vertical stresses in soil below a sheepsfoot and heavy rubber-tired roller.

tremely erratic. Since modern, controlled compacting methods are available, jetting and flooding should not be used.

Fill Operation[8:11,8:12,8:13] The selection of the proper compaction method, layer thickness, contact pressure, and moisture is the joint responsibility of the engineer and the constructor, for these affect the quality and uniformity of the soil structure and the speed and cost of construction.

The most important factor is the pressure in the layer being compacted. As shown in Fig. 8:5, the pressure beneath the compaction device decreases with depth. A high pressure applied over a small area, such as by the sheepsfoot roller, decreases rapidly, while a moderate pressure over a large area produces a more uniform pressure throughout the layer. The average pressure in a layer can be increased by decreasing the layer thickness or increasing the surface load. Ordinarily the best compaction efficiency is obtained with the maximum possible pressure that will not produce bearing-capacity failure. This is found by experiment. Bearing failure is indicated by rutting of the surface by rubber tires or failure of the sheepsfoot roller to rise out of the ground or "walk out" with each successive pass.

A loose, uncompacted soil has a low bearing capacity even when the compacted soil has high capacity. Heavy equipment operating on the loose soil is likely to create bearing failure and accompanying loss of compaction efficiency until the soil is densified enough to support the loading. If the soil is first partially compacted by a light roller, the bearing can be increased enough to support the heavy roller. Such *stage compaction* can be very effective where high densities are required.

The best moisture for compaction is the optimum for that particular method. The laboratory optimum has no exact counterpart in the field, but it serves as a guide. The Standard Proctor optimum is indicative of the needs of light rollers; the Modified Proctor optimum (a few per cent less than the Standard) is indicative of the needs of the heaviest equipment.

On large projects a test area is constructed to try different combinations of equipment, pressure, layer thickness, and moisture to determine the best for each different soil. Such testing ultimately saves much time and money.

Rock Fills   Both coarse gravel and broken rock make excellent fills because they are free draining and frost free. However, they require compaction to obtain their best strength and to minimize settlement. If the largest particles are smaller than about 12 in., the fill is best compacted by 50- to 100-ton rubber-tired rollers. Water is sprayed or *sluiced* on the surface during the rolling at a rate of one-half to two volumes of water for each volume of fill. The water enables the roller to force the larger rock or gravel pieces together by washing the finer particles from between their points of contact.

Coarse rock is compacted by dumping and sluicing. The rock is dumped from the dam abutment, or from one end of the embankment being built, so that it falls freely or slides and rolls down the slope. The momentum causes the pieces to wedge tightly together. At the same time huge jets of water from 3-in. nozzles at more than 100 psi play on the rock face, washing the fines inward so that the coarsest particles can make contact with one another. Dumped rock fills are strong but tend to settle from $\frac{1}{2}$ to 1 per cent of their height over a period of five to ten years.

Density Control   Continuous testing of the moisture and density of the compacted fill is essential to ensure that the finished product meets the requirements. The number of tests depends on the fill size and the workmanship: Typically, one test is required for every 1000 to 10,000 cu yd of fill, spaced so that there are tests in each lift and in each day's work.

The density test procedure depends on the character of the soil. If little gravel is present, a thin-walled tube 4 in. in diameter and 5 in. long, with a sharp cutting edge (Fig. 8:6), is used to secure a sample of known volume which is weighed and then tested for moisture to determine the dry density. For gravelly soils the *sand cone method* is often used. A hole 4 to 6 in. in diameter and 6 in. deep is dug, and the soil from it is weighed and tested for moisture. The volume of the hole is measured by filling it with loose, dry sand that falls from a fixed height through a cone-shaped

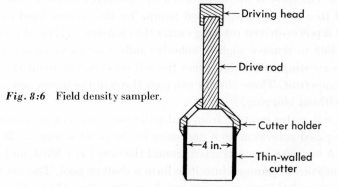

Fig. 8:6 Field density sampler.

— Driving head

— Drive rod

— Cutter holder

←4 in.→

— Thin-walled cutter

stand. An alternate method of measuring the hole volume is to line it with a thin rubber membrane and fill it with water. A number of different devices, called *balloon density* meters, incorporate a retracting rubber membrane and self-indicating water supply to expedite measuring the hole volume.

The moisture content can be measured in the ordinary way by oven-drying at 105 C. A number of alternate methods are used to speed the drying, including burning out the moisture with alcohol, frying the soil at a temperature of about 300 C, and by direct-reading moisture meters. Although these alternates are seldom accurate, they are useful in securing a quick answer.

Moisture and density determinations can be made by measuring the effects of nuclear radiation through the compacted soil. Both surface tests of the uppermost foot of fill and deep tests throughout the fill depth are possible, and the results are available immediately. The results should be checked by direct density tests from time to time because in some soils there is a tendency toward erratic calibration.

Hydraulic Fills   When large volumes of soil must be excavated and transported, hydraulic methods may be economical. This is particularly true in water-front construction or dam construction where sufficient quantities of water are available.

Hydraulic excavation can be employed in cohesionless or slightly cohesive soils. Jets of water, forced by pressures as high as 150 psi through 2-in. to 4-in. nozzles, wash the soil from the borrow pit into sluices. The mixture of soil and water can then be pumped and transported by pipe for miles.

Suction dredging can be employed to excavate sands below the water surface. The sand is literally sucked up through a large flexible pipe attached to a powerful centrifugal pump. To the suction head can be attached a power-driven rotating cutter that loosens sands and even makes it possible to remove slightly cohesive soils. Clays can be excavated by using a rotating cutter that slices the soil into chunks about the size of a large grapefruit. These chunks can pass through the pump and hydraulic lines without clogging.

The soil–water mixture from hydraulic excavation or suction dredging can be piped several miles if necessary to the point where the fill is to be made. A low dike is constructed around the area to be filled, and the soil–water mixture is pumped into it to form a shallow pool. The soil particles settle out and the excess water overflows the edges of the dike or seeps away. The height of the dike is increased as the fill grows, by pulling some of the settled soil from the bottom of the pool onto the top and shoulders of the dike. When the soil contains both fine and coarse grains, the coarse particles settle out close to the outlets of the hydraulic lines, and the fines settle out in the stiller portions of the pool. In constructing dams by the hydraulic fill method, it is possible to make use of these different rates of sedimentation to create an impervious core of fines with shells of coarse, pervious soil. The outlets are placed at the outside of the fill where the coarse materials settle out, and the fines for the core settle in the pool in the middle, as shown in Fig. 8:7.

Compacting Hydraulic Fills   Hydraulic fills of sand and gravel are formed in a relatively loose state. Since it is impractical to compact them during filling, they are ordinarily loose throughout their entire depth. The methods of compaction are pile driving, explosives, and vibroflotation, and it is difficult to get uniformly high densities.

Silt placed by hydraulic methods is usually in an extremely loose condition. Pile driving is effective in compacting deep silt fills, but the results may be somewhat erratic. If the silt has cohesion, pile driving will be somewhat less successful, but compaction by consolidation may be possible. A thick layer of sand or gravel on top of the fill and the weight of the fill itself will provide the consolidation load. In order to increase the rate of consolidation, well points or vertical sand drains may be inserted into the soil. They provide short paths for drainage of the water expelled from the soil during the consolidation process.

Hydraulic fills of impervious clays consist of clay balls in a matrix of very soft clay. Such fills can be compacted only by consolidation or, in some cases, by drying out, although the latter takes place only near the

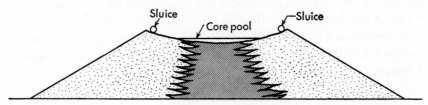

Fig. 8:7 Cross-section of a hydraulic fill dam. Core is composed of fines and shell of coarser materials.

surface. Under the load of a thick bed of gravel, the clay balls will deform plastically and the soft clay between the balls will consolidate and become stiffer.

Hydraulic methods of fill manufacture are very cheap and have been used for many years in marine and dam construction. Unfortunately the quality of the resulting fill is often poor, and expensive methods of compaction may be required to make the fill suitable for its purpose.

8:5 Soil Stabilization[8:15,8:16]

Frequently the soils available for construction cannot meet the requirements, such as strength and incompressibility, imposed by their use in embankments or subgrades. The process of improving the soil so that it can meet the requirements is known as *stabilization*. In its broadest meaning, stabilization includes compaction, drainage, preconsolidation, and protection of the surface from erosion and moisture infiltration. However, the term *stabilization* is gradually being restricted to one aspect of soil improvement: the alteration of the soil material itself.

Requirements of Stabilization[8:18] The mode of alteration and the degree of alteration necessary depend on the character of the soil and on its deficiencies. In most cases additional strength is required. If the soil is cohesionless, this can be provided by confinement or by adding cohesion with a cementing or binding agent. If it is cohesive, the strength can be increased by making the soil moisture-resistant, altering the clay-adsorbed water films, increasing cohesion with a cementing agent, and adding internal friction. Reduced compressibility can be obtained by filling the voids or cementing the grains with a rigid material or by altering the clay-mineral adsorbed water forces. Freedom from swelling and shrinking can be provided by cementing, altering the clay-mineral water-adsorbing ability, and by making the soil resistant to moisture changes. Permeability can be reduced by filling the voids with an impervious material or by altering the clay-mineral adsorbed-water structure to prevent flocculation. It can be increased by removing fines or creating an aggregated structure.

Many different methods for stabilization have been proposed. From the standpoint of their function or effect on the soil they can be classified as follows:

(1) Moisture-holding: retain moisture in soil.
(2) Moisture-resisting: prevent moisture from entering soil or from affecting clay materials.
(3) Cementing: binding the particles together without their alteration.
(4) Void-filling: plugging the voids.
(5) Mechanical stabilization: improving the soil gradation.
(6) Physicochemical alteration: changing the clay mineral or the clay-mineral adsorbed-water system.

A satisfactory stabilizing agent must provide the required qualities and in addition must satisfy the following criteria: (1) compatible with the soil material; (2) permanent; (3) easily handled and processed; and (4) low cost. Many materials have been employed but with varying degrees of success. No one material meets all the requirements and most are deficient in the last criterion—cost. The principal methods and materials and their typical applications are described in the subsequent paragraphs.

Moisture-holding Admixtures Moisture in the soil provides some cohesion in sands and silts by capillary tension and prevents dust in all materials. It prevents shrinkage and cracking of cohesive soils and thereby reduces their disintegration in the first rain following a dry spell. Ordinary salt is an excellent moisture-holding material in hot but relatively humid regions; it is applied at a rate of about 25 lb per cu yd. Calcium chloride, at 15 lb per cu yd, is very effective, particularly in dry areas, because it is deliquescent (capable of taking moisture from the air).

Moisture-resisting Admixtures Moisture-resisting or waterproofing materials help keep water away from the soil particles and prevent softening or swelling. This is done in two ways: coating the grains or by preferential adsorption. Bituminous materials, such as RC-3 or 5 or MC-3 or 5 cutback asphalts, are the most widely used waterproofing agents. The amounts required vary from 2 to 7 per cent, increasing with the percentage of fines. They are most successful in soils of low plasticity but in many soils tend to lose their effectiveness with time. Resinous waterproofing agents have been used but are expensive and likely to deteriorate badly.

Hydrophobic agents, which are adsorbed on the particles in preference to water, show considerable promise. Silicones and stearates have been used for this purpose and appear to be relatively permanent in their effect. Processing is difficult, for each clay particle must be treated. The method is promising but requires development.

Cementing A wide variety of cements or binding agents are employed in cementing, the most widely used and most successful method for stabilization. While the most pronounced benefit is an increase in strength by cohesion, there is also a reduction in permeability of most soils through filling of the voids with the cementing agent. When the cementing agent is relatively rigid, the modulus of elasticity of the soil can be increased and its compressibility decreased.

Soil-cement stabilization employs portland cement to form a mixed-in-place concrete in which the soil is the aggregate. It has proved very successful in making low-cost pavements for light traffic and rigid base courses for the heaviest traffic.

The proper mix is determined by a trial procedure to obtain the required durability and strength.[8:17] Samples of soil are prepared with different amounts of cement and compacted at optimum moisture by the Standard Proctor method. After curing seven days, these are subjected to 12 cycles of freezing and thawing or 12 cycles of wetting and drying. The maximum volume change (swell plus shrink) permitted is 2 per cent. The maximum loss of weight permitted (after brushing) ranges from 7 per cent for A-6 and A-7 soils to 14 per cent for A-1, A-2, and A-3 soils. In some cases a minimum unconfined compressive strength is also specified. The required cement content is the least percentage which will satisfy these criteria. Typical cement requirements are 8 per cent for sandy soils to 15 per cent by weight for clayey soils.

Soil-cement modification uses about one-fifth the usual amount of cement to improve the strength and rigidity of soils that do not require complete stabilization. This is particularly useful when proper soil compaction is prevented by excessive soil moisture, and when sufficient time is not available to wait for dry weather.

Lime-fly ash stabilization resembles soil cement in that a pozzolanic cement is created by the reaction of lime on the silica of the fly ash. The proportions of lime to fly ash and the amount of cementing material are found by trial. Typical requirements are 10 to 15 per cent of a mix consisting of two parts of ash to one part of lime mixed with the soil and compacted in the same way as portland cement.

Bituminous binders, usually asphaltic cutbacks such as RC-1, RC-3, MC-1, and MC-3, have been used for both subgrades and low-cost pavements. Emulsified asphalts are also used, but they require a long period of dry weather to permit the mix to cure properly. The amount of bitumen is determined by trial or from past experience, and usually is from 4 to 7 per cent by weight. Bituminous stabilization finds its widest use in sandy soils having little or no clay, such as SW, SP, and SM classes.

Chemical cementing consists of binding the soil with materials that harden by a chemical reaction. While portland cement and lime-fly ash involve chemical reactions, they are ordinarily not placed in this category. Because their cost is five to fifty times that of portland cement, these materials are employed only in special circumstances.

Soluble silicates react with a number of salts to produce insoluble gels that harden with time. The principal silicate is a solution of sodium silicate or water glass, and the gel is precipitated with calcium or magnesium chloride, aluminum sulfate, or a weak acid. The reaction is so rapid that the soil cannot ordinarily be processed after it occurs. Therefore the process is used principally for in-place stabilization of soil deposits by injection, using from 10 to 20 per cent of the mixed solutions by volume.

The *chrome-lignin* process utilizes the reaction between the waste lignin-rich liquor from sulfite paper manufacture and potassium or sodium dichromate. The result is a dark-colored resin that becomes harder with time. The reaction is slow enough so that the soil can be mixed and compacted after the chemicals are added. Because the chemicals initially are in solution, the process finds its greatest application in injection into fine-grained soils.

Analine, a liquid coal-tar derivative, and *furfural*, an organic liquid from corn products refining, in the ratio of two parts to one, react to form

of the proportions that will provide the optimum binder. A number of standard gradation specifications have been developed for this purpose, based on past experience, but most do not consider the effect of the grain shape and the volume of water adsorbed in the clay. A rational procedure[8:19] separates each soil into aggregate and binder. The aggregates and the binders are compacted separately, to determine the volume of voids in the compacted aggregate and the density of the compacted binder. The mix is proportioned so that the total binder (from all the ingredients) is from 75 to 90 per cent of that required to fill the voids. Typical binder requirements for maximum strength are 20 to 27 per cent and are somewhat less than the amounts that result in the maximum compacted density. Mechanical stabilization is primarily used for pavement subgrades and for low-cost pavements where some improvement in the soil is needed but where great expense is not justified.

Physicochemical Alteration   Physicochemical alteration, including *chemical stabilization*, consists of changing the properties of the soil grains, principally the clay minerals, and their adsorbed water. Ion exchange or *base exchange* is the changing of the cations in the adsorbed water films. The plasticity of the clay tends to decrease with increasing valence of the cations. By the addition in sufficient concentrations of chemicals with high valence cations, the soil is forced to exchange with a resulting lowering of its plasticity. Lime and calcium chloride provide calcium ions with a valence of 2 which bring about a marked improvement of high plasticity clays having sodium or potassium cations. Aluminum sulfate and certain organic chemicals have also been used for this purpose experimentally. The amount of the chemical required is small, as low as 0.1 per cent in some cases.

Electrochemical stabilization involves base exchange induced by an electric current. Aluminum cations leave a positive electrode of aluminum in the soil and migrate toward the negative, and in the course of their movement, bring about base exchange. At the same time electro-osmotic drainage toward the negative electrode in the form of a well helps harden the soil.

Dispersing agents, such as sodium silicate and sodium polyphosphate, increase the repulsion in the clay-adsorbed water layers and cause the soil to develop a dispersed or oriented structure (Fig. 1:10). The liquid limit, plasticity index, and permeability are reduced, and the maximum compacted density is increased. The procedure is inexpensive, for it requires only from 0.1 to 0.2 per cent of cheap chemicals. The method has been employed successfully for sealing leaky ponds.[8:20]

Coagulating or aggregating chemicals provide the opposite effect to dispersion. The particles link themselves together in chains with large voids between. The permeability and plasticity are increased and the maximum compacted density is decreased. They improve cultivation and drainage and are used to help establish grass on steep slopes.

Thermal alteration is the application of intense heat to desiccate the soil and even produce limited fusion. Fuel-oil burners are introduced through holes in the soil to raise the temperature to more than 1500 F. The brick-like mass, 7 to 10 ft in diameter, that forms is permanently stabilized.[8:21]

Stabilization Processing Processing is the most critical part of stabilization because the effectiveness of any method depends on what proportion of the soil particles are treated. The ease of processing depends on the cohesion: Cohesionless soils break up readily and are easily processed, whereas cohesive soils tend to form impenetrable lumps that defy treatment. Dry materials such as cement are spread mechanically on each soil layer, while soluble materials and liquids such as asphalt are added by sprinkling.

Disc plows and harrows that turn the soil are effective in soils of low cohesion when large amounts of a stabilizer must be mixed. Traveling mechanical mixers that pulverize the soil with pug mills or high-speed rotary blades are very effective in all but highly plastic clays and are essential when only small amounts (less than 2 per cent) of stabilizer are used. After mixing, the soil is compacted as previously described. A period of curing is required for many of the cementing materials, ranging from a few days of hot weather for RC asphalts to a month for soil cement.

Injection Stabilization: Grouting Stabilization by injection, usually termed *grouting*, makes it possible to improve the properties of natural deposits and existing fills without excavation, processing, and recompaction. Grouting ordinarily has two objectives: to improve the structural properties and to reduce the permeability. This is done by filling cracks, fissures, and cavities in rock and voids in the soil with a stabilizer in liquid form or in suspension which subsequently solidifies.

A grouting material must meet a number of requirements. First it must be fluid or fine-grained enough to penetrate the finest openings that require filling. Second the hardening must take place before the grout is washed away by circulating ground water but after the grout has had time to penetrate. Third the grout must impart the required physical properties to the material being stabilized; and fourth the effect must be permanent. Many different materials have been used in grouting. The principal ones are: (1) portland cement with from one to five parts of water; (2) mixtures of portland cement, clay, fine sand, fly ash, and rock dust; (3) sodium silicate, with a reactor, and chemical solutions (chrome lignin and AM-9). Portland cement is suitable for cavities, cracks, and for coarse sand. The silicate mixtures are used principally for gravels and coarse sands where a rapid reaction is necessary to avoid dilution with ground water. The chemical solutions, particularly AM-9, are effective in sands and silts. None of the materials permeates clays. Instead they develop grout fingers, which may partially reinforce the mass but which do not really stabilize it.

The grout is injected under pressure through holes drilled in rock or perforated injection pipes that are driven into the soil. The grouting plant includes mixers, pumps, and valve systems that permit the grout to circulate and which allow control of the grout volume and pressure.

8:6 Subgrades and Pavements[8:23]

A *pavement* is a structure whose primary function is to spread the concentrated load of a vehicle wheel sufficiently that the underlying soil can support it without failure or excessive deflection. In addition the pavement should provide a smooth, non-skid, running surface that resists weathering. Finally it protects the underlying soil from loss of its qualities due to exposure to sun, rain, and cold.

The earliest pavements were narrow treads of stone spaced as far apart as the chariot and cart wheels, which allowed ancient military vehicles to service remote outposts in the worst weather. In heavily forested areas, 4- to 6-in. diam poles were laid side to side across the roadway to form a stable but rough "corduroy" pavement. The ancient road building was climaxed by the Romans, who laid large slabs of stone in overlapping layers on beds of broken stone and natural cement mortar. While the Roman road was strong and durable, it was so expensive that such construction was abandoned in the Middle Ages. Modern pavement design began with the Scottish engineer MacAdam, who formulated rules for drainage of the pavement and for developing load-spreading ability through the use of interlocking bulky fragments.

Components of Pavement Systems   Two different systems of load spreading are in use: *rigid* and *flexible*. The rigid pavement utilizes beam action of a relatively rigid member to distribute the load. The overlapping stone slabs and the wood poles of the primitive roads and the concrete slab of modern construction function in this way. The flexible pavement system distributes the load by particle-to-particle contact throughout its thickness.

As shown in Fig. 8:8a, the rigid system includes three components. The pavement slab provides the riding surface and the load-spreading slab. The *sub-base* (sometimes omitted) serves a number of purposes: insulation against frost penetration, drainage, and a layer resistant to erosion and *pumping*. The *subgrade* is the underlying natural soil or the surface of a compacted fill that ultimately supports the load.

The flexible pavement (Fig. 8:8b) includes four components. The surface course provides the riding surface and an impervious membrane that sheds water. The *base course* is the main load-spreading layer. It is strong enough to withstand the shear stresses produced by the wheel, incompressible, and rigid enough to distribute the load over the underlying layers. The sub-base (sometimes omitted) also spreads the load. In addi-

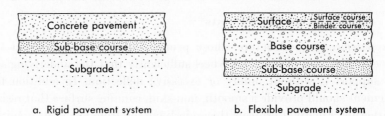

a. Rigid pavement system   b. Flexible pavement system

Fig. 8:8 Components of pavement systems.

tion it serves as a transition filter to prevent the base course materials from punching down into a fine-grained subgrade, as an insulator to prevent frost action in the subgrade, and as a drain. The subgrade is the ultimate support of the loads and is either natural soil or compacted fill.

Subgrades   In general a subgrade has the same requirements as a fill: strength, incompressibility, and freedom from swelling and shrinking. In addition it must be rigid enough to prevent excessive deflection under live loads. Susceptibility to frost action is important in regions where the depth of frost penetration is as great as the pavement thickness.

The investigation of materials for proposed use in subgrades is similar to that for fills. Large numbers of small samples are secured in prospective borrow areas and of the upper layers of virgin soil where no fill is to be used. These are classified visually and by laboratory tests. A preliminary evaluation of their qualities is made on the basis of empirical correlations of performance with the soil classes. Such a rating, based on the Unified System, is shown in columns 4, 5, 6, and 7 of Table 8:1. Similar ratings have been developed for other classification systems; the choice of which to use depends on the experience of the engineer.

Special tests for subgrades have been developed by a number of highway departments. The Georgia Highway Department[8:24] first obtains the maximum dry density by the Standard Proctor method. Two samples are then compacted to maximum density and one is allowed to shrink and the other to swell. The soil is rated on the basis of its compacted density and percentage of swell, plus the percentage of shrinking.

Subgrade Evaluation for Pavement Design   The design of the pavement is essentially the fitting of the wheel load to the capabilities of the subgrade. While this can be done by empirical rules based on past experience, economical engineering practice requires an evaluation of the significant physical properties of the subgrade and the design of a pavement to fit. A brief discussion of the evaluation of the subgrade follows. The design procedures can be obtained from texts on highway engineering and pavement design.[8:23]

The significant property of the subgrade for the design of a rigid pavement is the deflection under short-term loads. This can be approximated by a plate load test that simulates the loading of the rigid pavement. A circular plate 30 in. in diameter is seated on the subgrade and loaded to a pressure σ of 10 psi. The deflection ρ of the plate is measured. The modulus of subgrade reaction, K, is defined by

$$K = \frac{\sigma}{\rho} \tag{8:3}$$

and has the dimensions of pounds per cubic inch. In most cases the field test is not conducted under the worst possible condition of saturation. To simulate the effects of saturation, two samples of the subgrade are subjected to a short-term laboratory consolidation test of 10 psi, one in the original condition and one inundated. The ratio of the "as is" settlement to the inundated sample is multiplied by the field K factor to obtain a K value that is corrected for saturation.

A number of methods are used to evaluate subgrades for flexible pavement design. The California bearing ratio, usually abbreviated CBR, is a semiempirical index of the strength and deflection characteristics of a soil that has been correlated with pavement performance to establish design curves for pavement thickness.[8:25] The test is performed on a 6-in. diam, 5 in. thick disk of either compacted or undisturbed soil that is confined in a steel cylinder. Before testing, the sample is inundated under a confining pressure equivalent to the weight of the future pavement in order to determine the potential swelling and to simulate the worst possible condition of moisture that could occur in the field. A piston approximately 2 in. in diameter is then forced into the soil at a standard rate to determine the resistance to penetration. The CBR is the ratio (expressed as a percentage) of the actual load required to produce a 0.1-in. (or 0.2-in.) deflection to that required to produce the same deflection in a certain standard crushed stone. A field version of the test is used to determine the existing CBR of subgrades by in-place tests without soaking. The CBR test and its accompanying design curves have been widely used for designing flexible pavements for highways and particularly for airfields in many parts of the world. It has been criticized as being overly conservative in requiring inundation of the soil before testing. While this is admittedly a severe requirement, so little is known about the actual maximum subgrade moisture conditions that this is probably justified.

Plate load tests, similar to the subgrade modulus test, have been used in a rational evaluation of the deflection characteristics of the soil.[8:26] A number of different procedures have been developed, each to simulate certain field conditions such as load or load repetition. The results are analyzed on the basis of deformation settlement, using elastic theories derived for uniform, horizontal layers.

Rational analyses, based on the strength and deflection properties of the soil as determined by triaxial shear tests, are proving to be a useful approach to design because it is possible to reproduce different conditions of load and soil moisture at a low cost and in a short time.[8:23] It is likely that such rational methods will eventually replace the semiempirical and empirical designs.

REFERENCES

8:1   R. R. Proctor, "Fundamental Principles of Soil Compaction," *Engineering News Record*, Aug. 31, Sept. 7, Sept 21, and Sept. 28, 1933.

8:2   "The Unified Classification: Appendix A—Characteristics of Soil Groups Pertaining to Roads and Airfields, and Appendix B—Characteristics of Soil Groups Pertaining to Embankments and Foundations," *Technical Memorandum 357*, U.S. Waterways Experiment Station, Vicksburg, 1953.

8:3   *Construction and Material Specifications*, Department of Highways, State of Ohio, 1949, p. 56.

8:4 T. W. Lambe, "The Engineering Behavior of Compacted Clay," *Journal of the Soil Mechanics and Foundations Division, Proceedings, ASCE*, Vol. 84, No. SM2, May, 1958.

8:5 H. B. Seed and C. K. Chan, "Structure and Strength Characteristics of Compacted Clays," *Journal of the Soil Mechanics and Foundations Division, Proceedings, ASCE*, Vol. 85, No. SM5, October, 1959.

8:6 H. B. Seed and C. K. Chan, "Undrained Strength of Compacted Clays After Soaking," *Journal of the Soil Mechanics and Foundations Division, Proceedings, ASCE*, Vol. 85, No. SM6, December, 1959.

8:7 G. A. Leonards, "Strength Characteristics of Compacted Clay," *Transactions, ASCE*, Vol. 120, 1955.

8:8 H. L. Nichols, *Moving the Earth*, North Castle Books, Greenwich, Conn., 1955.

8:9 "Compaction of Embankments, Subgrades, and Bases," *Bulletin 58*, Highway Research Board, Washington, 1952.

8:10 W. J. Turnbull and C. R. Foster, "Stabilization of Materials by Compaction," *Transactions ASCE* Vol. 123, 1958, p. 1.

8:11 J. W. Hilf, "Compacting Earth Dams with Heavy Tamping Rollers," *Transactions ASCE*, Vol. 124, 1959, p. 509.

8:12 "Soil Compaction Investigation—Effect on Soil Compaction of Tire Pressure and Number of Coverages of Rubber-Tired Rollers and Foot-Contact Pressure of Sheepsfoot Rollers," *Technical Memorandum 3-271*, No. 7, U.S. Waterways Experiment Station, Vicksburg, 1956.

8:13 F. C. Walker and W. G. Holtz, "Control of Embankment Materials by Laboratory Testing," *Transactions, ASCE*, Vol. 118, 1953, p. 4.

8:14 H. F. Winterkorn, "Soil Stabilization," *Proceedings, Second International Conference on Soil Mechanics and Foundation Engineering*, Vol. 5, Rotterdam, 1948, p. 209.

8:15 "Stabilization of Soils," *Bulletin 98*, Highway Research Board, Washington, 1955.

8:16 "Soil and Soil Aggregate Stabilization," *Bulletin 108*, Highway Research Board, Washington, 1955.

8:17 *Soil Cement Laboratory Handbook*, Portland Cement Association, Chicago, 1959.

8:18 "Chemical and Mechanical Stabilization," *Bulletin 129*, Highway Research Board, Washington, 1956.

8:19 E. A. Miller and G. F. Sowers, "Strength Characteristics of Soil Aggregate Mixtures," *Bulletin 183*, Highway Research Board, 1958.

8:20 T. W. Lambe, "Improvement of Soil Properties with Dispersants," *Journal, Boston Society of Civil Engineers*, April, 1954.

8:21 I. M. Litvinov, "Discussion on Thermal Consolidation," *Proceedings, Fourth International Conference on Soil Mechanics and Foundation Engineering*, Vol. 3, London, 1957, p. 169.

8:22 R. H. Karol, *Soils and Soil Engineering*, Prentice-Hall, Inc., Englewood Cliffs, N.J., 1960, p. 174.

8:23   E. J. Yoder, *Principles of Pavement Design*, John Wiley & Sons, Inc., New York, 1959.

8:24   S. Williams, H. Lee, W. F. Abercrombie, and D. M. Burmister, *Bulletin 177*, Highway Research Board, Washington, 1958.

8:25   "Development of CBR Flexible Pavement Design Method for Airfields, a Symposium," *Transactions, ASCE*, Vol. 115, 1950.

8:26   U.S. Navy, "Airfield Pavements," *NAVDOCKS Technical Publication TP-Pw-4*, Department of Navy, 1953.

Suggestions for Additional Study

1. References 8:4, 8:5, 8:7, 8:9, 8:15, 8:18, 8:19.
2. *Proceedings, Conference on Soil Stabilization*, Mass. Institute of Technology, Cambridge, 1952.
3. "Soil Compaction Investigation," *Technical Memorandum 3-271*, Reports 1–8, U.S. Waterways Experiment Station, Vicksburg, 1951–1957.
4. *Soil Cement Laboratory Handbook*, Portland Cement Association, Chicago, 1959.
5. *Procedures for Testing Soils*, ASTM, Philadelphia, 1958.
6. "Symposium on Rock Fill Dams," *Journal of the Power Division, Proceedings, ASCE*, Vol. 84, No. PO4, August, 1958.
7. "Chemical Grouting," *Journal of the Soil Mechanics and Foundations Division, Proceedings, ASCE*, Vol. 83, No. SM4, November, 1957.
8. *Bibliography on Soil Stabilization*, Indian National Society of Soil Mechanics and Foundation Engineering, New Delhi, 1954.

PROBLEMS

8:1   The following data were secured from a moisture-density test. The soil $G_s = 2.71$.

Water Content	Unit Weight	Water Content	Unit Weight
10	97	20	127
13	105	22	126
16	117	25	121
18	123		

    a. Plot the moisture-dry density curve. Find the maximum density and optimum moisture.

    b. Plot the zero air voids curve.

    c. If the contractor is required to secure 90 per cent compaction, what is the range in water contents that would be advisable?

8:2   Compaction tests were made on the same soil, using first the Standard Proctor Method and second the Modified Proctor Method. The following results were obtained:

Standard Proctor		Modified Proctor	
Water Content	*Dry Density (lb/cu ft)*	*Water Content*	*Dry Density (lb/cu ft)*
6	102	6	107
9	106	9	113
12	108	12	118
14	109	13	118
16	108	14	117
19	105	16	112
22	100	18	108

a. Plot both curves on the same graph and determine maximum density and optimum moisture for each.

b. Plot the zero air voids curve if the specific gravity of solids is 2.67.

c. How much increase in maximum density results from the modified compaction? What decrease in optimum moisture occurs when using modified compaction?

d. The soil is classed CL by the Unified System. What densities would be required for a highway fill 40 ft high? What would the range in permissible moisture contents be if the field methods were comparable to the effort of (1) the Standard Proctor Test, and (2) the Modified Proctor Test?

8:3 A Standard Proctor Test on a ML soil having a specific gravity of solids of 2.68 was

Water Content	*Dry Density (lb/cu ft)*	*Water Content*	*Dry Density (lb/cu ft)*
12	86	24	91
15	89	27	88
18	91	30	84
21	93		

a. Plot the moisture density and zero air voids curve. What is the maximum degree of saturation of the soil?

b. The soil is to be used in a fill 15 ft high that supports a one-story building. What densities should be specified, based on Table 8:2?

c. The soil moisture is 25 per cent. The constructor is able to obtain a dry density of 96 lb per cu ft, using a sheepsfoot roller developing 700 psi. The roller fails to walk out. What should he do to obtain the required density (1) in the deeper part of the fill, and (2) in the upper part?

8:4 Make an estimate of the suitability of each of the soils listed in problem 3:3 for

a. Fill for a highway.

b. Subgrade for an airfield pavement in Illinois.

c. Core of an earth dam.

d. Shell (structural supporting part) of an earth dam.

8:5 List in the order of their importance the properties necessary for a soil to be used in the following ways:

a. Highway fill.

   b. Railroad embankment
   c. Earth dam.
   d. Subgrade for major airport
   e. Surface for a secondary road.
8:6 Prepare a report on available compaction equipment, showing width compacted, pressure, coverage for
   a. Sheepsfoot rollers.
   b. Heavy rubber-tired rollers.
8:7 Prepare a report, based on an article appearing in an engineering or construction journal, that describes the construction of a large fill. Include the following points:
   a. Soil description
   b. Method of excavation
   c. Method of compaction
   d. Control of compaction
8:8 Prepare an outline of the procedure required for testing soil-cement mixtures. (Secure information from bulletins of the Portland Cement Association.)
8:9 Prepare a table similar to 8:1 showing the probable adaptability of each of the soil groups to stabilization by the different methods given in Art. 8:6.
   a. Mixed-in-place stabilization of a subgrade.
   b. Injection stabilization.
   c. Where any soil or material is not included, state why.

9... STABILITY of EARTH MASSES

When portions of large earth masses become detached and move, the results are usually spectacular and often disastrous. Tremendous landslides have buried entire cities and dammed up rivers; slides in open cuts have caused the abandonment of canals, highways, and railroads; levees have broken during periods of high water, flooding valuable farm land and driving people from their homes; and earth dams have failed, producing tremendous surges of water that scoured out valleys and left death and destruction behind.

9:1 Analysis of Stability

The safety of an earth mass against failure or movement is termed its *stability*. It must be considered not only in the design of earth structures but also in the repair and correction of failures. The design of open-cut slopes and embankment, levee, and earth dam cross-sections is based primarily on stability studies—unless the project is so small that occasional failures can be tolerated. When failures such as landslides and subsidences do occur, their correction requires stability studies to determine the cause of failure and the best method of preventing future trouble.

Causes of Earth Movements Earth failures have one feature in common: There is a movement of a large mass of soil along a more or less definite surface, as shown in Fig. 9:1. In most cases the earth mass remains intact during the first stages of the movement, but finally it becomes distorted and broken up as movement progresses. Some failures occur suddenly with little or no warning, while others take place leisurely after announcing their intentions by slow settlement or by the formation of cracks.

317

b. Cross-section
of failure

a. Failure on a hillside

Fig. 9:1   Failure of an earth mass.

Movements occur when the shear strength of the soil is exceeded by the shear stresses over a relatively continuous surface. Failure at a single point in the mass does not necessarily mean that a soil mass is unstable. Instability results only when shear failure has occurred at enough points to define a surface along which the movement can take place. It is hard to determine the cause of many earth movements. Actually anything that results in a decrease in soil strength or an increase in soil stress contributes to instability and should be considered in both the design of earth structures and in the correction of failures. Table 9:1 will serve as a guide in analyzing for stability.

Table 9:1   CAUSES OF INSTABILITY

Causes of Increased Stresses

1. External loads such as buildings, water, or snow.
2. Increase in unit weight by increased water content.
3. Removal of part of mass by excavation.
4. Undermining, caused by tunneling, collapse of underground caverns, or seepage erosion.
5. Shock, caused by earthquake or blasting.
6. Tension cracks.
7. Water pressure in cracks.

Causes of Decreased Strength

1. Swelling of clays by adsorption of water.
2. Pore water pressure (neutral stress).
3. Breakdown of loose or honeycombed soil structure.
4. Hair cracking from alternate swelling and shrinking or from tension.
5. Strain, and progressive failure in sensitive soils.
6. Thawing of frozen soil or frost lenses.
7. Deterioration of cementing material.
8. Vibration of loose, granular soils.

In cases of failures that result in property damage or loss of life, the engineer is often called upon to determine *the* cause of the failure. In most cases a number of causes exist simultaneously, and so attempting to decide which one finally produced failure is not only difficult but also incorrect. Often the final factor is nothing more than a trigger that set in

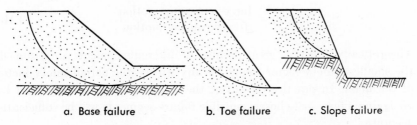

a. Base failure   b. Toe failure   c. Slope failure

Fig. 9:2 Types of circular arc failures.

motion an earth mass that was already on the verge of failure. Calling the final factor *the cause* is like calling the match that lit the fuse that detonated the dynamite that destroyed the building *the* cause of the disaster.

Stability of Slopes Among the most common of earth-mass failures are those resulting from unstable slopes. Gravity, in the form of the weight of the soil mass and of any water above it, is the major force tending to produce failure, while the shearing resistance of the soil is the major resisting force. The failure surface has the shape of the bowl of a teaspoon or half an egg sliced lengthwise, with the smaller end at the top of the slope and the wider end at the bottom, as shown in Fig. 9:1.

The failure usually occurs in one of three forms (Fig. 9:2). The *base failure* develops in soft clays and soils with numerous soft seams. The top of the slope drops, leaving a vertical scarp, while the level ground beyond the toe of the slope bulges upward. *Toe failures* occur in steeper slopes and in soils having appreciable internal friction. The top of the slope drops, often forming a series of steps, while the soil near the bottom of the slope bulges outward, covering the toe. The *slope* or *face* failures are special cases of toe failures in which hard strata limit the extent of the failure surface.

Theory of Stability Analysis of stability problems is largely a trial-and-error procedure to determine the safety factor of an assumed design or of an actual soil mass. First a potential failure surface is assumed, and the shearing resistance acting along the surface is calculated. The forces acting on the segment of soil bounded by the failure surfaces are determined, and then the safety factor of the segment is calculated as follows:

Safety against rotation

$$SF_m = \frac{\text{resisting moments}}{\text{moments causing failure}};$$ (9:1a)

Safety against translation (straight-line movement)

$$SF_t = \frac{\text{forces opposing motion}}{\text{forces causing motion}}. \qquad (9:1b)$$

Theoretically, if a very great number of different segments are assumed, the smallest safety factor found for any will be the actual safety factor of the mass. In practice, however, the smallest safety factor found by analyzing a few, well-chosen, possible failure segments will be sufficiently accurate.

Circular Arc Analysis   The general method for analysis of the stability of slopes was first suggested by the Swedish engineer K. E. Petterson[9:1] as a result of studies of a landslide in the harbor of Gothenburg. The

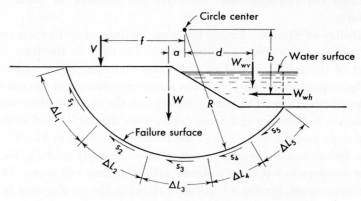

Fig. 9:3   Circular arc analysis of an earth movement.

actual surface is approximated by a segment of a cylinder which in cross-section is an arc of a circle (Fig. 9:3). The overturning moment M_0 per foot of width about the circle center is the algebraic sum of the moments due to the weight of the mass W, the horizontal and vertical components of water pressure (if the slope is inundated) acting on the surface of the slope, W_{wh} and W_{wv}, and any other external forces acting on the mass V.

$$M_0 = Wa - W_{wh}b - W_{wv}d + Vf. \qquad (9:2a)$$

In this expression a, b, d, and f are the respective moment arms of the centroids of the weights or action lines of the forces about the circle center. The resisting moment is provided by the soil strength. If the shear strength is s along each segment of the arc ΔL, whose radius is R, then the resisting moment for each foot of width is

$$M_r = R\Sigma s \,\Delta L = R(s_1\,\Delta L_1 + s_2\,\Delta L_2 + \cdots). \qquad (9:2b)$$

The safety factor of the circular segment is found by

$$SF = \frac{M_r}{M_0}. \tag{9:3}$$

The basic circular analysis can be applied to any slope and combination of forces where the shear strengths of the soils are independent of the normal stresses on the failure surface, such as saturated clays in which failure occurs so rapidly that there are no changes in water content or soil strength.

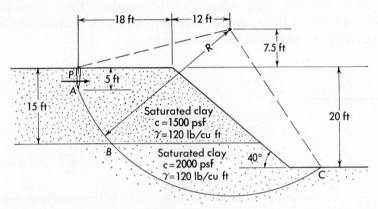

Fig. 9:4 Example 9:1 Circular arc analysis of a slope in a stratified deposit of saturated clays.

Example 9:1 Calculate the safety of the following assumed segment (Fig. 9:4) if the crack, which is 5 ft deep, is filled with water. Arc radius is 32.5 ft.

(1) Divide arc into two segments, AB and BC. Determine length of each.
    $AB = 12$ ft; $BC = 44$ ft.

(2) Calculate resisting moment.
    $M_r = 1500 \times 12$ ft $\times 32.5 + 2000 \times 44 \times 32.5 = 3,445,000$ lb-ft.

(3) Calculate weight of segment and find centroid by methods of statics.
    $W = 76,000$ lb; $a = 10.2$ ft.

(4) The moment caused by the weight is $76,000 \times 10.2 = 775,000$ lb-ft.

(5) The resultant force of water pressure in the crack P is $\dfrac{5 \times 62.4 \times 5}{2} =$
    780 lb per ft. It acts horizontally at a distance of 10.8 from the center of the arc; $M = 8400$ lb-ft.

(6) The total moment tending to cause overturning is
    $775,000 + 8400 = 783,400$ lb-ft.

(7) The safety factor SF is given by
    $$SF = \frac{3,445,000}{783,400} = 4.4.$$

Method of Slices In order to compute the stability of slopes in soils whose strength depends on the normal stress, it is necessary to determine the effective normal stress along the failure surface. A rigorous solution for the normal stress is not available, but the method of slices developed by Fellenius[9:2] has proved to be a workable approximation.[9:3]

The failure zone is divided into vertical slices, as shown in Fig. 9:5. They need not be of equal width, and for convenience in computation, the boundaries should coincide with the intersections of the strata with the circle and with the slope face. In making the analysis, it is assumed that each slice acts independently of its neighbor: There is no shear developed between them, and the normal pressures on each side of a slice produced by the adjoining slices are equal.

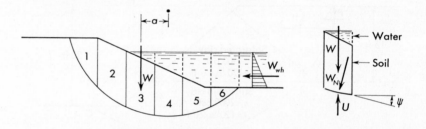

a. Circular segment divided into slices   b. Forces acting on slice 3

Fig. 9:5   Method of slices for circular arc analysis of slopes in soils whose strength depends on the confining pressure.

The vertical force acting on each slice W is the weight of the soil in the slice plus the weight of water directly above the slice. The weight of any external load on the slice, such as a structure, is also included. The net or effective downward force acting on the curved bottom of the slice is the total weight minus the upward force due to neutral stress, $\overline{W} = W - U$. The upward force U is found by multiplying the neutral stress u (computed from the flow net as described in Chapter 4) by the slice width.

If the slice is sufficiently narrow, the curved boundary can be approximated by a straight line that makes an angle of ψ with the horizontal axis. The component of the vertical force normal to the plane, $\overline{W}_N$, is computed by $\overline{W}_N = \overline{W} \cos \psi$. The shear strength along that segment of arc can be expressed as follows:

$$s = c' + \bar{p} \tan \phi', \qquad\qquad\qquad (2\!:\!24\mathrm{b},\ 2\!:\!28)$$

$$s = c' + \frac{\overline{W}_N}{\Delta L} \tan \phi'. \qquad\qquad\qquad (9\!:\!4)$$

The total resisting moment for all the arc segments is found as before by equation 9:2b.

The overturning moment can be found, as previously described, by equation 9:2a. The moment due to the vertical forces is the algebraic sum of the moment of the total weight W of each slice about the circle center Wa. To this must be added algebraically the total moments due to the horizontal component of water pressure on the slope, and water pressure in cracks.

Many variations and refinements of this basic method have been developed.[9:3,9:4,9:5] While none are rigorous, they have proved to be sufficiently accurate for analysis and design.

Cracking at the Top of the Slope   As described in Chapter 7, the upper part of a slope in a cohesive soil is in a state of tension. Under continued tension, vertical cracks develop which destroy part of the shear strength and which can contribute to failure if they fill with water. The depth d of the tension cracks can be approximated by

$$d = \frac{2c}{\gamma}. \qquad (9:5)$$

The soil above this level does not contribute to the resisting moment of the failure arc, as shown in Example 9:1. If the crack fills with water, water pressure contributes to the overturning moment.

Effect of Submergence and Seepage   Submergence of a slope has three effects. First the weight of the circular segment is increased by the weight of the water above the slope and the greater soil unit weight, which increases the overturning moment. Second the increase is more than offset by the resisting moment due to horizontal water pressure. Third, neutral stress increases on the failure surface, depending on the seepage flow net that develops, and offsets much of the gain in strength produced by the additional weights of the soil and water. The result is that the submerged slope usually has a higher safety factor than the same slope without submergence.

When the level of submergence is reduced so rapidly that the neutral stress within the slope cannot adjust itself to the new water level, the condition is termed *sudden drawdown*. The helpful moment due to horizontal water pressure is reduced. The weight of the soil and water is also reduced, but the neutral stress is not greatly changed. As a result the safety factor drops sharply, usually below that for the non-submerged condition. This is often the most critical condition in the design of the upstream face of an earth dam.

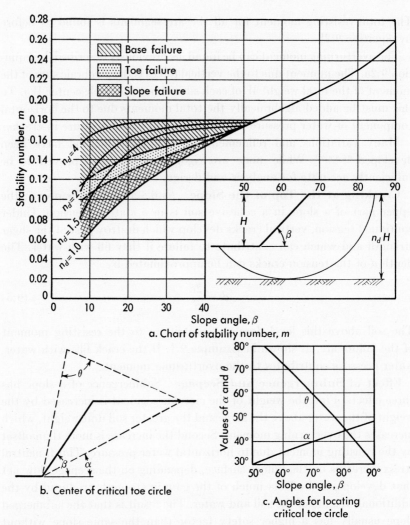

Fig. 9:6 Chart for finding the stability of slopes in homogeneous saturated clay where $\phi = 0$. (After D. W. Taylor and W. Fellenius.)

Seepage through the soil toward the face of a slope is caused by excess neutral stress within the soil mass and results in lower strength and a smaller safety factor compared with that of the same slope without seepage. This condition is often critical in deep excavations, highway and railroad cuts, the downstream face of earth dams, and in natural slopes.

Slopes in Homogeneous, Soft Clay The special case of a uniform slope in a homogeneous, soft clay whose shearing resistance is given by the relation $s = c$ can be solved analytically, and the results are presented in the form of a dimensionless number, m, termed the *stability number*. The stability number depends only on the angle of the slope, β, and on the *depth factor*, n_d, which is the ratio of the depth of a hard, dense stratum measured from the top of the slope to the height of the slope. The height of slope, H_c, at which a failure will occur is given by the relation:

$$H_c = \frac{c}{m\gamma},\tag{9:6a}$$

and the safety factor of a slope of height H is given by

$$SF = \frac{c}{mH\gamma}.{}^{*}\tag{9:6b}$$

A chart (Fig. 9:6a) showing the relation of the stability number to the slope angle and to the depth factor has been prepared from the results of a study by D. W. Taylor.[9:6]

From the chart it can be seen that toe failures occur for all slopes steeper than 53°. The location of the center of the failure arc can be found from a chart (Fig. 9:6c) developed by W. Fellenius,[9:2] a Swedish engineer who pioneered in the analysis of slope stability. For slope angles less than 53° three possibilities of failure exist, depending on n_d. When n_d is 3 or more, a base failure will occur whose failure surface is tangent to the hard stratum and whose center is above the mid-point of the slope. For values of n_d between 1 and 3, a base failure, toe failure, or slope failure may take place, depending on the slope. For values of n_d less than 1, only slope failures can take place. The different possibilities of failure and the stability factors can be determined directly from the chart.

Example 9:2 Find the safety factor of a proposed slope of 30° on an embankment 60 ft high with rock 40 ft below the base of the embankment. The soil weighs 120 lb per cu ft and the shear strength, $s = 4700$ psf.

(1) $n_d = \dfrac{60 + 40}{60} = 1.7$.

(2) $m = 0.17$ from chart.

(3) $SF = \dfrac{4700}{0.17 \times 120 \times 60} = 3.9$.

Slopes in Homogeneous, Cohesive Soil Similar analytical studies have been made of the special case of uniform slopes in homogeneous soils

* This is *not* the same safety factor as found by equation 9:3 but instead is the safety factor with respect to cohesion.

whose shearing resistance can be expressed by

$$s = c' + p \tan \phi' \qquad \text{(2:24b, 2:28)}$$

A chart of the stability number for different values of the slope angle β is shown in Fig. 9:7.[9:6] All failures are toe failures unless a hard stratum appears above the toe of the slope. In such cases the height of the slope should be measured from the top of the slope to the level of the hard stratum.

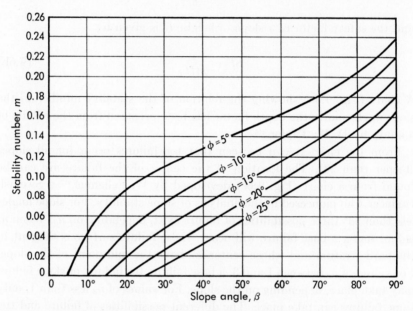

Fig. 9:7 Chart for finding the stability of slopes in homogeneous, partially saturated clays and similar soils. (After D. W. Taylor.)

Slopes in Homogeneous, Cohesionless Soil   Instead of failing on a circular surface, sand slopes fail by sliding parallel to the slope. Each sand grain can be considered as a block resting on an inclined plane at the slope angle β. When the slope angle exceeds the angle of friction of sand on sand (the angle of internal friction), the sand grain will slide down the slope. The steepest slope that a sand can attain, therefore, is equal to the angle of internal friction of the sand. Usually this is the minimum value of ϕ, since near the surface the sand is very likely to be in a loose condition. The *angle of repose* of sand as it forms a pile beneath a funnel from which it is poured is therefore about the same as the angle of internal friction of the sand in a loose condition.

Stability of Blocks In many cases the presence of extremely soft strata or strata weakened by neutral stress causes failure to take place by translation or straight-line movement along the plane of weakness instead of by rotation on a circular surface. This often occurs when earth dams are founded on stratified deposits, since the horizontal force of the water acts parallel to the possible planes of failure.

The procedure is essentially one of trial and error. A possible failure plane (usually a weak stratum) is selected, and vertical boundaries $\overline{ab}$ and $\overline{cd}$ are arbitrarily assumed (Fig. 9:8). The wedge *abdc* is acted upon by its own weight W, the force of active earth pressure P_A at the right, and

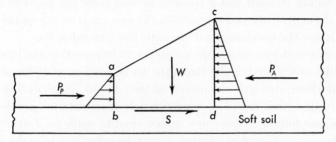

Fig. 9:8 Sliding-block analysis of a slope.

the force of passive earth pressure P_P at the left. Shear along the failure plane $\overline{bd}$ resists the unbalanced forces acting on the block. If the total shear force is S, then the safety factor *SF* is given by

$$SF = \frac{S}{P_A - P_P}. \qquad (9:7)$$

In the case of an earth dam, water pressure should be added to the effective active earth pressure causing movement. When thin, horizontal seams of cohesionless soil are present, the neutral stress must be computed in order to determine the effective strength and shearing resistance in the soil.

Shear Strength for Analysis The shear strength of a soil varies greatly, depending on the environment and particularly on the degree of saturation, the effective stress and its changes due to neutral stress variations, and the effects of progressive strain. Saturation destroys capillary tension and causes the buildup of neutral stresses under quickly applied loads. Therefore, if the environmental conditions indicate any possibility of soil saturation, the shear strength in that state is employed in analysis.

The effective stress depends on the rate of loading compared with the rate of drainage within the soil. If the loads will be placed on the soil quickly, such as by rapid construction of a large embankment, the undrained strength is used. If the loads are applied slowly, the undrained strength will be safe, but the drained strength with proper consideration of neutral stress will result in more economy. For excavated or natural slopes that are exposed for long periods of time, it is necessary to use the drained strength because the unloading produced by erosion or excavation eventually reduces the effective stress on the soil and thereby the strength.

Progressive failure brings about failure at one point before the adjoining point is highly stressed and a transfer of load from one point of the soil mass to the next. If the soil is sensitive, the average strength on the failure surface is not the maximum soil strength but somewhat less.

Judgment and experience are necessary in interpreting the laboratory test results and selecting the strengths to be used in stability analysis. The best shear strength for design is that found by analyzing actual failures in that same soil. This is particularly true when the problem is to correct a past failure. When a new design must be made for a situation for which there is no record of failures, it may be expedient to make an artificial failure—a full scale model of the proposed slope, embankment, or dam, that can be made to fail under careful observation and control. The results of such a full-scale test, when correlated with the laboratory data for the same soil, furnish the engineer with the effective strength for design of similar structures.

Safety Factors for Design   When existing slopes and embankments have been analyzed for safety, it has been found they have relatively small factors of safety when compared with those of other structures. Although a safety factor of 2 or 2.5 is not uncommon in building design, the same factors applied to embankments would make the cost so high that they could not be constructed. Many earth structures having a *computed* safety factor as low as 1.0 have been proved stable by the test of time. The following table gives the significance of different values of the safety factor for soil masses. The safety factors in Table 9:2 apply to the most

Table 9:2   SIGNIFICANCE OF SAFETY FACTORS

Safety Factor	Significance
Less than 1.0	Unsafe
1.0–1.2	Questionable safety
1.3–1.4	Satisfactory for cuts, fills, questionable for dams
1.5 or more	Safe for dams

critical combination of forces, loss of strength, and neutral stresses to which the structure will be subjected. Under ordinary conditions of loading, an earth dam should have a minimum safety factor of 1.5. However, under extraordinary loading conditions, such as a design superflood followed by sudden drawdown, a minimum safety factor of 1.1 to 1.25 is often considered adequate.

9:2 Open Cuts

Open cuts are excavations in which no bracing is used to support the soil. They are used in constructing excavations when hard soil is encountered that needs no support and in highway, railroad, and canal cuts where the cost of long lines of bracing would be great. Cuts less than 30 ft deep are ordinarily designed on the basis of experience. Railroad design manuals and standard highway specifications give 1½ (horizontal) to 1 (vertical) as a standard slope for most conditions and 2 to 1 for very soft soils.

Deep Cuts   Deep cuts should be investigated first on the basis of a preliminary soil study and a slope-stability analysis utilizing the drained shear strength. If the soil is a swelling or fissured clay or subject to unusual seepage, further investigation is necessary. The condition of nearby cuts in similar soil should be checked and, if necessary, a trial cut excavated on a slope steep enough to cause failure. The soil strength determined by an analysis of the failure, correlated with the laboratory data on the soils in the cut, should be used to determine the safe slope. In extreme cases where accurate analysis is impossible because of erratic soils, it may be necessary to place bench marks at the top of the finished slopes to warn of any unusual movements that could lead to failure.

Improvement of Cut Stability   The stability of a cut can be improved by decreasing the soil stress or by increasing its strength. Soil stress can be reduced in most cases by making the slope flatter. If the sections that require improved stability are short, the slope may be partially supported by a small retaining wall or by cribbing. Water pressure in cracks in cohesive soils can be relieved by surface drains above the slope to intercept water and by horizontal drains driven into the face of the slope.

Soil strength in cohesionless and slightly cohesive soils can be increased by relieving neutral stresses with surface drains and horizontal drains in the face of the slope. The strength of cohesive soils is difficult to improve permanently. In some instances large ventilation ducts, driven into the slope, have been able to reduce the soil's water content and increase its strength, but the method is very expensive.

Cuts in Loess   True loess, a cemented soil, has high shear strength in spite of its loose structure. It will stand vertically in cuts as deep as 40 to 50 ft. Sloping cuts are stable only until rain falls. The bare, porous soil absorbs the water, which seeps downward rapidly because of the high vertical permeability. The cementing of the soil breaks down in water, and so the slope disintegrates by slumping until it becomes vertical. Vertical cuts (Fig. 9:9) will stand for years with only occasional slumping

Fig. 9:9   Highway cut in loess. Note vertical slopes and wide shoulders.

or scaling along the vertical cleavage planes. Cuts should be made wider than is necessary in order to allow room for the debris that collects.

9:3   Embankments

An embankment is an artificial mound of soil used to carry railroads and highways across low spots, or to impound water. Since embankments are constructed of filled-in material, they are often termed *fills*, but this term applies also to other earth construction.

Highway and Railroad Fills   Highway and railroad fills are usually designed on the basis of experience unless heights greater than 30 or 40 ft are involved. The standard slopes are usually 1½ (horizontal) to 1 (vertical) or 2 to 1 unless the embankment is subject to flooding. Highways fills are carefully constructed of selected soils compacted to prevent settlement and a rough surface (see Chapter 8), but railroad fills are seldom highly compacted because rough surfaces can be prevented by proper maintenance of the ballast.

High Fills and Fills Subject to Flooding High fills and those subject to flooding require careful analysis and design based on the shear strength and compressibility of soils to be used in the fill construction. The different soils that could be used should be selected and tested as described in Chapter 8, and their shear strengths and other characteristics should be made available to the design engineer. The slopes required by each different soil to provide a safe embankment should be determined by stability analyses. From these data trial designs can be made, using the different soils, and the cost of each design can be estimated. The best soil is the one that gives a satisfactory fill at the lowest cost.

Fills subject to flooding are especially critical. Railroad fills that have stood the pounding of heavy trains for years often collapse during periods of flooding. They should be designed on the basis of the shear strength, determined after soaking samples of the soil in water as described in Chapter 8. Typical slopes for such fills may be as flat as 3 (horizontal) to 1 (vertical) or even 4 to 1 when made of soils that soften readily on absorbing water.

Levees Levees are small, long earth dams that protect low areas of cities and towns, industrial plants, and expensive farm land from flooding during periods of high water. Unlike highway and railroad embankments, settlement is not an important consideration; and unlike earth dams, levees must often be placed on poor foundations. Since levees usually extend for many miles, the cost of borrow materials and of construction is extremely important. Ordinarily a dragline working on top of the completed sections of the levee is used for construction, as shown in Fig. 9:10. It is capable of excavating and placing large volumes of soil quickly and cheaply, but it must utilize the soils found adjacent to the levee. Compaction of the soil interferes with the dragline operating cycle and so is seldom done. Because of poor soils and no compaction, levees in the United States are ordinarily constructed with very flat slopes, such as 6 (horizontal) to 1 (vertical) on the outer slope and 3 to 1 or 2 to 1 on the inner. The slopes are determined by experience in most cases.

High levees, levees in restricted space where flat slopes cannot be used, or levees protecting critical areas such as power plants should be designed

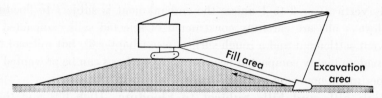

Fig. 9:10 Dragline at work building an embankment.

on the basis of soil tests and stability analyses. In such cases careful soil compaction is required, but since steeper slopes can be used, the saving in soil volume compensates, to some extent, for the added cost of construction.

9:4 Embankment Foundations

Most difficulties with embankments come from faulty foundations. It is not difficult to construct a fill that is strong, free from volume change, and incompressible; but if the soil below it is poor, failure may occur in spite of careful construction. The failure commences below the fill and in some cases can spread into the fill itself, obscuring the actual cause of the trouble.

Fills on Thick Strata of Weak Soil Fills on deep soils of little strength fail because of inadequate bearing capacity. The formulas for bearing capacity can be used to analyze such failures if the weak stratum is at least half as thick as the base of the fill is wide. Otherwise the possibility of failure must be determined by trial and error, using the circle method of analysis. If a hard crust overlies the soft soil, its strength should not be relied on to support the load. In one case a levee 40 ft high was built on top of a thin crust of hard clay that lay over a thick stratum of soft clay. Twelve hours after the levee was completed, it had sunk until it was only a few feet above the ground surface. The hard clay, which held up the partially completed fill, broke under the full load and allowed the fill to drop. Bulges or mud waves appeared in the ground surface adjacent to the toe of the fill.

Failures of this type can be prevented in a number of ways. Lightweight fill materials, such as slag, or wide, flat slopes can reduce the stresses beneath the fill to a safe amount. A gravel berm adjacent to the toe of the slope acts as a counterweight to prevent the bulging from taking place and thus may prevent failures. If the soil is normally consolidated, its strength can be improved by consolidation under the weight of the fill. Construction must proceed slowly, however, in order to give the soil time to consolidate. Vertical sand drains or sand piles can decrease the length of the drainage paths and may increase the rate of consolidation.

If the soft stratum is relatively thin (5 to 10 ft thick), it will be cheaper to excavate the soil beneath the fill area and replace it with something better. If the soft soil is from 10 to 20 ft thick, it can be replaced by *displacement*.[9:7] In this method the fill is constructed on the top of the soft soil as high and as steep as possible. In some cases it is expedient to allow it to sink under its own weight, displacing the soft soil. In other cases, it is feasible to remove the soft soil from beneath the fill by blasting. Dynamite is introduced under the fill, as shown in Fig. 9:11. The innermost charges have a slight delay. The first blast removes the soil from

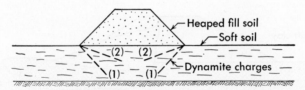

Fig. 9:11   Blasting to remove soft soil beneath a fill. Dynamite charges marked (1) explode first and are followed by those marked (2) a fraction of a second later.

the sides of the proposed fill position, and the second, a few thousandths of a second later, removes the soil beneath the fill and allows it to settle into place. The method has been very successful in many cases but requires trained, experienced personnel. A pile foundation can be used to support fills in especially critical areas, such as dock and harbor installations. On top of the piles is placed a concrete slab, known as a *relieving platform*, which supports part of the weight of the fill. The method is extremely expensive, however.

Fills on Compressible Soils   In some cases the soil may be strong enough to support the fill without failure but is so compressible that the fill settles badly. This is particularly true of organic silts and clays and true to an extreme degree in peat. Highways across marsh areas often assume wavy profiles because of irregular settlement.

Excessive settlement due to compression may be corrected by preconsolidating the soil through slow construction, by the use of sand piles, or by excavating the compressible soil. Any procedures involving consolidation require careful study to determine their effectiveness in each different situation.

Fills on Thin Strata of Soft Clay Fills on relatively thin strata of soft clay fail by sliding horizontally along a complex failure surface that extends upward through the fill, as is shown in Fig. 9:12. Failures of this type usually occur during or shortly after construction before the clay stratum has a chance to consolidate under load. The safety against this type of failure can be determined by the sliding-block analysis, using half the unconfined compressive strength of the clay stratum as the shear strength. Increased safety against this type of failure can be provided by a lightweight fill, flat slopes, and slow construction that permits the soil to consolidate and gain strength under the load. Vertical drains into the soft stratum in some cases can accelerate the rate of consolidation.

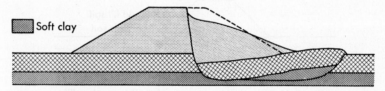

Fig. 9:12   Failure of an embankment by shear in a stratum of soft clay in the foundation.

If the stratum is close to the ground surface, it may be most economical to remove it completely.

Fills above Thin, Cohesionless Strata Subjected to Neutral Stress When water pressure builds up in thin, cohesionless strata beneath a fill, failure may take place suddenly without any warning. Entire sections of the fill move outward, leaving a depressed area in the middle. Failures of this type can occur at any time when the water pressure builds up sufficiently.

Fills on hillsides sometimes seal natural outlets for seepage and cause pressures to build up in the embankment foundation and in the natural slope above. Dams and levees create high pressures by the reservoirs they form. Temporary high water pressures sometimes develop during construction because the weight of the embankment acts on discontinuous silt and fine sand seams from which water cannot drain.

The safety against failure due to water pressure in cohesionless seams is analyzed by the sliding-block method, by considering the neutral stress and its effect on strength along the surface of sliding. This is easily done where the head is known, such as when it is produced by a man-made lake or reservoir. In other cases the head must be estimated from ground water observations or from the weight of the embankment. The safety can be increased by drains that intercept the pervious strata.

9:5 Earth Dams[9:8,9:9,9:10]

Earth dams are special embankments designed to impound water more or less permanently. Dams are the most critical of all engineering structures, for their failure can cause great property damage and loss of life. Earth dams, if not properly designed and constructed, are particularly vulnerable because the very material of which they are constructed can be weakened or disrupted by the water they are supposed to hold. In spite of these dangers, earth dams have proved to be among the most enduring of structures. Dams built in India and Ceylon over 2000 years ago are still storing water for irrigation. The largest structure ever built is the Fort Peck earth dam in Montana, with over 124,000,000 cu yd of embankment. Many earth dams over 250 ft high are in use in many parts of the world.

Criteria for Use Dams of earth are employed for a number of reasons. First, earth suitable for dam construction is available at a large proportion of dam sites. Second, earth is easily handled, either by hand in remote areas with cheap labor or by great machines. Third, earth dams are often suited to sites where the foundations are not strong enough or sufficiently incompressible for masonry dams. Finally, the earth dam is frequently cheaper than any other type. Of course there are some disadvantages: Suitable materials are not always available; greater maintenance is usually necessary; and a separate spillway is required.

A successful earth dam must satisfy two technical requirements: safety against hydraulic failure and safety against structural failure. These include failure of the foundation and the embankment, acting together as a unit, and any part of either.

Hydraulic failure can be external or internal. Externally the dam must have enough spillway to be safe against overtopping, and both the upstream and downstream faces must be protected against surface erosion. Safety against internal hydraulic or seepage failures was discussed in Chapter 4. The dam and the foundation must be sufficiently impervious that the loss of water is not objectionable, and they must be resistant to seepage erosion or piping. The latter has been an important cause of failure of earth dams, and provisions to prevent seepage erosion are essential features of design.

Structurally the dam and the foundation must support the weight of the embankment and the load of the water under the worst possible combinations of maximum reservoir, seepage forces, changes in reservoir level, and earthquake acceleration. The embankment is analyzed in the same manner as other earth structures but the required safety factors are higher, as given in Table 9:2. Settlement of the embankment can create cracks through which seepage erosion could develop. Ordinarily, settlement of the foundation of 1 per cent of the dam height and settlement in the embankment of 1 or 2 per cent of the height will not be serious, provided there are no sharp differences between adjacent parts of the dam.

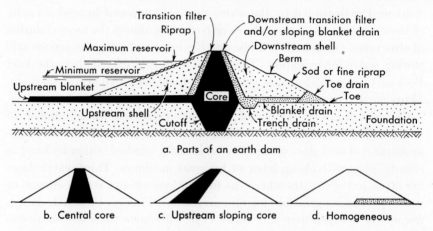

Fig. 9:13 Basic earth dam cross-sections.

Components of an Earth Dam   The components of an earth dam are shown in Fig. 9:13a. The basic parts are: (1) the foundation, (2) the cutoff and core, (3) the shell, and (4) the drainage system. The *foundation*, either earth or rock, provides support for the embankment and also may resist seepage beneath the dam. The *core* holds back the water, and if the foundation is pervious, the core is extended downward to form a *cutoff*. The *shell* provides structural support for the core and distributes the loads into the foundation. The internal drains carry away any seepage that passes through the core and cutoff and prevent the buildup of neutral stress in the downstream part of the embankment. The internal drains take many forms, depending on the anticipated seepage: trench drains and sloping drains just downstream from the core, blanket drains between the dam and the downstream foundation, the toe drains at the downstream toe. All must be provided with filters, as described in Chapter 4, to prevent internal erosion and clogging.

Transition filters are frequently necessary between the core and shell to prevent migration of the fine-grained core into the shell (which is usually coarser). They are sometimes omitted if the grain sizes of the core and shell are not greatly different or if the seepage gradient through the core is small. *Riprap* is required on the upstream face to prevent erosion and wash by waves. Sod or fine riprap is required on the downstream face to prevent rain wash. Berms are often provided to permit access to the face of the dam during construction or for maintenance afterwards. They also help prevent rain wash by breaking the long continuous slope.

Cross-Section   The three basic cross-sections are the central core, the upstream core, and the homogeneous, as shown in Fig. 9:13. The *central core* provides equal support for the core and is most stable during sudden drawdown. It utilizes the minimum amount of core material. The *upstream core* or sloping core is most stable with a full reservoir and provides the cheapest design when there is little or no sudden drawdown. The *homogeneous* cross-section results when both the core and shell are made of the same material. Unless a core zone is defined by extensive internal drainage, a homogeneous cross-section requires flatter slopes than a core type and for that reason is seen more frequently in dams less than 50 ft high.

Cutoff and Core Design   Cutoffs and cores are made of earth, steel sheet piling, concrete, or a curtain of grout injected into the soil. Earth is cheap and can be made sufficiently flexible so that it will remain watertight in spite of small movements in the dam or foundation. Almost any soil can be used if its permeability is sufficiently low (less than 10^{-4} cm per sec) and provided it does not develop swelling pressures. Earth is used for cutoffs if it is possible to cut a trench in the foundation with slopes steep enough so that the volume of soil required is not excessive. Earth is always used for the dam core unless no suitable material is present. The minimum thickness of the core or cutoff depends on the soil; clay cores as thin as 5 per cent of the head have been used, but better practice calls for the minimum thickness of clay cores to be 10 to 20 per cent of the head and for silty cores to be 30 to 40 per cent of the head.

Steel sheet piling and grouting are used for cutoffs where it is impractical to excavate for an earth core. Steel sheeting is sometimes used as a core for dams made of sand but is seldom worth the cost otherwise. Concrete is sometimes used for cutoffs but is rarely used today for cores because it cracks under the inevitable movements of the dam.

Shell Design The design of the shell consists of selecting the material on the basis of its strength and availability for construction, as outlined in Chapter 8, and then determining the slopes necessary to provide stability for the embankment. The design process is essentially trial and revision: Tentative slopes are selected, the stability is analyzed, and the design is then revised to provide greater economy or greater stability.

Typical upstream slopes range from $2.5(H)$ to $1(V)$ for gravels and sandy gravels to $3.5(H)$ to $1(V)$ for micaceous sandy silts. Typical downstream slopes for the same soils are $2(H)$ to $1(V)$ to $3(H)$ to $1(V)$. A seepage analysis is made of the trial design to determine the flow net and the neutral stresses within the embankment and foundation. Safety against seepage erosion and the amount of leakage through the dam are computed.

Stability analyses are made of both faces of the dam, using the method of slices previously described. The upstream face is usually analyzed for three conditions: full reservoir, sudden drawdown, and reservoir empty before filling. The downstream face is analyzed for full reservoir and minimum tailwater and also for sudden drawdown of tailwater from maximum to minimum if that condition can develop.

If the stability is insufficient, there are several possibilities for improvement. First the slope can be flattened. Frequently only the lower half or third need be changed, making a composite slope that is steep at the top and flatter at the bottom. Second the soil strengths can be improved by increasing the required density or by using different materials. Third, weak zones in the foundation can be corrected by preconsolidation or by their removal. Fourth the position of the core and cutoff can be shifted. Finally, internal drainage can be designed to reduce neutral stresses in the downstream foundation and shell.

9:6 Earth Movements in Nature

Classification of Natural Earth Movements Earth movements are commonplace geologic phenomena that are part of the process of mass wasting. Tremendous quantities of weathered materials are constantly on the move down slopes and into streams where they are carried away to be deposited elsewhere. The impelling force for all these movements is gravity, assisted at times by water pressure, expansion and contraction forces, earthquake shock, and man's interference with nature.

There are four different classes of natural movements:

(1) Creep—the slow, relatively steady movement of soil down slopes.
(2) Landslides—fairly rapid movements of soil masses in combined horizontal and vertical direction.
(3) Subsidences—movement of earth masses vertically downward.
(4) Rockfalls—vertical superficial rock movements.

Creep   Creep is a slow, nearly continuous movement of soil resembling the creep of metals under small stresses or the plastic flow of concrete. It is manifested by the tipping of fence posts, trees, and other vertical objects on hillsides and by the movement of fence lines and bench marks from their original positions. Creep is a sort of "caterpillar motion" caused by alternate shrinking and swelling of soils that lie on slopes steeper than 3 or 4°. It may extend into the soil as deep as 15 or 20 ft but is most rapid near the ground surface.

Creep cannot be stopped, but its rate of movement can be decreased materially by drainage, to increase the strength of the soil and to prevent the periodic swelling and shrinking. In most cases the best method of preventing trouble is to make allowances for it. Bench marks should be set in solid rock or in level areas not subject to movement by creep. Pipe lines should be made with flexible joints when laid in slopes on which creep is taking place. Building foundations must be strong enough and deep enough to resist movement or should be tied together so the entire structure can move. The latter procedure, of course, would be practical only for very small buildings.

Landslides   Natural landslides are difficult to analyze because of their complex nature. The strength of natural deposits is so variable and the number of different forces acting is so great that theoretical studies are at best only indications of what is likely to occur. Most landslides do not occur spontaneously. The soil slope is usually unstable for years and gives warning of its instability from time to time by slow settlement or the formation of cracks.

Finally, some event takes place that increases the soil stress or decreases its strength to the point that failure can take place. This event triggers the failure, although it actually may be insignificant by itself. Loud noise has been known to start slides in loose debris in mountainous areas, and the added weight of water due to a hard rainfall is often responsible for the start of slides in humid regions.

Many different ways of classifying slides have been devised. Some systems classify them according to the type of soil deposits or the appearance of the failure, while other systems classify them according to the forces causing failure or by the force that triggered the movement. Actually each failure should be considered by itself, and any classification should be used for descriptive purposes only.

Flow Slides   If a soil or rock mass should suddenly lose its strength, it will behave like a liquid and flow downhill and spread out over the flat land below. The basic cause of failure is ordinarily neutral stress that builds up until the strength becomes insufficient to support the load. If the material is loose, structural collapse as described in Chapters 1 and 2 contributes to the water pressure increase and loss of strength.

Loose, saturated cohesionless soils are particularly vulnerable. In one case a loose, fine sand marine deposit, with a surface slope of less than 10°, collapsed and flowed like water when the tide fell rapidly and induced seepage out of the slope. In another case, pile driving triggered a flow in a similar deposit that carried houses and people into the bottom of a shallow lake. Talus and rock debris that accumulate in steep mountainous regions can be unstable when saturated by rainfall and snow melt. Failure is triggered by intense rain, earthquakes, or sudden thawing, and the semiliquid mass flows down into the valleys below to engulf towns and to cover farm lands with a veneer of debris. Similar flows have occurred in badly fractured rock and whole mountainsides have moved downward in a stream of flowing rock.

A peculiar type of flow occurs in highly sensitive clays such as the marine clays of eastern Quebec. While the undisturbed strength of the clay is moderately high, the remolded strength is extremely low. Failure at one point in the soil mass, induced by shear, brings about a flow in which large masses of intact clay float on a stream of viscous remolded clay.

Linear Shear Slides   The linear shear slide or sliding-block movement occurs in a number of forms. The most common takes place in relatively thin, uniformly deep deposits of residual soils or weathered rock lying above a tilted base of sound materials. Sliding occurs on the contact between soil and rock or on bedding planes or joints of the rock itself. Movement is caused by a loss of strength of the soil, brought on by neutral stress or softening of partially saturated clay either from rainfall and snow melt percolating down from the surface or seeping upward from joints and fissures in the rock. These slides can also be triggered by cutting into the soil, which removes the support from the lower side of the potential zone of failure. The movement begins with the detachment of a small part of the mass which leaves the remainder unsupported. This subsequently slides until the entire hillside is moving.

Linear slides also occur on horizontally stratified hillsides in which there are seams of very weak materials. The lateral earth pressure produced by the overburden weight causes a sliding-block-type failure in the weak seams. The sounder materials above move horizontally away from the hillside in detached blocks as though they were being carried on a conveyor belt.

Rotational Slides Rotational slides take place in homogeneous soils, particularly clays, and in thick deposits where there are numerous non-continuous planes of weakness. The classic examples of the rotational slides are the deep base failures that occur in the soft clays of the coastal areas of Norway and Sweden. Failure is triggered by undercutting of the toe by dredging or erosion and by external loads on the upper part of the slope.

Steep slopes in stiff clays fail in rotational toe slides. The clay cliffs of the Great Lakes suffer from such movements when they are undercut by wave action. Several successive slides are often seen at the same point, forming narrow, arc-shaped terraces or steps leading down the slope, their surfaces intact and with trees and shrubs growing on them.

Modified rotational slides occur in clays with seams or lenses of cohesionless soils. When water pressure (neutral stress) builds up, the strength drops, sometimes so low that shear failure occurs. Failure begins with a horizontal movement, but this leads to an elongated rotational slide that often cuts across the cohesionless seams and allows them to drain. An example of such a slide is shown in Fig. 9:14. It took place after snow melt, spring rainfall, and finally a leaking water pipe augmented the normal ground water pressure in numerous thin sand seams in a thick clay deposit.

Correcting Landslides Most landslides are caused by a combination of factors. Before any remedial action can be taken, a careful study must be made to determine which factors are the significant ones for that particular situation. The structure of the soil and rock formations and the physical properties of the different materials must be established. The ground water levels and the pressures in cracks and fissures are particularly important.

Correction involves controlling as many of the factors as possible. Often the best method is found by trial. Drainage, flattening the slope, stabilization of the soil by grouting, removing external loads, erosion protection at the toe, and providing support with piling and retaining walls—all have proved to be successful under certain circumstances, but no method is of value unless it fits the specific needs of the particular slide.

Subsidences Subsidences are actually vertical earth movements.

They are of two types: rapid, caused by undermining or failure of the underlying strata; and slow, caused by consolidation. Rapid subsidence occurs frequently in areas of abandoned mines. Disintegration of old timbering in shallow workings causes caving of the rock above and the formation of a cavity beneath the soil. Sooner or later the soil bridging the cavity will break apart until an intact mass slides vertically downward. The same phenomenon occurs in areas underlaid by cavernous limestone. The countless sinkholes that dot the landscape in many parts of Kentucky,

Fig. 9:14   Landslide caused by water pressure in thin seams of cohesionless silt and fine sand in a thick stratum of clay.

Tennessee, Virginia, Georgia, Ohio, and other states are the results of small subsidences. In a few cases subsidences have been caused by the underground erosion of cohesionless strata by artesian water.

Rapid subsidence can be caused by excavation for sewers, tunnels, and buildings. If more soil is removed from an excavation than the finished volume of the excavation, it indicates that the soil is squeezing into the hole as it is being removed. This phenomenon, known as *lost ground,* is particularly troublesome in soft clays such as are found in Chicago, Detroit, Cleveland, and other cities in glaciated areas. The lost ground results in subsidence of the surrounding ground surface and often causes damage to adjacent buildings. Careful bracing of excavations and checks to determine possible building settlement are required to prevent such troubles.

Slow subsidence caused by consolidation occurs in areas in which the soil stresses increase materially. The Long Beach area of California subsided at a rate of 10 in. per year for the period 1941 to 1945 and is still sinking. The excessive pumping from the many oil wells in the area is reducing the neutral stresses in the oil-bearing rocks and is increasing the effective stresses. The rocks therefore consolidate as the oil is removed and the ground surface sinks correspondingly. Mexico City is also subsiding at a rate of several inches per year. This is probably caused by the pumping of the city water supply from the sand strata that are interbedded with the soft, volcanic clays beneath the city. The only remedy for such subsidences is to make allowances for them in design of structures. They cannot be prevented without correcting the causes.

Rockfalls Rockfalls are movements of detached rock fragments down steep slopes. They often occur in cuts in badly jointed rock and in cuts where all the materials loosened by blasting were not removed. Periodic checks should be made on the condition of rock cuts or other steep slopes in rock and all unstable pieces removed. Some roads must be closed during periods of heavy rain or freezing and thawing when water pressure or frost wedging can set loose rock in motion. In some cases it has been practical to anchor loose rocks with rods and cables to prevent their movement.

REFERENCES

9:1 L. Bjerrum and Nils Flodin, "The Development of Soil Mechanics in Sweden, 1900–1925," *Geotechnique*, Vol. X, No. 1, March, 1960.

9:2 Fellenius, *Erdstatische Berechnungen*, Rev. ed., W. Ernst u. Sohn, Berlin, 1939.

9:3 D. W. Taylor, *Fundamentals of Soil Mechanics*, John Wiley & Sons, Inc., New York, 1948.

9:4 "Stability of Slopes and Foundations," *Engineering Manual for Civil Works Construction, Part CXIX*, Chapter 2, Department of Army, Corps of Engineers, Washington, 1952.

9:5 A. W. Bishop, "Use of the Slip Circle in the Stability Analysis of Slopes," *Geotechnique*, Vol. V, No. 1, March, 1955.

9:6 D. W. Taylor, "Stability of Earth Slopes," *Journal, Boston Society of Civil Engineers*, July, 1937.

9:7 *Blasters Handbook*, E. I. Dupont de Nemours and Company, Wilmington, Delaware, 1958.

9:8   A. Casagrande, "Notes on the Design of Earth Dams," *Journal, Boston Society of Civil Engineers*, Vol. 37, 1950.

9:9   J. D. Justin, J. Hinds, and W. P. Creager, *Engineering for Dams, Vol. III, Earth, Rock Fill, and Timber Dams*, John Wiley & Sons, Inc., New York, 1945.

9:10 G. F. Sowers, *Earth and Rockfill Dam Engineering*, Asia Publishing House, Bombay, 1961.

9:11 K. Terzaghi, "Mechanism of Landslides," *Application of Geology to Engineering Practice, Berkey Volume*, Geological Society of America, 1950.

9:12 J. M. Tompkin and S. B. Britt, "Landslides, A Selected Annotated Bibliography," *Bibliography No. 10*, Highway Research Board, Washington, 1951.

Suggestions for Additional Study

1. References 9:4, 9:10.
2. "Proceedings, European Conference on the Stability of Earth Slopes," *Geotechnique*, Vol. V, No. 1 and 2, March and June, 1955.
3. *Landslides and Engineering Practice*, Special Report 29, Highway Research Board, Washington, 1958.
4. D. P. Krynine and W. R. Judd, *Principles of Engineering Geology and Geotechnics*, McGraw-Hill Book Co., Inc., New York, 1957.
5. Publications of the Swedish and Norwegian Geotechnical Institutes.
6. *Proceedings, International Conferences on Soil Mechanics and Foundation Engineering*: I, Cambridge, Mass., 1936; II, Rotterdam, 1948; III, Zurich, 1953; IV, London, 1957; V, Paris, 1961.
7. *Design of Small Dams*, U.S. Bureau of Reclamation, Denver, 1960.

PROBLEMS

9:1   A slope of 2 (horizontal) to 1 (vertical) is cut in homogeneous, saturated clay whose $c = 1100$ psf and whose $\gamma = 112$ lb per cu ft. The cut is 42 ft deep and the clay deposit extends 17 ft below the bottom of the cut. The clay rests on rock.

a. Compute the safety of this slope, using the charts for homogeneous soils.

b. Check, using the circular arc analysis.

9:2   A cut is excavated at an angle of 45°. It is 30 ft deep. The soil profile from the surface down is:

Depth (ft)	Soil	Shear Strength (psf)	Unit Weight (lb/cu ft)
0–10	Stiff clay	$c = 1500$	$\gamma = 118$
10–25	Stiff clay	$c = 1200$	$\gamma = 105$
25–40	Firm clay	$c = 1000$	$\gamma = 112$
40	Shale (rock)		

a. Find the safety factor with respect to base failure, assuming the center of the failure circle to be above the mid-point of the slope.

b. Find the safety with respect to toe failure, assuming the center of the circle to be the same as for the homogeneous case.

c. Check the results, using the stability factor chart and assuming that the effective c is the weighted average c of all the strata.

9:3 A cut at an angle of 65° with the horizontal is to be made in a partially saturated clay with $c' = 500$ psf, $\phi' = 15°$, and $\gamma = 115$ lb per cu ft. How deep can this cut be made before a minimum safety factor of 1.2 is reached? Use charts for homogeneous soil.

9:4 An excavation 30 ft deep and 65 ft wide at the bottom is to be made in clay with $c = 780$ psf and $\gamma = 110$ lb per cu ft. How wide should the top of the excavation be if the minimum safety factor is 1.3? (Use chart of stability number.)

9:5 An embankment of sand is 40 ft high, 30 ft wide at the top, and has side slopes of $1\frac{1}{2}$ (horizontal) to 1 (vertical). The embankment soil $\phi = 42°$ and $\gamma = 124$ lb cu ft. The foundation soil consists of clay with $c = 800$ psf. Compute the safety of the embankment against a sliding-block failure along the line of contact of the foundation and the fill.

9:6 A canal is dug in a soil whose characteristics when saturated are $c = 600$ psf, $\phi = 16°$, and $\gamma = 124$ lb per cu ft saturated. The canal is to be 22 ft deep and the slopes are 2 (horizontal) to 1 (vertical).

a. Compute the safety factor when the canal is full of water. (Use chart.)

b. Compute safety factor if canal is suddenly drained, leaving the soil saturated.

c. Which condition is worse?

HINT: When canal is full of water, the unit weight is reduced by buoyancy, an amount of 62.4 lb per cu ft.

9:7 An embankment 75 ft high and 40 ft wide at the top is constructed with a slope of 50°. The soil is partially saturated clay. The uppermost 50 ft of soil has $c' = 2000$ psf, $\phi' = 15°$, and $\gamma = 114$ lb per cu ft. The remaining 25 ft has $c' = 900$ psf, $\phi' = 12°$, and $\gamma = 111$ lb per cu ft. Compute the safety factor with respect to toe failure. Use the method of slices. Assume that the center of the critical circle is the same as in homogeneous saturated clays (Fig. 9:6c).

9:8 A highway fill 25 ft high, 30 ft wide at the top, with slopes of 1.5 (horizontal) to 1 (vertical) is constructed across an area of soft, compressible soil. The fill weighs 120 lb per cu ft and is well-compacted, homogeneous, sandy clay. Foundation soil has $c = 420$ psf, $\gamma = 106$ lb per cu ft saturated. Compute the safety against a bearing-capacity failure, assuming that the entire fill remains intact.

9:9 An earth dam is 100 ft high and 20 ft wide at the crest. The upstream slope is 3 (horizontal) to 1 (vertical), and the downstream slope is 2.5 to 1. The dam consists of a clay core 20 ft wide at the dam crest and 30 ft wide at the base. The clay core $c = 200$ psf and $\gamma = 100$ lb per cu ft. The remainder of the dam is sand with $\gamma = 121$ lb per cu ft and $\phi = 41°$. The foundation soil is clay with $c = 2500$ psf, $\gamma = 115$ lb per cu ft. A thin seam of sand with $\phi = 42°$ extends from the reservoir under the dam at a depth of about 4 ft below the embankment. The seam ends a few feet upstream of the toe. If the maximum head on the dam is 85 ft above the foundation, compute the safety of the downstream half of the dam against sliding. Assume that the pressure in the sand seam is equivalent to the full head.

9:10 Prepare a discussion of a landslide or slope failure from the published description in an engineering journal or magazine. Include the following points:

(1) Description of failure;

(2) Chain of events leading to failure;

(3) Probable cause;

(4) Corrective measures, if any.

10... UNDERGROUND INVESTIGATION

One of the most important steps in the solution of a structural engineering problem is determining the underground conditions that will affect the design. In reality the soil is just as much a part of a structure as is the concrete and steel. The engineer has control over the characteristics of the man-made materials and can specify them to suit his design. Unfortunately he has little or no control over the characteristics of the soil deposits, and so in many cases he must design the superstructure to fit the existing soil conditions.

The underground characteristics of a particular site cannot be determined from a handbook or even from experience with nearby sites. Each site requires individual analysis; experience will serve to guide the engineer in making his study, but there is no substitute for adequate, accurate, and specific information obtained from the site. A typical case is that of a designer who felt that a study of underground conditions was unnecessary because nearby multistory buildings had been built with no foundation problems and because the proposed structure was to be only two stories high. The new building cracked badly long before it was completed. It was found to rest on a cinder fill 30 ft deep in an old ravine, whereas the nearby buildings had been founded on dense clay beyond the edges of the ravine.

The designer is not the only one interested in underground conditions. Even before a site is bought, many purchasers insist on underground exploration to determine the suitability of the site. One such investigation disclosed to the prospective owner that the uppermost 20 ft of soil consisted of a loose rubbish fill. The design engineer estimated that the foundation for the building proposed for this site would cost more than the superstructure, and so the property was not purchased.

When bidders and contractors are furnished with accurate information about soil and water conditions, they can estimate their costs more accurately and plan their work more intelligently. The result is a better job at a lower cost, and less time is consumed in waiting for changes in design to compensate for unforeseen soil conditions.

10:1   Planning a Soil Investigation[10:1]

Information Required   A complete investigation of underground conditions includes the following points:

(1) Nature of the soil deposit (geology, recent history of filling, excavation, and flooding; possibilities of mineral exploitation).
(2) Depth, thickness, and composition of each soil stratum.
(3) The location of ground water.
(4) The depth to rock, and the characteristics of rock.
(5) The engineering properties of the soil and rock strata that affect the performance of the structure.

In many cases all this information is not necessary and in others estimates will suffice. The best investigation is the one that provides adequate data at the time it is needed and at a cost consistent with the value of the information.

Costs   The value of an investigation can be measured by how much money might be spent for the structure if no investigation were made. When a designer is confronted with inadequate data, he compensates for the lack by overdesign; when a contractor is furnished with incomplete information, he increases his estimates to allow for possible trouble. In most cases the cost of inadequate data is considerably more than the cost of the investigation. When unforeseen soil conditions necessitate a change in design or a construction procedure, the cost of the structure increases rapidly. If a failure of the structure should result, the entire project may become a loss. In such cases, the cost of an adequate investigation would be but a small fraction of the money lost.

The cost of an adequate investigation (including laboratory testing) has been found to be from 0.05 per cent to 0.2 per cent of the total cost of the entire structure. For bridges and dams, the percentage may be somewhat higher.

Procedure for Investigation   A complete investigation consists of three steps:

(1) Reconnaissance, to determine the nature of the deposit and to estimate the soil conditions.
(2) Exploratory investigation, to determine the depth, thickness, and composition of the soils, the depth to water and to rock, and to estimate the engineering properties of the soil.
(3) Detailed investigation, to secure accurate information about critical strata from which design computations can be made.

In some instances, such as for small buildings, only a minimum of reconnaissance and exploration will be necessary; in others, such as for large bridges and heavy power plants, extensive reconnaissance, exploration, and detailed investigation will be required to secure adequate data for economical, safe design.

Planning and conducting a soil investigation is among the most intricate of engineering problems. Careful coordination is necessary between the engineer, the laboratory, and the men in the field in order to secure the best information in the least time and at the lowest cost. If the field men send soil samples to the laboratory immediately, time-consuming tests can be started before the field work is finished. If the soils engineer is promptly furnished with test data, he can make changes in the field and laboratory procedures without expensive delays and without having to repeat some operations.

10:2   Reconnaissance

Geologic Study   A geologic study, no matter how brief it may be, is very useful in planning and interpreting a complete soil investigation. The primary purpose of such a study is to determine the nature of the deposits underlying the site. The types of soil and rock likely to be encountered can be determined, and the best methods of underground exploration can be selected before boring, sampling, or field testing is commenced. The geologic history may reveal changes such as faulting, flooding, or gullying that have taken place and which have changed the original character of the soil or rock. The possibility of defects in the rock, such as cracks, fissures, dikes, sills, sinkholes, and caves, may be indicated. This information will greatly aid in the interpretation of the results of sampling and field tests. Another important function of geologic studies is to establish the possible presence of minerals having economic value. If there is a possibility of future mining or well drilling on the site, this must be considered both in the design of the structure and in planning for the use of the site. Legal and engineering problems have arisen where structures settle because of the collapse of mine workings beneath them or where valuable minerals are discovered below expensive buildings.

A geologic study may indicate the possibility and probability of earthquakes and tremors that would affect the structure. The presence of minor but active faults beneath a proposed structure might justify changing sites.

Sources of Geologic Information   Geologic studies have been made of many parts of the earth by state and national geologic surveys, oil companies, mining interests, and industrial concerns. Water-well or oil-well records are frequently available that will show the depth of soil and whether it is sand, gravel, or clay. In many cases, soil and rock profiles along highway or railroad cuts may be studied. Geologic maps often show ancient shore lines and river and lake locations, with their terraces, deltas, and fills that are now soil strata of gravel, sand, and clay. The "deltas" of Mississippi and Louisiana and the shore lines of glacial Lake Maumee in Ohio are examples of such deposits.

The U.S. Geological Survey, state geological surveys and mining departments, the U.S. Department of Agriculture, and state highway departments have collected data dealing with soils. Bulletins and special reports may be secured by writing for them.

The county soil-survey bulletins of the U.S. Department of Agriculture are particularly useful to the highway engineer whose work extends across areas of many different soil types. Some state highway departments have correlated the performance of subgrade soils with the soil names shown on the soil-survey maps. When a new roadway is projected, the engineers can predict with a minimum amount of field work the soil problems they may expect in construction and maintenance.

Site Inspection   An examination of the site and the adjacent areas will reveal much valuable information. The topography, drainage pattern, erosion pattern, vegetation, and land use reflect the underground conditions, particularly the structure and texture of the soil and rock. Highway and railroad cuts and stream banks often disclose the cross-section of the formations and indicate the depth of rock. Outcrops of rock or areas of gravel and boulders may indicate the presence of dikes and more resistant strata. Ground water conditions are often reflected in the presence of seeps, springs, and the type of vegetation. For example, marsh grass on what appears to be a dry hillside shows that the area is wet during the growing season. The water levels in wells and ponds often indicate ground water, but these also can be influenced by intensive use or by nearby irrigation.

The shape of gullies and ravines reflects soil texture. Gullies in sand tend to be V-shaped, with uniform straight slopes. Those in silty soils often have a U-shaped cross-section. Small gullies in clay often are U-shaped, while deeper ones are broadly rounded at the tops of the slopes.

Special features such as sinkholes, sand dunes, old beach ridges, and tidal flats are often obvious to the layman. More obscure forms require intensive geological training for their recognition.

Valuable information about the presence of fills and knowledge of any difficulties encountered during the building of other nearby structures may be secured by talking to old residents of the area adjacent to the site. Settlement cracks in nearby buildings often indicate that poor foundation conditions will be encountered. However, it must be remembered that good soil conditions at one site do not necessarily mean good conditions at an adjacent site.

Aerial Reconnaissance Examination of the site from the air can reveal the broad patterns of topography and land form, drainage, and erosion even more effectively than site inspection on the surface. Features that are obscured because they cover too large an area or because of poor access are easily observed from the air. Large areas can be inspected in a short time, especially if the site is in rugged country.

A study of low- and high-altitude aerial photographs, termed *air-photo interpretation*[10:2,10:3] provides the most thorough visual evaluation of the site if the photographs are made with sufficient overlap so that stereoscopic examination is possible. Land forms, drainage patterns, and such topographic details as sinkholes (Fig. 10:1) stand out sharply. Even the texture of the soil and the drainage can be estimated from the tone (shade of gray), the vegetation, and the shape of erosion ditches and gullies.

A personal inspection from a small aircraft often permits examination of outcrops as close as 100 or 200 ft, as well as observation of the site as a whole from altitudes as high as 8000 ft. A permanent record of the inspection made with a good camera, particularly in color, is extremely useful in later detailed studies of the soil conditions.

The Value of Reconnaissance A reconnaissance investigation establishes the probable soil conditions at the site. If the site appears to be unsuitable for the structure, then it may be abandoned without further study. In most cases, however, the results of reconnaissance are used in planning the exploratory investigation and in interpreting the results of such an investigation. Geologic information and the data from a visual inspection are too general in character to be used as a basis for engineering design but must be augmented by specific, detailed data obtained by boring, sampling, and field and laboratory tests.

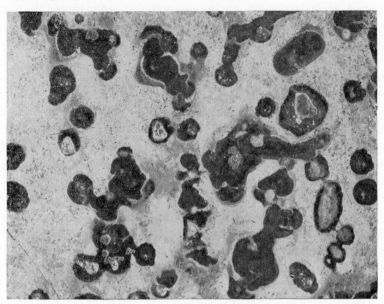

Fig. 10:1   Aerial photograph of sinks developed in sands and clayey sands overlying porous limestone in southern Florida. The dark areas are shallow ponds in the sinks, with some partially choked with vegetation. The diagonal line at the lower left is a road and the small specks, trees.

10:3   Geophysical Methods of Exploration

Geophysical methods of underground exploration were developed in oilfield exploration work and are now being used to some extent in soil investigations.[10:4] All these methods are based on the principle that force patterns, such as those produced by sound waves or an electric current, assume a certain definite shape in a homogeneous material, regardless of the magnitude of the force or of the type of material. When a material is non-homogeneous, the force pattern is distorted at the points where the properties of the material change. The depth of such points may be determined by an analysis of the force patterns.

Seismic Method The seismic method is based on the principle that sound travels more rapidly through dense materials than through loose materials. Velocities as high as 20,000 fps have been recorded in dense gneiss, and velocities as low as 600 fps have been found in coarse sand and gravel. At the boundary between materials of different densities a sound wave is refracted or bent in the same way that a light wave is bent as it goes from air into the glass of a lens.

An explosive charge is placed in the ground at one point, and automatic sound detectors are placed along a straight line at intervals of from 25 to 50 ft. The charge is detonated, and the time required for the sound to reach each detector is measured. A curve of time against distance is made and analyzed to find the depth to the boundaries between strata of different densities. Usually the most violent change in density occurs between soil and bedrock; thus the depth to rock can be easily determined. Occasionally changes in density between different soil strata are great enough to be detected, but borings should be made to confirm the existence of the change in soil strata. The method is particularly useful when dense rock underlies great depths of soil. When the rock is badly jointed or covered with large boulders, the results of the seismic method may be inconclusive.

Electrical Resistivity Method The electrical resistance of different strata varies inversely with the ionized salts present. Since dense rock contains little moisture, its ionization is low and it will have high resistance; on the other hand, a soft, saturated clay may have a very low resistance.

In operation, two electrodes are placed in the ground a short distance apart and an electric current passed through the soil between them. Two other electrodes, equally spaced in a line between the outer two, are used to measure voltage. Many different electrode spacings from a few feet up to more than a hundred must be used to develop a diagram of resistance against electrode spacing. This is analyzed to determine the depth to a boundary where resistance changes greatly. The method is particularly adapted to depths less than 100 ft. It works very well when used to determine the thickness of widely different soil types such as clean sand overlying soft clay, or soft clay overlying dense granite, and can often be used to locate the water table.

Application of Geophysical Methods Geophysical methods are particularly suited to reconnaissance or exploratory work of a general nature, such as determining the approximate depth to rock in a valley or

determining the depth to rock along the line of a proposed highway. They
have also proved of value in measuring the size of deposits of sand and
gravel and of other relatively uniform soils surrounded by widely different
soils. In many materials reasonably accurate results can be obtained, but
in others the results have been of little value. Since geophysical methods
indicate only the depth to different soil strata, borings should be made
to determine the nature of the strata. The methods are of limited value in
the design of foundations for bridges and buildings because the results
are not sufficiently accurate.

10:4   Exploratory Investigations[10:1]

Planning Exploratory Work   The purpose of the exploratory investigation is to secure accurate information about the actual soil conditions
at the site. The depth, thickness, extent, and composition of each soil
stratum; the depth of the rock; and the depth of ground water are the
primary objectives of exploration. In addition approximate data on the
strength and compressibility of the strata are secured in order to make
preliminary estimates of the safety and settlement of the structure.

A carefully planned program of boring and sampling is the best method
of obtaining specific information at a site and is the heart of an exploratory investigation. Many different methods have been developed for doing
this work, and construction organizations, well drillers, and commercial
laboratories offer such services. Too frequently exploratory work is so
poorly planned, carelessly performed, incompletely reported, and incor-
rectly interpreted that the results are inadequate, erroneous, and misleading. Soil or rock boring and sampling to obtain information that will give
an accurate picture of underground conditions is an engineering problem
requiring resourceful, intelligent personnel trained in the principles of
geology and soil mechanics.

Spacing of Borings   It is impossible to determine the spacing of borings before an investigation begins because the spacing depends not only
on the type of structure but also on the uniformity or regularity of the
soil deposit. Ordinarily a preliminary estimate of the spacing is made;
this is decreased if additional data are necessary or is increased if the
thickness and depth of the different strata appear to be about the same
in all the borings. Spacing should be smaller in areas that will be subjected
to heavy loads; greater, in less critical areas. The following spacings are
often used in planning boring work.

Table 10:1 SPACING OF BORINGS

Structure or Project	Spacing of Borings (ft)
Highway (subgrade survey)	1000
Earth dam, dikes	100–200
Borrow pits	100
Multistory buildings	25–50
One-story manufacturing plants	75–100

For uniform, regular soil conditions the above spacings are often doubled or tripled.

Depth of Borings In order to furnish adequate information for settlement predictions, the borings should penetrate all strata that could consolidate materially under the load of the structure. For very important heavy structures, such as large bridges or tall buildings, this means that the borings should extend to rock. For smaller structures, however, the boring depth may be estimated from geologic evidence, the results of previous investigations in the same vicinity, and by considering the extent and weight of the structure.

Experience indicates that damaging settlement is unlikely when the added stress in the soil due to the weight of the structure, $\Delta\sigma$, is less than 10 per cent of the initial stress in the soil due to its own weight, $\bar{\sigma}_0$. A rule adopted by E. De Beer of the Geotechnical Institute of Belgium requires that borings penetrate to the depth where $\Delta\sigma = 0.1\bar{\sigma}_0$.[10:4] Typical depths for exploratory boring, based on the above stress relationship, are given in Table 10:2.

Table 10:2 DEPTH FOR EXPLORATORY BORING

Building Width (ft)	Boring Depth (ft)				
	Number of Stories				
	1	2	4	8	16
100	11	20	33	53	79
200	12	22	41	68	108
400	12	23	45	81	136

An old rule is that the boring depth should be twice the width of the building; however, this would be ridiculous for wide one-story structures such as modern industrial plants. A more reasonable, simple rule is to bore 8 to 12 ft for each story of building height or its equivalent in load.

For dams and embankments the depth should be at least twice the height. The borings for deep excavations should extend 5 to 10 ft below the excavation bottom, and deeper if soft clay or loose sand and silt are encountered. Borrow pit borings should go a few feet below the anticipated excavation depth to determine if any artesian water pressures are present.

10:5 Boring and Sampling

Auger Boring   The *soil auger* (Fig. 10:2) is the simplest equipment for making a shallow hole in the ground and securing samples of the soil material in a much loosened condition. Several different styles are available. The stump auger, which resembles a long wood-auger bit and was originally designed for drilling dynamite holes beneath stumps and boul-

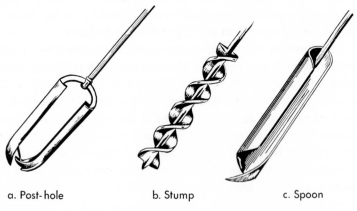

a. Post-hole   b. Stump   c. Spoon

Fig. 10:2   Soil augers.

ders, is useful in drilling holes up to 10 ft deep and about 1½ in. in diameter. The most effective auger is the post-hole auger, consisting of two curved blades that retain the soil as it is cut. These are available in sizes from 2 to 6 in. in diameter. Small earth augers are generally fitted with handles, so that they can be turned by hand, and extensions can be added to the handle so that depths as great as 30 ft can be reached. Motor-driven augers are available which are capable of drilling holes in some soils as deep as 80 ft in a few minutes. However, it is difficult to identify the layers of soil encountered, since the materials from all depths are fairly well mixed together in one composite sample.

Soil augers have the advantage of obtaining a dry hole until the water table is reached and of providing easy visual recognition of changes in soil composition. On the other hand, they are difficult to use in soft clays and coarse gravel and impossible to use in most soils below the water table. Hand augers are seldom economical when boring deeper than 20 ft.

The auger sample is a well-disturbed mixture of all the materials penetrated. It is useful for determining the average water content, grain size, and plasticity characteristics and is sufficient for most borrow pit exploration. It gives little information on the character of the undisturbed soil.

Wash Boring Wash boring was once widely used in soil exploration work and is still useful when only limited information, such as the depth to a hard stratum, is needed. The soil is drilled with a combination of jetting and chopping by the use of a chisel-shaped bit attached to hollow drill rods. Water is pumped through the rods and through the bits, which loosens the soil and washes to the ground surface the cuttings dislodged by chopping. The cuttings are retrieved in a tub or sump. They are a composite of the coarser particles of all the strata drilled and give only a hint of the nature of the materials penetrated. The hardness of the soil can be estimated from the speed of drilling. However, determining the characteristics of the soil from the cuttings (washed sample) is like trying to determine the size of the peas from the color of the pea soup.

Test Boring Test boring is the most widely used method of soil exploration. It consists of two steps: drilling, to open a hole in the ground; and *dry sampling* to secure an intact sample that is suitable for visual examination and tests for water content, classification, and even unconfined compression.

Drilling is done by augering, wash boring, or rotary drilling, using a high-speed revolving cutter and circulating water to remove the cuttings in the same way as in wash boring. In firm soils the hole remains open by arching. In soft clays and in sands below the water table, it is kept open by inserting steel tubing (casing) or preferably by keeping the hole filled with a viscous fluid known as *drilling mud*. Drilling mud, usually a mixture of bentonite clay and water, has the advantage of supporting both the walls and the bottom of the hole. The mud also serves as the circulating liquid in wash and rotary boring and maintains a cleaner hole by washing out coarse sand and gravel which tend to accumulate in the bottom.

The *sampler* (Fig. 10:3), also called a split spoon, consists of a thick-walled steel tube split lengthwise. To the lower end is attached a cutting shoe; to the upper end, a check valve and connector to the drill rods. The standard size is 1.4 to 1.5 in. ID and 2 in. OD,[10:5] but similar samplers with 2 in. ID × 2.5 in. OD and 2.5 in. ID × 3 in. OD are occasionally used.

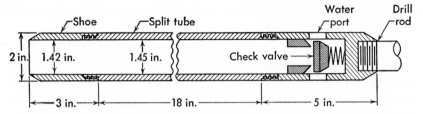

Fig. 10:3 Standard split-barrel sampler. (Courtesy of Law-Engineering Testing Co.)

The hole is drilled as previously described until a change in the soil is detected. The drill tools are removed and the sampler lowered to the bottom of the hole by attaching it to drill rods. It is first driven 6 in. into the soil to ensure that the cutting edge is seated in virgin material. It is then driven 1 ft with blows from a 140-lb hammer falling 30 in. The number of hammer blows required to drive the sampler 1 ft is the *penetration resistance* of the soil. Sampling is shown in Fig. 10:4.

The sample is examined and classified by the field technician in charge of boring and then sealed in a glass or plastic container for shipment to the laboratory. The sample maintains the water content, composition, and stratification of the soil, although there may be appreciable distor-

a. *Mobile test boring rig.*   b. *Removing sample from split barrel sampler.*

Fig. 10:4 Exploratory test boring. (Courtesy of Law Engineering Testing Co.)

tion of the structure. Good samples can often be used for unconfined compression tests but are not of sufficient quality for triaxial testing.

The penetration resistance is an indication of the density of cohesionless soils and of the strength of cohesive soils. In effect, it is an in-place dynamic shear test. Tables 10:3 and 10:4 have been proposed to describe density and strength from the standard penetration test results.

Table 10:3 RELATIVE DENSITY OF SAND
(After Terzaghi and Peck[10:6])

Measured with 1.4 in. ID, 2 in. OD sampler driven 1 ft by 140-lb hammer falling 30 in.

Blows	Relative Density
0–4	Very loose
5–10	Loose
11–20	Firm
21–30	Very firm
31–50	Dense
Over 50	Very dense

Table 10:4 CONSISTENCY OF COHESIVE SOILS
(After Terzaghi and Peck[10:6])

Measured with 1.4 in. ID, 2 in. OD sampler driven 1 ft by 140-lb hammer falling 30 in.

Blows	Consistency
0–1	Very soft
2–4	Soft
5–8	Firm
9–15	Stiff
15–30	Very stiff
Over 30	Hard

The resistances measured with a 2 in. ID, 2.5 in. OD sampler driven with a 300-lb hammer falling 18 in., as specified by the New York City Building Code,[10:7] are roughly equivalent to those measured by the standard test.[10:1]

Test boring is the most widely used method for securing data on the depth, thickness, and composition of the soil strata and approximate information on the soil strengths. It is economical and rapid and adapted to most soils (except coarse gravel) and even to soft rock.

Core Drilling   When a soil boring encounters a material so hard that its penetration resistance exceeds 100 blows (measured with a 140-lb hammer falling 30 in. on a 1.4 in. ID spoon driven 1 ft), further progress with soil-boring equipment is difficult and often impossible. This resistance is termed *refusal,* and it may indicate a highly compacted soil, a boulder, or rock.

Core drilling is used to penetrate such hard materials in order to determine whether refusal indicates a hard lens or boulder underlaid by softer materials, or sound rock. Large-diameter holes (30 to 54 in.) drilled in rock permit an engineer or geologist to examine the strata in place, but the cost of drilling is great. Small-diameter cores that are brought to the surface make it possible to determine the composition, soundness, and defects of the rock for great depths at a moderate cost.

Diamond drilling is the most common method for obtaining small-diameter cores. The sampler, or *core barrel*, is a piece of hardened steel tubing from 2 to 10 ft long with a *bit* attached to the lower end. The bit (Fig. 10:5) is ordinarily set with borts (black diamonds), although tung-

Fig. 10:5   Rock drill bits. Two are diamond bits and one is a hard metal-faced saw-tooth bit for soft rock.

sten carbide or other very hard, tough materials can be used for drilling soft rocks. The six most popular sizes standard in the United States are given in Table 10:5.

Table 10:5 SIZES OF DIAMOND BITS

Size	Outside Diameter (in.)	Core Diameter (in.)
EX	$1\frac{1}{2}$	$\frac{13}{16}$
AX	$1\frac{15}{16}$	$1\frac{3}{16}$
BX	$2\frac{3}{8}$	$1\frac{5}{8}$
NX	3	$2\frac{1}{8}$
$2\frac{3}{4} \times 3\frac{7}{8}$ in.	$3\frac{7}{8}$	$2\frac{11}{16}$
$4 \times 5\frac{1}{2}$ in.	$5\frac{1}{2}$	$3\frac{15}{16}$

To obtain good cores in soft or fractured rock, BX or larger is desirable.

In drilling, the core barrel and bit rotate while water under high pressure is forced down the barrel and into the bit. The cuttings, ground to a powder, are carried up the hole with the wash water. The rock core extends upward into the barrel. The ratio of the length of core obtained to the distance drilled is known as the *core recovery* and is expressed as a percentage. The core recovery is an indication of the quality of the drilling and of the soundness of the rock; in homogeneous, sound rock a recovery of over 90 per cent may be expected; in rocks with seams a recovery of about 50 per cent is typical; however, in decomposed rock the recovery may be little or nothing.

In badly fractured or soft rock a double-tube core barrel helps obtain better core recovery. This employs a thin steel tube that fits snugly around the core and which remains stationary while the outer tube rotates. It protects the core from vibration and from erosion of the drilling wash water.

Ground Water Level Determining the ground water level is an essential part of the exploratory investigation. In most cases it is measured in the exploratory borings after waiting a sufficient time after the drilling has been finished for the water level to become stable. In sandy soils a few hours will usually be enough, but in clays, or if drilling mud has been used to stabilize the hole, several days may be required.

Perched water tables and artesian heads complicate the ground water picture. Perched water is indicated by ground water that appears at shallow depths and which disappears when the boring extends deeper. A series of auger borings, each to a different level, may be necessary to identify this condition fully. Artesian pressure is indicated when deeper borings show a higher ground water level than shallow ones. Sometimes it is necessary to seal a casing into deeper pervious strata in order to establish definitely whether artesian pressures are present.

Long-term observations are necessary to show the seasonal fluctuations in ground water. Perforated or slotted casings are left in the borings to serve as observation wells in which measurements can be made periodically.

10:6 Analyzing the Results of an Exploratory Investigation

Laboratory Tests While a visual examination of the soil samples obtained from exploratory borings may provide the engineer with a rough picture of the soil conditions, a study of the results of laboratory tests clarifies the picture and makes it possible to analyze the soil conditions on the basis of factual data.

The samples are ordinarily described in the field by the engineer in charge of the boring and sampling work, but they should be re-examined in the laboratory and the field identifications should be verified. Tests can then be made on the samples to confirm their identification and to determine their physical properties. Table 10:6 summarizes the tests most useful in exploratory work.

Other tests, such as the loss of weight by ignition which identifies organic materials, or treatment with hydrochloric acid which indicates the presence of soluable carbonates, may be useful in identifying some soils. A microscopic examination of coarse soils and of the particles coarser than 0.074 mm in fine-grained soils may be very useful in correlating similar strata in different borings.

Table 10:6 LABORATORY TESTS FOR EXPLORATORY INVESTIGATIONS

Test	Types of Soils	Size of Sample (lb)	Type of Sample	Use of Data
Specific gravity of solids	All	$\frac{1}{10}$	Auger or split barrel	Determine composition, void ratio.
Grain size	Cohesionless (sands, gravels)	$\frac{1}{4}$	Auger or split barrel	Classification. Estimate permeability, shear strength, frost action, compaction.
Grain shape	Cohesionless (sands, gravels)	$\frac{1}{4}$	Auger or split barrel	Classification. Estimate shear strength.
Liquid and plastic limits	Cohesive (silts, clays)	$\frac{1}{4}$	Auger or split barrel	Classification. Estimate compressibility, compaction.
Water content	Cohesive	$\frac{1}{4}$	Auger or split barrel	Correlate with strength, compressibility, compaction.
Void ratio	Cohesive	$\frac{1}{4}$	Split barrel*	Estimate compressibility and strength.
Unconfined compression	Cohesive	$\frac{1}{4}$	Split barrel*	Estimate shear strength.

* Sample must be relatively undisturbed.

Plotting Boring Records The first step in analyzing the data obtained by exploratory investigations is to plot the boring records graphically on a large *work sheet*, as shown in Fig. 10:6. Each boring is represented by a vertical bar graph, with the different soils indicated by appropriate symbols or abbreviations. All should be plotted to the same scale with elevation (above the site datum) as the vertical ordinate. If possible, borings that are adjacent on the site should be plotted adjacent to one another, but a space of 2 or 3 in. should be left between the plot of each boring to provide room for the laboratory data.

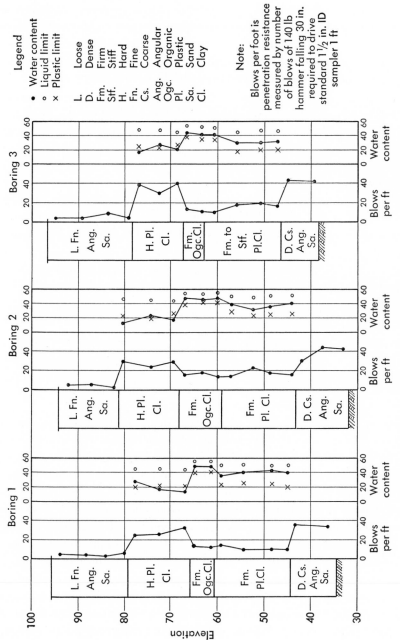

Fig. 10:6 Plot of the results of the exploratory phase of a soil investigation.

The soil penetration resistances are plotted as a broken-line graph next to the boring plot. This makes it possible to correlate the resistances of the different soils encountered. On the same graph can also be plotted the unconfined compressive strength data from the laboratory tests.

A second graph, also plotted adjacent to the boring record, shows water content and the liquid and plastic limits. The water content may be plotted as a broken-line graph and the limits as isolated points. The characteristics of cohesionless soils such as grain size and shape cannot be represented so conveniently on such a graph but may be indicated by notes or symbols.

Preparing Soil Profiles Soil profiles or geologic cross-sections (Fig. 10:7) for critical parts of the site are prepared by correlating the soils encountered in each of the borings. For example, a hard clay layer found in each of three adjacent borings at about the same elevation is probably

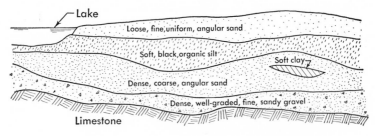

Fig. 10:7 Soil profile (geologic cross-section).

the same continuous stratum, especially if the liquid limits and plasticity indexes are the same. By interpolating between borings, a reasonable soil profile may usually be established. In some very erratic soils, such as glacial moraines, interpolation may be dangerous, since apparently continuous strata may be discontinuous lenses. Silts and organic soils often occur in limited lens-shaped deposits and should be viewed with suspicion.

In attempting to correlate the boring records and determine the soil profiles, the engineer often finds that additional borings would be very helpful. If the records are plotted at the same time the boring work is progressing, then the number or spacing of the borings can be changed to produce a clearer picture of the soil strata. In many cases low-cost auger borings can be used effectively to determine the extent of strata between the more expensive test borings, and in some cases geophysical methods prove very useful for the same purpose.

Preliminary Computations The unconfined compressive strength, void ratio, and compressibility of clays, and the unit weight and angle of internal friction of sands and gravels are necessary for most studies involving the safety and settlement of earth masses and the structures they support. The average values of these for each stratum in the soil profiles may be estimated from the laboratory data and the penetration resistance.

Preliminary computations for safety and settlement may be made by utilizing the soil profiles and the estimated soil properties. The results of these computations can be placed in four categories:

(1) The structure is so safe from failure and excessive settlement that further study is unnecessary, and the estimated soil properties can be used as a basis of design without the sacrifice of economy.
(2) The structure is safe and free from excessive settlement, but additional detailed soil studies may lead to a more economical design.
(3) The structure appears to be unsafe or will probably settle too much; therefore additional detailed soil studies will be necessary before a satisfactory design can be developed.
(4) The structure is so unsafe or will settle so much that further soil studies would be useless.

On the basis of these computations, therefore, the designer can decide whether to go ahead with his plans without further study, to secure additional, more accurate data, or to abandon the project as originally planned.

10:7   Detailed Soil Investigation

When the results of the exploratory investigation indicate that the soil has questionable safety, or that the settlement may be excessive, detailed soil studies will be necessary before a satisfactory design can be developed. When heavy, complex structures are involved, or when the foundations are expected to cost a great deal, a detailed investigation usually pays for itself by providing accurate data for exacting design.

The detailed investigation is ordinarily limited to those strata that are shown by the exploratory investigation to be critical. For example, if the preliminary computations indicate that the bearing capacity of footing foundations is adequate but that settlement of the proposed building will possibly be excessive, the detailed investigation will be limited to the strata that are responsible for the settlement.

Data Required   When the safety of the soil mass or structure is critical, then data on soil shear strength are required. The strength of cohesive soils may be determined by laboratory tests on undisturbed samples, while the strength of cohesionless soils may be estimated with sufficient accuracy from the results of tests on disturbed samples correlated with penetration test results. When settlement is critical, accurate data on compressibility and elasticity are required. The modulus of elasticity of cohesive soils can be determined by triaxial compression tests on undisturbed samples or from the results of plate load tests (if the soil is at the ground surface). The elasticity of cohesionless soils can be estimated from triaxial compression tests of disturbed samples correlated with relative density. The compressibility of cohesive soils must be determined by consolidation tests of undisturbed samples. Since cohesionless soils are so incompressible, they are rarely ever subjected to this test. In instances where seepage or drainage are important, permeability data are required. The permeability of cohesive soils may be determined by laboratory tests of undisturbed samples, while the permeability of cohesionless soils is best determined by field tests on the actual deposit.

Samples Required In most investigations the critical strata prove to be composed of cohesive soils—clays, organic silts, and organic clays— which require undisturbed samples of sufficient size for laboratory tests. Table 10:7 lists the typical sizes of samples for testing.

Table 10:7   SIZES OF SAMPLES FOR TESTING

Test	No. of Samples for One Test	Size of Sample Tested
Unconfined compression	2	1.4 in. diam × 3 in. long
	2	2.8 in. diam × 6 in. long
Triaxial shear	4–6	1.4 in. diam × 3 in. long
	4–6	2.8 in. diam × 6 in. long
Direct shear	4–6	1. in. × 4 in. × 4 in.
Consolidation	1	2.5 in. diam × 1 in. thick
	1	4.25 in. diam × 1 in. thick

The number of samples to be made depends on the uniformity of the stratum to be sampled. A perfectly homogeneous soil would require only one sample large enough for the necessary tests, but unfortunately, most actual soil deposits are far from uniform. The range in variation in soil properties can be determined from the results of the exploratory investigation. Typical points and extreme points within the stratum are selected from the boring logs and the plots of penetration resistance, water content, Atterberg limits, and unconfined compressive strength. The undisturbed samples are secured as close to these points as it is practical to do so. In many instances, however, it is necessary to secure an unbroken or continuous series of undisturbed samples throughout the depth of the critical stratum. Ordinarily, one series of undisturbed samples is made beneath each important structure or beneath each different part of large structures, but more or less may be necessary, depending on the uniformity of the soil.

10:8 Undisturbed Sampling

The most important step in the detailed investigation is securing a sample with as little disturbance as possible. Unfortunately it is impossible to secure a completely undisturbed sample. The removal of a portion of soil from the ground produces changes in the soil stresses which change the soil structure to some extent. The best "undisturbed samples" are

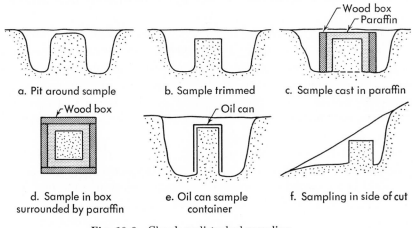

a. Pit around sample   b. Sample trimmed   c. Sample cast in paraffin

d. Sample in box surrounded by paraffin   e. Oil can sample container   f. Sampling in side of cut

Fig. 10:8   Chunk undisturbed sampling.

those in which the soil water content and composition remain unchanged and the void ratio and structure are changed as little as possible.

Chunk Sampling A *chunk sample* excavated carefully by hand is usually the best undisturbed sample obtainable. Figure 10:8 illustrates the steps for securing a chunk sample. A pit or shaft is excavated in the proper location to the depth from which the sample is desired. The soil is carefully removed from around the sample, leaving it projecting in the side or bottom of the excavation like a small stump. If the sample is strong and rigid, it can be cut free with a flat shovel, then wrapped with plastic film to preserve its water content, placed in a substantial box for support, and transported to the laboratory by automobile. If the sample is weak, or if it must be transported by railroad or truck, additional protection is required. One very good method is to place a heavy wooden box, with lid and bottom removed, around the sample so as to leave a space of 1 in. on all sides. This space is filled with melted paraffin. The sample and the box are removed from the excavation, paraffin is poured on the top and bottom of the sample, and the top and bottom lids replaced. Another method is to slide a cylindrical container over the sample which has been carefully trimmed to make a snug fit. Five-quart oil cans with their tops removed, sections of stove pipe, and large water pipes have been used successfully. Wood or metal caps should be provided to protect the open ends of the samples from damage. A layer of paraffin should be poured over the open ends to prevent evaporation of the moisture. These containers should be placed in a substantial wooden box and surrounded with sawdust or shavings in order to protect them for shipment.

The test pit not only makes it possible to secure undisturbed samples, but also provides a "window" from which to observe the soil structure in place. A visual examination of the soil strata that are uncovered by excavation of the pit will disclose the arrangement, uniformity, and the inclination or dip of the strata—information that is not easily secured from borings. Photographs made of the sides of the pit will provide a permanent record of this information.

Deep Undisturbed Sampling   Many types of equipment have been designed to secure undisturbed samples from deep bore holes, but not all types will be successful in every soil. The undisturbed quality of the sample has been found to be dependent on the following factors:

(1) Displacement of the soil by the sampler.
(2) Method of forcing sampler into ground.
(3) Friction on inside of sample tube.
(4) Squeezing of soil, owing to pressure of overburden.
(5) Handling and storing of samples until tested.

The displacement of the soil by the walls of the sampler is probably the most important source of disturbance. The soil is forced aside and upward, which severely distorts it and changes its structure. This can be minimized by excavating around the sample, by using a long, thin cutting edge on the sampler, and by keeping the cross-sectional area of the walls of the sampler as small as possible. The relative displacement of the sampler can be expressed by the area ratio A_r:

$$A_r = \frac{D_o{}^2 - D_s{}^2}{D_s{}^2} \times 100 \text{ per cent.} \qquad (10\!:\!1)$$

where D_o is the outside diameter of the sampler and D_s the diameter of the sample. According to Hvorslev,[10:4] displacement disturbance is minimized by keeping the area ratio less than 10 to 15 per cent.

The method of driving the sampler into the ground is important in loose sands and very sensitive clays. In such soils continuous hammering with the accompanying shock and vibration are harmful, although a single blow of a heavy hammer does not appear detrimental. The best method is to force the sampler into the ground with a steady movement such as is provided by hydraulic-feed drilling machines or by blocks and tackle that pull against anchors set in the ground.

Friction between the sample and the walls of the sample tube produces disturbance in the edges of the sample that is readily visible in stratified or laminated soils but is present in all cases. This friction can be reduced by drawing in the cutting edge of the tube about $\frac{1}{50}$ in. The diameter of the sample is then about $\frac{1}{25}$ in. less than the inside diameter of the tube. If too much draw-in is used, the sample may expand, changing its structure; if too little is used, the sample will be distorted. Friction is also minimized by limiting the sample length and by excavating around the sample.

Removal of soil from the boring reduces the downward stress at the hole bottom without changing the lateral and upward stresses produced by the weight of the overburden. As a result the soil squeezes inward and upward, distorting itself in the process. This condition is very serious in soft clays but exists to some extent in all materials. In cohesionless soils any attempt to lower the water level in the hole below the ground water table by pumping or bailing will have the same effect because the unbalanced water pressure in the hole bottom creates a quick condition. The unbalanced stress can be overcome by keeping the hole filled with liquid at all times. Water is adequate in many soils, but in loose sands and soft clays, drilling mud (described in Art. 10:5) is better. In extremely soft clays it is sometimes necessary to match the unit weight of the drilling fluid to that of the soil by adding baroids or iron filings to the mixture.

Improper handling and storing result in shock, distortion, and drying. By sealing the sample immediately, packing it in a cushioned container, and exercising extreme care in transportation these causes of disturbance can be minimized.

Thin Walled Sampler The simplest and most widely used deep undisturbed sampler is the *thin-wall* or *Shelby tube* (Fig. 10:9a). It is made of cold drawn steel tubing (sometimes known as *Shelby* tubing) from 2 in.

to 5 in. in diameter and with walls of 18 gage ($\frac{1}{20}$ in.) for the 2-in. tube to 11 gage ($\frac{1}{8}$ in.) for the 5-in. The lower end is beveled to form a tapered cutting edge, and it can be drawn in to reduce the wall friction. The upper end is fastened to a check valve that helps hold the sample in the tube when it is being withdrawn from the ground.

The sampler is introduced in the bore hole and forced into the soil a distance of no more than 15 diam so as to minimize friction between the sample and the walls of the tube. The sample is sealed in the tube with melted wax and shipped intact to the laboratory.

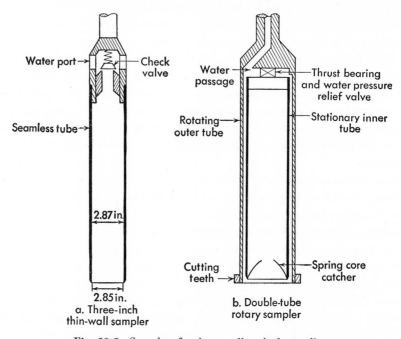

Fig. 10:9 Samplers for deep undisturbed sampling.

The thin-wall sampler minimizes the most serious sources of disturbance: displacement and friction. When used in a bore hole that is stabilized with drilling mud, excellent results can be had in a wide variety of soils.

Piston Sampler   In extremely soft soils, even the small displacement of the thin wall tube tends to cause the soil to squeeze into the tube faster than the sampler is advanced, causing distortion. The distortion due to friction also can be serious, but if friction is reduced too far by draw-in and by limiting the sample length, the sample will slide out of the tube when it is being withdrawn from the ground.

These difficulties can be reduced by placing a piston in the thin-wall sampler. At the start of sampling, the piston is at the tube bottom and in contact with the soil surface. The piston is fixed in this position by its actuating rods, which extend to the ground surface and which are locked to a rigid support. The sample tube is driven ahead of the piston into the soil below. The fixed piston prevents the soil from squeezing upward. If the sample tends to slip out of the tube, a vacuum is created between the piston and the soil, which helps hold it. Good samples can be secured in the softest soils by this method but at a considerable increase in cost.

A number of variations of the piston sampler are in use. The free piston is locked in the lower end of the tube while the sampler is being lowered into the hole. This keeps loose cuttings from choking the tube. When sampling begins, the piston is unlocked and floats up the tube on top of the soil. When the tube is withdrawn, the piston again locks and helps hold the sample in place. It does not, however, prevent squeezing of the soil during sampling. In another form the piston is torpedo-shaped, which allows the sampler to be advanced through very soft soil without a bore hole. None of these variations is so effective as the fixed piston.

Foil Sampler The Swedish foil sampler minimizes the friction between the sample tube walls and the soil by feeding thin strips of metal foil into the tube. These form a moving liner of thin metal that prevents the soil from touching the tube. The foil is pulled ahead by a piston at the same rate the sampler is advanced, so that there is no tendency to distort the soil by squeezing or wall friction. By this method continuous undisturbed samples as long as 50 ft have been obtained in soft to firm clay or silts. It is of little use in sands and gravels, however.

The foil lining is made up of 16 strips, each nearly $\frac{1}{2}$ in. wide so as to nearly cover the surface of the 2.7-in. diam sample. The foil is supplied from rolls that fit in a retainer 12 in. above the cutting edge so that the displacement of the retainer will not cause undue soil disturbance. The strips feed to the sample 5 in. above the edge.

Rotary Samplers The rotary samplers combine drilling and sampling, which minimizes disturbance due to sampler displacement. An example is the *Denison sampler* (Fig. 10:9b), which consists of two concentric tubes. The inner tube is actually the sampler and is a 5-in. diam, 24 in. long pipe with a thin steel liner and a heavy cutting shoe at the lower end. The outer tube rotates, cutting the soil, and the cuttings are washed up the bore hole by water that is pumped down the drill pipe and flows between the two tubes. The inner tube remains stationary and protects the sample from the wash water. At the same time, both tubes are forced downward into the soil. The samples secured by this device are excellent, particularly in hard clays and slightly cohesive sands that are difficult to sample in any other way. The equipment is comparatively expensive to buy and to operate.

Deep Sampling in Sand   It is difficult to secure undisturbed samples of cohesionless sand and gravel from bore holes, since the sampling operation may rearrange the grains and the samples often run out of the sampler. One method has been to freeze the soil and then drill through it with a rotary drill, but the disadvantage is that freezing increases the void ratio. Another method has been to sample with a thin-wall sample tube and then freeze the lower end of the sample to prevent the soil from escaping.

Undisturbed samples of sand can be secured below the ground water table if a very heavy drilling mud is employed. The mud forms a coating over the lower end of the sample, which prevents the sand from running out. The sample is drained of excess water before sealing so that capillary tension will help to maintain its structure during shipment. It is also helpful to measure the sample so that any change in density during shipment can be detected and the original void ratio can be computed from the weight as received in the laboratory.

Liner Tube Samplers   An early type of undisturbed sampler that is still in use is similar to the split-barrel sampler except that it is equipped with a seamless liner tube that fits snugly in the barrel. The sample is shipped and stored in the liner to minimize handling disturbance. The large area ratio often causes severe displacement distortion, and for this reason such samplers are not widely used.

10:9   Soil Tests for Detailed Investigations

Sample Preparation   Undisturbed samples delivered to a laboratory are of two types: continuous and intermittent. The continuous samples are cut into sections representing 0.5 ft or 1.0 ft of depth. The samples are weighed and then small portions may be removed for visual classification and water content determinations. The average unit weight and void ratio for each section can be computed. The average unit weight and void ratio for each intermittent sample can also be determined. The test results are plotted on the same work sheet as the exploratory boring data.

A thin, vertical slice from each section or sample may be set aside to

dry. This is examined at intervals to determine the presence of lamina-
tions or thin strata which ordinarily became more visible after partial
drying. The disturbing effects of sampling can often be seen from the distortion of the strata. Finally the clay thickness is measured.

Tests of Cohesive Soils A study of the classification test and void-
ratio results will show that the soil characteristics vary within any one
stratum. The points where the soil characteristics of a stratum appear to
be both typical and extreme can be determined from the plots of water
content, void ratio, plasticity, and penetration resistance. The undisturbed samples to be tested for shear or consolidation are usually selected
from the typical and extreme points in order to determine the variation
of soil properties. Only a few samples are tested, for the cost of testing
every one would be very great. The test results can be correlated with the
other soil properties to determine the average strength or compressibility
of the stratum.

Tests of Cohesionless Soils Strength tests of cohesionless soils are
made at different void ratios with disturbed samples. The angle of internal
friction, correlated with the relative density of the soil, can be used to
estimate the strength of the actual soil deposit.

In-Place Tests The ideal conditions for testing a soil for its physical
properties would be in its undisturbed state in the ground. Unfortunately
the difficulties involved in performing such tests beneath the surface
make the costs prohibitive except in special situations.

The load test described in Chapter 5 is one of the more widely used
in-place soil tests. It is an excellent test for determining the angle of
internal friction and elasticity of sands and the shear strength and elasticity of clays. The test is performed as previously described, and the soil
properties are computed by the formulas in Chapter 5. It must be remembered that the load test gives the *average* soil properties throughout the
depth equal to the width of the test plate.

Load tests on the soil far below the ground surface must be made in deep
test pits or with special casings. One method of making a deep load test
is to drive an open-ended, 12-in. pipe into the soil to the depth at which
the test is to be made. The pipe is cleaned out and then a circular load
plate placed inside it. The load plate acts as a piston in the bottom of the
open pipe. It is forced against the soil beneath the pipe in the same way
that a load plate is loaded in the conventional test.

The vane shear test is a method of determining the in-place strength of soils far below the ground surface. The vane consists of four vertical steel plates welded to a vertical rod. The projection of the vane on a horizontal plane would be a +. The vane is attached to drill rods and is forced into the undisturbed soil at the bottom of a drill hole. The vane is rotated, and it shears the soil along a cylindrical surface at the outer ends of the +. The torque required to produce rotation of the vane is a measure of the soil shear strength. The vane test provides reliable shear strength data for soft clays that are difficult to sample without disturbance.

Correlating Test Results   It is often possible to correlate the results of the detailed testing with the data obtained in the exploratory phase of the work. In this way limited test data can be extended on the basis of the exploratory boring results to save time and money.

The penetration resistance can usually be correlated with the undrained shear strength of clays and even with their safe bearing capacity. In most cases the average strength c in 1000 psf is proportional to the standard penetration resistance N in blows per foot and can be expressed by

$$c = CN. \tag{10:2}$$

The constant C depends on the character of the clay. For clays of low plasticity it has been found between 0.1 and 0.2, with the average value at 0.15. For very silty or sandy clays the range in C is somewhat lower: 0.05 to 0.15, with the average at 0.1.

In sands and gravels the penetration resistance can often be correlated with the angle of internal friction. The average relation for a number of sites in alluvial and marine sands has been found to be

$$\phi = 28 + \frac{N}{4}. \tag{10:3}$$

The relations between liquid limit, void ratio, and compression index were discussed in Chapter 2 (equations 2:12 and 2:13). The preconsolidation load can often be correlated with the water-plasticity ratio R_w:

$$R_w = \frac{w - \text{PL}}{\text{PI}}. \tag{10:4}$$

The relation appears to be different for each stratum, depending on the character of the clay minerals present.

The results of all the testing, extended by correlations, are indexed on the underground cross-sections prepared from the exploratory phase of the investigation. Superimposed on the same sections are the outlines of the proposed structure, so that these sections become the starting point for the engineering analyses of stability, bearing capacity, and settlement.

REFERENCES

10:1 G. F. Sowers, "Modern Procedures for Underground Exploration," *Proceedings, ASCE*, Vol. 80, Separate 435, May, 1954.

10:2 D. R. Lueder, *Aerial Photographic Interpretation*, McGraw-Hill Book Co. Inc., New York, 1959.

10:3 *Manual of Air Photo Interpretation*, American Society for Photogrammetry, Washington, 1960.

10:4 M. J. Hvorslev, *Subsurface Exploration and Sampling of Soils for Civil Engineering Purposes*, U.S. Waterways Experiment Station, Vicksburg, Miss., 1949.

10:5 "Soil Exploration and Sampling of Soils," *Procedures for Testing Soils*, American Society for Testing Materials, Philadelphia, 1958.

10:6 K. Terzaghi and R. B. Peck, *Soil Mechanics in Engineering Practice*, John Wiley & Sons, Inc., New York, 1948.

10:7 *Foundation Code, City of New York*, 1948.

10:8 "Standards," *Bulletin 2*, Diamond Core Drill Manufacturers Association, New York, 1956.

Suggestions for Additional Study

1. References 10:1, 10:2, 10:3, 10:4, 10:5.

2. R. W. Moore, "Geophysical Methods of Subsurface Exploration Applied to Highway Engineering," *Public Roads*, August, 1950.

3. Catalogs and bulletins of manufacturers of soil-sampling equipment, such as Sprague and Henwood, Inc., Scranton, Pennsylvania; Acker Drill Company, Inc., and Soiltest, Inc., Chicago, Illinois.

PROBLEMS

10:1 Prepare a typical soil profile for your locality. Secure data from contractors, city and county engineers, engineers specializing in underground exploration work, and from geologic and engineering reports.

10:2 A single test boring made for a water tank led to the following data:

	Soil Data		Sampling Data		
				Penetration	
Depth (ft)	*Soil Stratum*	*Depth (ft)*	*Data*	*w*	*LL*
0–4	Fill: cinders, brick	2	3	—	—
4–7	Hard, slightly plastic clay	5	32	21	44
7–25	Firm, uniform, coarse, subrounded quartz sand	8	15	—	—
		13	19	—	—
		18	27	—	—
		23	20	—	—
25–32	Firm, highly plastic clay	26	7	55	62
		31	6	57	64
32–51	Dense, uniform, fine, angular sand	33	35	—	—
		38	37	—	—
		43	40	—	—
		48	46	—	—
51–75	Dense to very dense graded, angular, coarse,	52	48	—	—
	sandy, subrounded, fine gravel. Coarser with	57	55	—	—
	depth.	62	72	—	—
		67	68	—	—
		72	63	—	—
22	Ground water				

a. Plot the boring log.

b. Determine which strata, if any, require more detailed study. List tests necessary.

c. Should more or deeper test borings be made? Tank weighs 450 tons and rests on four columns arranged in a square 30 ft apart.

10:3 Sketch and list the essential equipment for test boring, using both hand auger and wash drilling, and spoon sampling.

10:4 A 10-story office building with a basement floor 7 ft below the ground surface is 100 ft wide and 240 ft long. The dead load per floor is 120 psf and the live load 50 psf. The soil weighs 110 lb per cu ft.

a. Show layout of borings for average conditions.

b. Determine depth of boring, using the rule of 10 per cent of increase in effective stresses.

10:5 A one-story manufacturing plant is 120 by 600 ft. It rests on new fill 3.5 ft thick. The geology of the area indicates that it is underlain by horizontally stratified coastal lagoon deposits covered with an old man-made sand fill.

a. Show the recommended boring layout.

b. Estimate the required boring depth. Under what conditions encountered during boring should this depth be changed? When should undisturbed samples be made?

c. Estimate the cost of making a soil investigation at this site, assuming that soil testing and engineering costs will be 40 per cent of the cost of boring and sampling.

APPENDIX

UNIT COSTS

Engineering analysis and design cannot be divorced from cost of construction. Science and technology have made it possible to do many remarkable things; whether or not they will be of use depends on their ultimate value compared with their cost. The following table will give the student some concept of the cost of soil and foundation work. It is based on typical costs in the United States in 1960 as published in *Engineering News Record* and similar publications.

Foundations

Basement excavation in soil	$ 0.50 to $ 2.00/cu yd
Basement excavation in rock	5.00 to 20.00/cu yd
Footing excavation in soil	2.00 to 5.00/cu yd
Footing excavation in rock	5.00 to 15.00/cu yd
Footing concrete, including any forming	40.00 to 60.00/cu yd
Drilled pier foundations, including concrete	40.00 to 50.00/cu yd
Wood piles, untreated, including driving	1.50 to 2.00/lin ft
Wood piles, treated, including driving	2.00 to 3.00/lin ft
Concrete 40-ton precast, including driving	6.00 to 8.00/lin ft
Concrete 40-ton cast-in-place, including driving	4.00 to 5.00/lin ft
Steel H-pile, 10 in., 50 ton, including driving	6.00 to 7.00/lin ft
Steel pipe pile, 10¾, 50 ton, including driving	6.00 to 7.00/lin ft

Excavation Bracing

Wood sheeting (20 ft deep)	3.00 to 5.00/sq ft
Steel sheeting, or H-beam and lagging, (20 ft deep)	4.00 to 8.00/sq ft

Drainage

Wellpoint installation and operation, 30 days	15.00 to 40.00/lin ft*
Trench excavation in soil	1.00 to 2.00/cu yd
Pumping, 20-ft head	.05 to 1.00/1000 gal
Drain pipe, 8-in. concrete	2.00 to 4.00/lin ft

* Of header pipe.

Earthwork (Dams, embankments, large fills)

Soil excavation, placement, compaction in embankments	0.40 to	0.80/cu yd
Rock excavation, placement, compaction	1.00 to	5.00/cu yd
Backfill, around structures, compacted	2.00 to	5.00/cu yd

Soil Stabilization

Soil-cement, cement, mixing and compaction	6.00 to	8.00/cu yd soil
Cement grouting, including injection	2.00 to	3.00/sack cement
Chemical grouting, including injection	30.00 to	50.00/cu yd soil

Exploration

Auger boring	1.50 to	3.00/lin ft
Test boring, including split barrel samples	4.00 to	6.00/lin ft
Diamond-core drilling	8.00 to	12.00/lin ft
Undisturbed sampling	10.00 to	40.00/sample

INDEX

379